THE MEDICINE TREE

Traditional Medicine in Wales from

Prehistory to the Present

1

THE MEDICINE TREE

Traditional Healing in Wales from Prehistory to the Present

Published by Llanerch Press 2009

ISBN 9781861431509

Llanerch Press, Cribyn, Lampeter.
Website www.llanerchpress.com.

The Publisher acknowledges the financial support of the Welsh Books Council.

How we squander our lives of pain.
How we gaze beyond them into the bitter duration
To see if they have an end. Though they are really
Seasons of us, our winter –
Enduring foliage, ponds, meadows, our inborn landscape,
Where birds and reed-dwelling creatures are at home.

Rainer Maria Rilke.

Chapbooks were small printed tracts formally sold by itinerant chapmen. The hawkers carried their hand-sized books from market to market, often publicly extolling their contents in song or blank verse to attract the attention of passing trade and to gather a crowd around them. The chapbooks were small, roughly four by six inches and made up of four pages, with multiples of four eight sixteen or twenty-four sheets stitched together. They contained legends, old tales, folk-lore, notorious crimes and criminals, fortune telling, astrology, nursery rhymes, biblical stories, recipes; even school lessons and dream lore with fanciful interpretations. Along with the religious and printed broadsheets they were the main sources of information for ordinary people until the inexpensive printed magazines bcame popular in the 18th century.

A Sharkey chapbook of Welsh traditional medicine follows in the spirit of an earlier age with healing anecdotes by the physicians and doctors, bone setters and horse quacks, folk charmers and *dyn hysbys* and even saints, and with an occasional word from the poor patients.

4

CONTENTS

The Medicine Tree: *An Introduction* 7

THE MEDICINE TREE

An Introduction

I often dream of the medicine tree. Poetically like one of those gnarled ancient yews encrusted with age whose massive trunk seems to have endlessly regenerated itself with old forgotten medicines. Its healing branches stretch far back into past ages; its leaf labels marked with Greek and Roman healing charms. Some holy Christian and medieval medicines are copper-plated in unknown ciphers. Here and there a flask of Paracelsium with vials of Cymru superstition and Celtic druidism lie scattered among the Bunsen burners. This book is in a setting that lives apart from the modern world. I can still remember working as a technician in a Dublin city hospital with its daily short-cut through a churchyard outside strewn with weathered stone carvings. Inside, the 18th century lab was like a picturesque backdrop to the old horror movies with that formaldehyde tang of ever-decaying amnesia of yesterday. Even then there was a vivid reminder of old style medicine with its emphasis on the examination of patients' urine in terms of colour, clarity, density, smell, to my final objective cell-count on a microscope you would not even find in a museum. A *memento mori* rather than a meeting place of what was then medicine's higher aspirations among the sick. A metaphorical view of a medicine tree might reveal older exotic branches, the trunk and its roots as part of a universal relationship between sufferer and healer. It is one that harks back to remote eras of prehistory rather than to the classically written works of the Mediterranean; to an environmental imprint that modified people as much as it was modified by those who lived here. This focus is anterior to the arrival of the Roman legions; as far back as when the western land-mass emerged from its glacial cover to become an almost recognizable geographic entity. The ice had covered all of this land apart from a stretch across the south-western peninsula. This earliest known period of habitation in what

7

is now Wales, was at the climatic downturn of the last glacial maximum when vast plains stretched beyond the raised beaches of the Gower Peninsula. Known as the Upper Palaeolithic period from thirty-six to twenty-five millennia BC, people camped in the Gower caves away from the fierce beasts that roamed in the lowlands below. Presumably headless, a hunter was buried in the Goat's Hole Cave with obvious care and preparation. The mammoth's skull and tusk nearby may indicate that man and beast might have conjoined in the spirit realm. The red ochre sprinkled over his body would show that he was both inside the sacred cave and yet outside on the plains with the ancestral beast and his fellow hunters. Many Palaeolithic cave paintings have a window-type configuration which pre-historians call a soul trap, as a symbol of such a union which could be a form of shamanistic medicine that was directed beyond the individual, to oscillate between the group and a liminal threshold of spirit entities which we can hardly imagine. Extinct bones were first found in the Gower at Goat's Hole and Hound's Hole Caves by two brothers from Reynoldston who brought the discovery to the notice of some amateur geologists of Penrice Castle. They were in touch with William Buckland the flamboyant, eccentric and articulate Professor of Geology at Corpus Christi College in Oxford. A renowned and witty public-speaker, he usually carried a black bag from which he would produce his latest find or would mimic the strange animals that lived in his imagination like the flying reptile he named the Pterodactyl. On being informed of the new finds the professor wrote back that he was impatient for further accounts, "and the moment I can stir, I will if possible run down to get a peep at what remains in the cave". He arrived quicker than his letter would suggest and almost immediately began to dig up the hard ground floor of Goat's Hole. Halfway up the cave wall among the thick occupational deposits he found a skeleton that had been laid out in an extended position. The skull, vertebrae, and parts of the right-hand side were missing. Close to the thigh bone were handfuls of perforated shells piled so neatly that they may originally have been strung together or in a pocket of a burial garment. In contact with the ribs were fifty fragments of small quite cylindrical ivory rods and fragments of ivory rings. In the shallow grave, the bones and ornaments had been powdered by deep red ochre. A mammoth's skull and tusk, shaped flint tools, and an ivory tongue shaped artefact carved from the metacarpal bone of a wolf were found among the cave deposits.[1]

Much later the caves were used as shelter by wolves and hyenas that left behind the gnawed bones of their prey; with evidence of use found in twenty of the ninety known caves hereabouts. After an intensely cold period Goat's Hole was again being used as temporary shelter by people who left a small number of 'Creswellian type' flints, also found in the Nanna's Cave on Caldey Island, at sometime between ten to eight thousand BC. In the Kendrick's Cave near Llandudno four human skeletons were found from this period, with a carved horse's mandible and a bear's perforated tooth. Thereafter in Goat's Hole the human traces discovered related to subsequent archaeological periods such as Mesolithic flints, a Neolithic axe head and Iron-Age pottery from a fort situated on the hill above. If it were not for the body of the hunter interred from the beginning of the sequence of occupation in this cave; the mute evidence from geology and the shaped flint assemblage of archaeological findings preclude known human interaction in terms of medicine, music or language, although we must presume that they were an essential part of their culture. The body surviving so long in such a cave and with the changing environmental conditions is extraordinary enough but the actual interment points to a variety of caring factors that can be implied and related to the group laying the body out full length on the stone shelf in a simple tunic through which the sprinkling of red ochre penetrated to the bones of the hunter. What such a ritual burial might have meant then, we have no knowledge, but as a starting point for a survey of human healing here, it is one of the oldest 'images' and a potent one that can be pinpointed in time and place long before the Wales we now know with its hills, trees and lakes came into existence.

9

———————☼☼☼———————

The region we now call Wales emerged into the sunlight about
ten millennia ago. In that geophysical sense it is a young country.
One may therefore situate a primitive medical interaction down
through the valleys of prehistory; to when the ecological imprint and
the relationship between plants and the small social groups we now
call hunter-gatherers can be discerned. There is a broad understanding of how such people used the natural plant world around
them for nourishment, shelter and healing. A credible first step in
understanding the intimate relationship of earlier people with the
land is to imagine the environment in which they lived. The tools
now available to pre-historians are scientific, with pollen analysis,
tree-ring dating and data from fossilized plants. Such advanced
microscopic techniques can show growth sequences from the grass
lands of a post-glacial tundra era to the deciduous mixed forests
which can also be disentangled from their underlying and
overlapping geophysical strata. A broad-leafed mixed hardwood
forest established itself as the most developed form of the plant
community. Its dominance was on the open hillsides while alder
swamps occupied damp valley floors. Although it is possible to
identify such early trees as the birch *(Betula)* and Scots pine *(Pinus
sylvestris)* from the warm and dry Boreal period; or the mixed oak,
elm and lime in the subsequent warmer and moist Atlantic period, it
may be that such flora were not environmentally identical with those
of the present-day we see around us.[2] Possession of fire and the
domestication of grazing animals like sheep, pigs, goats and red
deer had a prolonged intrusive effect on the woodlands. As people
became more sedentary and dependent on such animals for food,
clothing and many other commodities they probably changed some
wild habitats in order to attract or retain certain species of game;
even to inducing the wild animals in for hunting purposes. The old
notion of early peoples in Britain chasing the elk, reindeer and the
wild horse to extinction has altered. It was climatic change affecting
the vegetation slowly over time that caused their decline, but helped

10

along the way no doubt by man the hunter. The overwhelming concentration by earlier generations of writers on the stone axe-head as the main tool for hacking and fighting, idealized the hunters' survival techniques. Such unstinting devotion to the wonderfully-shaped icon tended to overlook the combination of family or group contribution to the social good. The evidence from Mesolithic (Middle Stone Age) midden heaps that have survived around the western coastal areas show they were composed of over eighty per cent shellfish along with small amounts of animal bones. It points to a more balanced view of the food gatherers in early communities. The female role as edible food collectors of the young green shoots for the pot, berries and nuts for processing, meant that it was probably they that initially formed an agricultural imperative through daily cooking and trial-and-error in the search of nutritious plants; as well as useful observations of seasonal growth and change. In their child-bearing and caring roles, the use of medicinal plants as well as the necessary obstetric skills would be part of their 'home' medicine; and certainly indispensable for any small group survival. Then again unless forced by catastrophe, natural disasters, epidemics or other circumstances in having to up-sticks and move elsewhere, people would tend to remain within a region where the known cyclic patterns of fishing, primitive farming, and flowering of edible plants and fruits assured their social stability. By a process of movement and splintering as such family units grew larger, a regional territory would soon become quite familiar to them. Accelerated radio carbon dating techniques now mean that even the minute bones found at Mesolithic sites can be analyzed. This type of data is changing much older received wisdom. Recent examination of the DNA from small animal bones reveals that domestication of animals was not only a process imposed by people but also partly a behavioural adoption by the animal species. House mice and house sparrows would appear to have been part of human settlements from their very inception. The remains of larger animals indicate that they were probably protected from natural predators and so helped to thin out the forests and facilitate human movement inland. In this way

11

the wild environment with its flora, fauna and animal habitat would also have undergone subtle but radical changes.[3]

The accounts of modern archaeological excavations usually include some medical findings unlike the hazardous methods of the 19th century when primary evidence of bone skeletons and the soil around them was often ignored. Many current scientific techniques can clarify the fate of artefacts and even individual bog bodies such as the 'Lindow Man' found quashed flat in its hardened outer skin from an ancient burial in a Cheshire mere. A team of medical experts were able to ascertain that his last meal was of burnt oat cakes and provide the gory details of his threefold ritual death. The body was dated to around the time of the arrival of the Roman legions in Anglesey. Yet even with such additional information from individual interment and bog burials, the general health picture of our prehistoric ancestors remains much as it was. People seemed to have had a shorter life span than we. Their molars were often ground down from chewing coarse cereals. They suffered back problems and their bones seemed particularly susceptible to arthritic decay. Throughout such long periods of time anomalies can be expected. The skulls of those in the Bronze Age were deemed to be longer than the norm in the earlier Neolithic or in the later Iron Age, when people were as tall as now. The blood groups of some peoples match those of the Basques which may account for some of the obvious Welsh 'small and dark' characteristics.[4]

Evidence of trepanned skulls show that people lived on after such operations. The surgical expertise seemed general throughout the ancient world and is still currently practiced in some tribal societies. The reasons given for these operations were usually to relieve pressure on the brain but there is a suggestion that since amulets of human cranial bone may have had magical qualities and trade value, this aspect of medical shamanism cannot be ignored. Perhaps it is well to remember that any overall archaeological vista of the past is gained from a limited sample of available human material due to the acidic soils that are so prevalent in Wales. Popular commentators on television are still fond of using absolute time-bands like the stone, bronze and iron ages for the prehistoric period but in general up to the time Roman soldiers marched across Wales and cut down the sacred groves of Mona, cultural trends were usually later here than in England. And probably the Stone Age with its cattle economy continued alongside the cereal cultivation of the megalithic builders as well as the later users of bronze and iron metals in their large-scale enclosed forts on prominent hilltops. The gradual decimation of the trees was a result of their activities over millennia but more especially due to the later Roman building activity here. The systematic clearing of woodlands around the military forts, roads and extensive stone buildings finally reduced the primal forests and helped denude the Welsh upland landscapes to somewhat like their present treeless state. Many of the primary inventions by early peoples probably came about through accident or from reasons other than were later suggested; copper mining for instance perhaps from the smelting of its mineral rock around fires. Knowledge of basic surgery may have come about from the butchering of animals and the use of splints on broken bones. Fast relief gained by bursting swellings from tics on cattle could also be applied to people; trepanning perhaps from decorating the head using flint knives — scarification is still popular in African societies — and a secondary need to remove pieces of devil bone for magical amulets. The word surgery derives from the Latin *chirurgia* out of the Greek *cheiros* (hand) and *erhon* (work). Early healing arts of working with the hands depended on a knowledge of plants such as the seasonal leaves used for covering open wounds and large abrasions. From what we now know of the healing properties associated with certain species of trees, some remedies could have been accidentally found and then if useful for one complaint might have been worth applying to others; in time such items would become part of the traditional pouch of the plant healer. Water trapped in the hollow of an oak would form a dilute of tannic acid. A hunter thirsty, wounded or suffering from fever might get some relief by drinking the still water. Once an easy-to-find remedy was available from the oak — venerated by almost all the peoples who subsequently lived here —

the spiritual association between magic and medicine would become sanctified by traditional or ritual usage.[5]

It is also likely that the art of botanical medicine arose from the religious induction of alkaloid producing plants. The toxins are often localized within a plant and they create powerful mind altering effects on those who ritually partake of it. In the search for other such plants or the necessary antidote to counteract effects of the poison, some people would become more aware of the natural pharmacological world surrounding them; either through trial and error or as in known from ethnographic studies into modern shamanism, as plants themselves taking on hallucinatory shapes to inform the seeker or healer where and what species to gather. The legend of the lady or fairy woman re-emerging from the waters of Llyn y Fan Fach near the Brecon Beacons to tell her sons which plants and herbs would heal people at a place still called *Pant y Meddygon* or the Physicians Hollow — was presented as the basis of the medical knowledge of the physicians of Myddfai. It has since the middle of the 19th century become the essential creation tale of Welsh traditional medicine.

The story of Llyn y Fan Fach is like one of those haunting melodies that are full of familiar passages but where the finale takes the listener somewhat by surprise. A girl is sitting on the unruffled surface of the lake. The young cattle herder is instantly besotted by an extraordinary sight of the young maiden calmly combing her long hair like a creature from a dream realm. Wrapped in this most feminine activity she was using glassy water as her mirror. Even so she deigned to notice him and his almost unconscious body gesture of both hands holding out his cheese and barley bread as an offering. During an endless moment as she moved across the still water to almost within his reach, he heard her speak, using the words *cras dy fara* to decline his offer of food. Then seemingly teasing him to chase her when she said *nid hawdd fy nala* and slid into the water to disappear completely from view almost without a ripple. She was right. It was not easy to catch her!

When he eventually got home to Blaensawdde on the other side of the Black Mountain, his mother was tempered and took it all as an everyday occurrence. She suggested he should take unbaked dough to tempt the lady the next time he was over that way, as there may have been some kind of spell connected with the old *bara cras.* The next time there he spent the whole day wandering the lake-side desperately searching for a sign. The sun was almost down when he noticed that his cattle were bunched on a steep slope, so he went over to get them and the fairy woman appeared again. It was a dream like the time before. Once more he offered her his food but she answered that like his bread, *ty ni fynna,* she would not have him. So shattered and confused, lovelorn and weary, he returned home. However his mother was not to be outdone, and clearly knowing a thing or two about the fairies, said she would part-bake the bread. It might be more to the taste of the lady in the lake. So again he hovered around it impatient for a glimpse of her, staring avidly into the shifting waters during that long day now fading into night. Leaving, but with one last glance over his shoulder he was astounded to see seven cows walking on top of the water. He rushed across the slope to the lakeside to see her gliding behind them. She moved across the surface to where he stood and this time let him hold her hand. After his offer of the half-baked bread she consented to become his wife but on condition that if he were to strike her three times without cause, she would have to return to the lake waters. So defused with love and probably without a thought for even such a future, he agreed to her condition — *tri ergyd diachos.* Once more he was dismayed for she and the magic cattle disappeared without trace almost like the day itself. He was beyond words and about to throw himself into the water after her when she appeared but with her exact double. The two maids floated on either side of an ancient man who had a most noble visage and extraordinary stature. Having set the scene of the mortal meeting his fairy woman, but knowing that the man will most certainly fail to keep his bargain about striking her three times, one can imagine the old storyteller in the corner of a cottage, pausing in anticipation, recounting an almost comic scene for the young man to choose the right girl: Neptune himself with two identical water nymphs waiting on the lad to make his choice. However she came to his rescue by tapping her foot in a delicate sandal that was knotted in the special way he recognized, so he took her by the hand. The old man gave the lad his blessing saying that he had chosen wisely and could have as many cattle as she could count in one breath. Again he reminded him that if he should strike her three times without cause, she would return to the lake taking all the stock and their offspring with her. She began to count tapping her fingers one two three four five and repeating until she had to exhale and after each count the cattle emerged from the waters to move up the slope to the mountain side. After the wedding they went to live at *Esgair Llaethdy* or the Ridge of the Dairy, about a mile from Myddfai. She had three children. The first blow occurred as they were about to go to a christening. She was reluctant saying that it was too far to walk. He then told her to get a horse from the field but she said only if he fetched her gloves from the house. (In other Welsh legends of the marriage between a fairy and a mortal it was usually the touch of cold iron from a horse's bridle that accidentally causes a return to the lake water.) When he came back she was still standing where he had left her, and irritated he slapped her on the shoulders with the gloves, saying *dod*, go go. She warned him to be careful as he had just given her the first causeless blow. The second occasion was at the wedding of a neighbour. Everyone there was enjoying themselves except his wife. She was full of tears and continued to weep. Anxious to make her cease crying he struck her asking what the matter was. She then told him that as the couple were entering into life's troubles she was crying for them. Now it's for you my husband as you have just struck me a second time without cause or reason. Years passed. The children had grown and the rich herder had never forgotten his pledge for he was always watchful to make sure he did not touch her in any way that might breach their agreement.

However at a funeral in the midst of his people weeping and mourning for the deceased, his wife could not control her loud outbursts of laughter. He was so shocked that he struck her saying hush hush do not laugh so. She told him that when people die they go away from life's troubles and as she turned to leave, she said to him: "you have struck me the final senseless blow and so broken the contract. Our marriage is now over. Farewell." Walking away slowly towards Esgair Llaethdy she began to call the cattle to her

> Brindled cow, white speckled, spotted cow,
> Bold freckled, the four field sward mottled.
> The old white-faced and the grey Geingon
> With the white bull from the court of the king.
> Even my little black calf slaughtered on the hook
> Come also. Quite well home.

All answered her call and followed, even the four field oxen tied to the plough.

> *Pedwar eidion glas*
> *Sydd ar y maes*
> *Deuwch chwithau*
> *Yn iach adre!*

The four grey oxen/ that are on the field/ come well home/ quite well home! The only trace left of their passing was a furrow made by the plough drawn by the four oxen over the six miles of moor land. What became of the herder is not recorded. His sons often wandered by the Llyn y Fan Fach hoping that she might reappear again. At a spot near Dol Howel, still called *Llidiad y Meddygon* or the Physician's Gate, she talked to Rhiwallon, the eldest one, to tell him that his work now was to relieve the pain and misery of the people through healing all manner of their diseases. He was to be a benefactor to mankind. For this purpose she gave him a bag of medicinal prescriptions and instructions for their use. She said that by paying strict attention to them, he and his family would become the most skilled physicians in the country, for generations to come.

On several occasions she met her sons by the edge of the lake and once even returned with them on their way home as far as the *Pant y Meddygon* or the Physician's Dingle. She pointed out the various plants and herbs growing there, revealing to them their medicinal qualities and virtues. The knowledge she imparted coupled with their skill made the family famous for generations and in order that it should not be lost, it was committed to writing for the benefit of mankind. And as the father of the grey old man in the corner had heard the story that his father heard and after them I have remembered it. Now so will you. A tale handed down.[6]

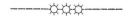

Llyn y Fan Fach is tucked in below the steep escarpment of the Carmarthen Van and part of a high ridge called Mynydd Ddu the Black Mountain. From where I live by the Preseli Hills in North Pembrokeshire, it is often visible as a horizontal marker and if one were to continue eastwards, the Ural Mountains would be the next highest point. Yet from the Carmarthenshire side, off the A40 through Llangadog, that landmark so familiar from countless photographs as a candy-coloured backdrop to the lake itself is not visible within the surrounding countryside. You have to traverse what can only be described as a green desert through dense clustering of overgrown hedges along undulating narrow unmarked roads and circular lanes until almost within reach of the hamlet of Llanddeusant, the church of the two saints. Wooden directional signs point the way along a track to a parking place below the reservoir. The original shorelines of the lake are quite doubtful. Sitting on a flat rock jutting out square and halfway up one slope, one can see the open treeless moor stretching beyond its dappled waters. It was in such a setting that the young herder waited for his love to emerge from the waters below. To move beyond the thrall of legend and actually visit the physical place and to sit in reverie above the small lake can be enlivening. The gap in time and many changes in the landscape around it due to the intrusion of modern life may destroy even a glimmer of its former beauty, as well as faith in the romance! But yet in that sparsely populated region, far from the main roads, it is just about possible to place oneself within a conjunction of mythic time and legendary history; to situate the physical contours of the present onto the herder's initial experience that somehow still permeates the ancient lake; with the eye of the imagination to move outside the irreversible flood of time composed of distant rivers and many time lines passing into the uncertain realms of a historical footnote.

Recently on my way up to the lake while passing two East Europeans I asked if they had seen the 'lady'. The immediate jocular response was no, but they did see the bubbles she left behind. Although much of the fabric of fairy beliefs had been swept away long before the publication of the legend which has been widely copied and promulgated from the 1861 editions and more recent reprints; the actual site of the encounter between the young man and the lake maiden has become a 'must-see' for visitors and people keen on myth and local lore.

From the mid-19th century the story of the lady from Llyn y Fan Fach had not only entered the literature of folklore and was as well known as any of the tales of the Mabinogion — initially translated into English by Lady Charlotte Guest — but it also had become firmly entrenched with the beginnings of Welsh medicine through the influence of the Rev. John Williams, editor of the bilingual versions of the *Physicians of Myddfai*. Both were crucial ingredients in the transformation of mid-Victorian scholarship into many of the current notions of a Welsh cultural nation that the heritage and tourist industry portrays to the rest of the world. Since the 1880's the eminent historian Sir John Rhys in recording many oral Welsh versions had formulated a collection of extant folklore associated with lakes in Wales. It was, he had written, partly to ascertain if the Myddfai legend were uniquely one of a kind. The folk motifs of the abduction of a fairy maiden were extensive and fairly common throughout the upland regions but apart from the variants he found here in Carmarthenshire, the story of a water maiden granting the gift of healing to a particular family of physicians did not appear to be known elsewhere. He was not overtly successful in his recording of the locals when visiting the area in search of storytellers whereas a century earlier the oral tradition had still been strong. At least three elderly residents had told their versions of the tale to a printer from Llandovery. The scholar bemoaned the loss of such original material that had been conflated and edited to form the single literary version published by Williams (ab Ithel) as if it were a prelude to the medical texts. However interesting the folklore associated with the area, if any of the additional motifs collected by Rhys such as the 'boiling' of the lake waters; the gathering of many people there on Lammas Sunday; a doctor eating the fairy bread so easily capturing one of three maidens; the appearance of a fearsome monster when they attempted to drain the lake; and a maiden in a golden skiff as the sun set on St. John's Eve; would not only have altered the tone of the published account but would certainly have distorted the 'gift of healing' and the beginning of Welsh medicine now generally associated with the lake.[7]

A recent archaeological examination of a Bronze Age burial mound above the lake was undertaken because of the erosive combination of the weather and the many walkers on the ridge of the Black Mountain. The dig revealed the burial site of a young girl beneath the earth mound of Fan Foel. She had been buried in a cist or stone coffin and alongside the human remains were the burnt bones of two pigs and possibly a dog. Scientific analysis of the surrounding soil found microscopic pollen grains to indicate that the burial was accompanied by a scattering of meadowsweet over the girl's body. The practice of placing floral tributes on the dead took place here at least four thousand years ago. The small white and cream faintly aromatic flowers usually appear in low lying damp areas during mid-summer or early autumn. Its common name 'Queen of the Meadow' is fairly apt for once it becomes established the five-petalled flowers can completely cover a low lying meadow. It was also known as mead wort which was formally an important ingredient in brewing mead or beer.[8]

What the discovery of this burial and its floral tribute brings up is an extraordinary connection over time that touches many points of ritual and the liminal aspect of this sacred place. It may be no more than an interesting connection of associations but the synergy between the meadowsweet tribute to the Bronze Age girl, the

20

common names of the plant as queen of the land and an ingredient in feasting and intoxication, and the deep waters of Llyn y Fan Fach below the ridge from which the fairy woman brought her gift of medicine to the Welsh people is remarkable. Even more so as salicylic acid was discovered in the flower buds in 1839 and from it aspirin was later synthesized which has become the most popular cure-all or pain relevant of modern times.

'The leaves and floures of meadowsweet farre excelle

all other strowing herbs for to decke up houses, to strawe

in chambers, halls and banqueting-houses in the summer-

time, for the smell thereof makes the heart merrie and

joyful and delighteth the senses'.   *Gerard's Herbal*

PART ONE

THE DARK AGES AND BEYOND

Chapter 1. Popular Roman Medicine

Hippocrates (486-377 BC) was known even in antiquity as the father of medicine with very good reason. He perfected a rational method for treating people, devoid of superstition and magical cant. The basis on which such an intellectual approach flowered was the system of the Four Humours. The humours of the blood, of bile, of phlegm and of choler would be evenly balanced in a healthy body. Imbalance of one or any combination of the four was the prime cause of peoples' sickness. Treatment of specific diseases centred on the understanding of how the bodily humours interacted and how they could be returned to be in harmony with each other. Blood-letting and purging were the quick methods of reducing the grip of imbalance. A judicious use of herbal remedies could bring slow relief as the body regained its capacity for the balanced state. Diet and general health-care facilitated the healing power of nature to enable the patient to make a complete recovery.

There were other schools of medicine besides the Alexandrian. The first medical teaching school in Rome was founded by a Greek epicurean called Asclepiades of Bithynia. He urged more active methods to process a cure. But it was Galen (AD 130-200) personal physician to the emperor Marcus Aurelius who was to become the most influential writer in the spread of western medicine. He combined the teachings of the Four Humours with the Doctrine of Contraries. This was in effect the treatment of and by opposites he learnt at the Hippocratic School in Alexandria. Galen's ideas became the basis of a highly pragmatic approach to physical illness. He maintained that all substances in nature have the same hot, cold, dry and moist elements as the qualities that are present in a human body. Furthermore since each quality or element had four degrees of intensity, so by modifying the original Hippocratic humoral doctrine

22

Galen created a more complex system on which the physician had to base his diagnosis and treatment. As all plants and mineral substances used in healing had four such elements so Galen altered the then accepted 'simples' tradition as used in Greek medicine by way of Egypt. This created a highly complex mixture of potions to accommodate his diagnostic theories. Later writers might modify or ignore the possible permutations in arriving at a diagnosis, yet the marriage of the Four Humours and the Four Elements pervade later medical treatises of European medicine; equally so with the Galen type mixture of herbal remedies that were popularly prescribed from the Middle Ages onwards. Such cocktails were for those who could afford it, and they were deemed the necessary adjunct for any treatment of royalty and the ruling classes. The poor had to make do with their traditional 'simples' or single therapeutic herbal remedy.

With the massive military invasion of Britain in AD 43 by Claudius was a Roman physician known as Scribonius Largus of the *Empiric* school. This meant that rather than relying on *a priori* knowledge or a system, his medical practice was based on personal experience and on trial-and-error in dealing with his patients' complaints. He was perhaps a forerunner of today's general practitioner! The visit to Britain makes him a significant figure in relation to what is known of Roman medicine and its influence here after the legions left. An army manual or his *Receipt Book* written at the time gives a number of prescriptions based on common herbs. Some of the unguents he employed for soldiers wounds had antiseptic properties such as the Madonna lily. Garlic was used as a staple food and useful to ward off infections for coping with coughs and lung infestations in the colder climates. Pliny the Elder (AD 23-79) was probably the most important Roman authority on science and medicine. He recommended garlic in hot milk to counter asthma and turnip (mashed and heated) as a useful cure for chilblains which the legionnaires standard sandal would have encouraged. The common dock was meant to counter scurvy. *Radix Britannica* or the British root was found stamped on a small ointment tin in the excavations of a Roman fort in Germany.[1]

Receipt Book of Scribonius Largus

De Compositione Medicamentorum of Scribonius Largus contained over two hundred and seventy prescriptions for the preparation of remedies which included plants, minerals and animal substances. The following are some of the plants listed: *aconite, aloes, anise, aniseed, belladonna, cardamoms, cedar wood oil, crocus, dill, gentian, ginger, iris, juniper, mistletoe, mustard, myrrh, olive oil, opium poppy, pepper, rose, rosemary, rue, santonica, valerian.* The manual also had directions on how to pack and transport herbal supplies. Each legion of ten cohorts (7,000 men) had its physician, a surgeon or bone-setter and a herbal quarter master. It was his job to guarantee stocks of medicines in their most usable form. If in short supply he had them transported quickly from elsewhere in the Empire. For instance the wormwood santonica was a bitter plant from the region of the Santones in Gaul. It contained santonin a poisonous compound. The Romans had brought the manufacture, storage and transport of drugs to a level previously unknown in the western world. But it was the Greeks who first wrote out extended lists of medicinal herbs along with their possible cures. Eventually a painted likeness of the plant was incorporated so that from the middle of the first millennium illuminated herbals began to appear.[2]

The definitive herbal was compiled by Pedacius Dioscorides, an army doctor who served under Nero during the first century AD. Based on his first-hand observation in the Near-East and in Europe, the work was originally written in Greek and included over a hundred plants already known to Hippocrates. Translated centuries later and under its Latin title *De materia medica* it became the authoritative herbal of the western world. The only known illustrated manuscript from early in the 6th century is the *Codex Vindobensis* which collates the *Materia Medica* written in Greek capital letters on parchment sheets as a bound book. The four-hundred brush illustrations of plants (with some birds) were by an unknown artist. It was prepared for Anicia daughter of the emperor of Constantinople and is now in the Austrian National Library in Vienna. The herbal was studied, extensively copied and translated down through the ages. An English version — opposite the Greek text — was hand-written in the 16th century by John Goodyer but was not published until centuries later.[3]

Medical historians, ignoring prehistory, tend to place the advent of medicinal arts in Britain with the Roman application of surgery and the use of magical charms from the Near East; with their reliance on Greek ideas such as the balance of the Four Humours as the key to health. Along with proper diet and a profuse dose of herbs, all made their entry here as part of the tool-kit of the Roman army doctors. The growth of Roman medicine was bound up with the army. Importance was given to its actual medical organization and the respect paid to the medical staff within the military hierarchy. From this arose the hospital system for treating soldiers, which according to Charles Singer was the greatest contribution of Rome to Western medicine. And furthermore it lay not so much in the rigid formulation of Greek ideas as was usual with the Romans but in the incorporation of sanitation and personal hygiene within the building of the first military hospitals. This was carried through on a massive architectural scale, initially in Rome and then in other cites throughout the empire. The layouts of such buildings were later to influence the Christian foundations for the sick, as can be seen from the plan of the hospice of St. Gall and the later basilica shape of the lazer or leper houses.

Originally the Republic was considered healthy without doctors. Cato the Censor decreed that cabbage was an excellent all heal for the sick and for anything more serious a magical formula could be intoned over the patient. Even though the Greek cities had long since introduced a kind of state medical care, the position of the doctor in Roman households was little better than a slave. It was Julius Caesar who conferred citizenship on all who practiced medicine within its walls. This was, according to Suetonius, to make them live in the city and induce others to resort there. A statute of Antoninus in 160 regulated the appointment of physicians in the army, the navy and in towns: stating that the smallest could have five doctors who were exempt from taxation, the larger towns seven and most important cities ten physicians. Part of their duty was to attend to the needs of the poor. They were also encouraged to train pupils in the arts of medicine. Presumably the same regulations applied to the British province. The scalpels, probes and spatulas that have been found in the debris of their towns here were standard Roman implements. Surgical saws, scissors, tweezers and forceps of all types including those for dental work were immured in the lava dust at Pompeii. Used initially in Greece, such medical instruments had been modified so they could be manufactured and produced on the same scale as the supply of herbal medicines.

Dental practice and even the wiring of loose teeth were clearly shown in the earliest scientific medical work written in Latin by Celsus in the first century AD. His *De re medica* begins with the proper emphasis on diet and the balance of the Four Humours relating to internal and external diseases. The final two of the eight sections of his treatise were devoted to surgery. He described various skin operations to the face and mouth, the removal of goitres and cutting out gall stones. This work by Celsus was unknown in Europe until it appeared in print in the late 15th century. Dr. Comrie writing about such medicine in Scotland stressed that Roman surgeons operated with steel-bladed knives; performed amputations when necessary as high as the knee and elbow; and afterwards provided the patient with artificial limbs. In their operations bleeding was arrested with the help of artery forceps and ligatures, and the edges of wounds were carefully stitched together. Complicated operations, such as those for hernia and cataract were performed, apparently with excellent results.[4]

Scribonius Largus seems to have been the earliest writer to make mention of 'an oath according to the Law of Medicine' that eventually become known as the Hippocratic Oath. Not many of us are aware of what a doctor swore to uphold but throughout the Roman Empire the relationship of pupil to master was explicit. A teacher was as dear to the novice as his own father and the teachers' sons as his brothers to whom he would teach the art of medicine in turn, without fee or stipulation. He could impart knowledge to his own sons and to disciples bound by contract and oath, but to none other. We can see that such a contract was the secret bond of the male medical lineage in later Welsh medicine. The oath of the medieval hereditary doctors was as much a bind as the family kin in their pre-modern medical genealogy. The Roman doctor also seems to be the first that we know of, after the early Egyptians, to name the parts of the outer physical body without relation to their connection with inner organs. He described a visual rather than the visceral anatomy. It began first with the head and then moved down to the soles of the feet; a formula extremely popular during the Middle Ages. Some of the Welsh manuscripts (of Myddfai) retain evidence of this form of presentation but the most complete example is the prayer called the *Lorica of Gildas* or *Gillus*. Six versions are known from extant Anglo-Saxon manuscripts which indicate the importance attached to the ancient descriptive form of the body; and to the power of the name of the Welsh saint linked with the protective healing prayer when recited over a sick or dying person.

Doctor Melus of Llangian.

An inscribed pillar stone at Llangian is a rare memorial from the Dark Ages in that it actually named a doctor. Situated at the extreme southeast corner of the Lleyn peninsula opposite Bardsey Island; St. Cian's churchyard was dedicated to the servant of Peris — a saint closely associated with many known place names around Llanberis in Snowdonia. In the manner that a few bones from an archaeological excavation can reveal vital information about the life of that individual so it is possible to deconstruct an inscription carved on an ancient stone. The clear cut Langian inscription runs in three vertical lines of Latin downward across the face of the stone. When translated directly it reads as, (the stone of) Melus the Doctor, the son of Martinus. He lies (here): MELI MEDICA / FILII MARTINI / IACIT. Concise dating of such inscriptions is difficult

27

without any historical correlation or epigraphic evidence. Yet the syntax in terms of formal layout, spacing and shapes of letters can be referenced to similar carvings throughout Wales from the early Christian era.[5]

The Celtic family designation of 'X son of Y' as in Mel son of Martin was a common formula in Latin, as well as on Irish Ogham stones; both were often conjoined on pillars in southwest Wales. Even the final *iacit* is indicative of its general usage here, indicating a date from mid to late 6th century, for the proper Latin spelling for 'here lies' was *iacet* usually found on stones elsewhere in Britain. The carving is in the form of the half uncial lettering and the vertical inscription was incised along the length of the stone. Earlier Roman memorials were generally uniformly chiselled out on smaller neat rectangular panels and carefully worked from left to right in well formed capitals. They were probably executed by masons using compass and ruler to ensure the proper standard of regularity to respect the dead person; and of course the status of the living family. The inscription to Melus the son of Martinus could not be simpler. Yet the fact that he was named as a doctor on this unique Dark Age memorial indicates a general public recognition among the Romano-British population. He may even have been a personal physician to Maelgwn Gwynedd, the local king who is recorded to have died of the yellow plague. Within the same area are two inscribed stones at Aberdaron with finely cut horizontal inscriptions dedicated to priests. The Verasius stone has forked serifs that are thought to show Greek influence but the Senacus stone is less regular with an incorrect phrasing of 'with a multitude of his brethen'. It may indicate the carver had some difficulty with Latin or that the mass burial was due to the plague.

Maelgwn the King of Gwynedd was often portrayed as a bogey-man in the *Lives* of the British saints. He was castigated by Gildas and later by Nennius for reverting, when he became ruler, to the ancient ways of a pagan Celtic overlord. With 'twenty-four fawning bards' his court may have had a resident mediciner, as set out in the later Welsh law codes, and from the unique commemoration after his death Melus may have been such a court physician. Maelgwn Gwynedd is recorded in the Annales Cambriae (oldest of the Welsh chronicles) as dying in the great mortality of 547. Later traditions concerning his death assert that to avoid the effects of the plague he moved from his royal fort at Dyganwy by the mouth of the Afon Conwy across to the headland of Rhos, for sanctuary in the church of Llanrhos by Colwyn Bay. However, impelled by curiosity, the King looked out through the keyhole and thereby caught the infection in his eye which brought him down. Maelgwn's death by peeping through the keyhole of the church door has an echo of divine retribution about it. It also suggests isolation and some facial disease affecting his eyes. In ancient Ireland no king was allowed to rule if he had a physical blemish. Gerald of Wales in the 12th century makes mention of a prince from north Wales called Edward Flatnose who was deprived of his rightful inheritance due to what may have been the effects of leprosy.[6]

There have been occasional disputes among epidemiologists on the authenticity of terms used by ancient writers to describe an outbreak of disease. The amended and often edited repetitions by later commentators were usually no better than informed guesswork or a symptomatic allusion to a general kind of illness. A classic example is the yellow fever that later writers reiterated as a form of jaundice. The medical historian and bibliographer John Cule in a paper read at a 1973 conference on Wales and Medicine in Swansea, showed in detail how this skin colouring was a later affected addition to the original brief references of an epidemic that wiped out hundreds of the saints of Wales and Ireland. The *Annals of Boyle* recorded a great mortality in Ireland for the year 543. A gloss on the text by a later hand added *buidhe chonaill* — an Irish term — for yellow fever. However some historians take these first recorded outbreaks here as local effects of the major Justinian pandemic of a bubonic nature that devastated the Eastern and Western Empire. Earlier, in 538, the sun had become darkened for at least eighteen months and the Roman world was enveloped in a grey mist. Although the effects of drastic climatic changes such as floods, drought and severe cold are often the unmentioned causes or carriers of famine and pestilence, a cryptic indicator for the year 543 in the Irish *Annals of Clonmacnoise* — 'bread was very scarce this yeare' — may be an effect related to the long term pall of dark skies throughout the Roman world. It is likely that Irish scribes may have then termed the later epidemic as yellow fever to differentiate it from the red dust or grey colouring of earlier outbreaks.[7]

An uncommon inscription, among a number of other stones at Penmachno church, is thought to refer to the time of Justinus the consul. It has two forms of lettering set vertically and horizontally. That stone pillar has now split in the centre so that part of the vertical message is gone leaving FILI AVITORI or the son of Avitorus (probably preceded by 'he lies here') sprawled along its broad face. Below this, a possible reference to Justinus is carved horizontally in three incomplete lines. The long flinty stone was found in 1915 built into a garden wall. Sir John Rhys wrote an account of it that was to be his final contribution to Welsh epigraphy before his death later in the year. His reading was accepted as such by Nash-Williams a later authority on early Christian carvings; although whether the year 540 when Flavius Justinius was consul of the Western Empire is the year that the stone was actually carved has been questioned; an issue that Rhys himself was cautious about when he deciphered its brief message — 'in the time of.' It may have been carved to indicate that it was an important occasion to be remembered by the monks of this early church, south of Betws y Coed. A most catastrophic and worldwide event that occurred during his reign in Constantinople was a bubonic pandemic that bears his name, the Justinian plague. The Emperor himself was affected and tens of thousands died in the capital. It was recorded in France and Spain in 545; in the Annales Cambriae and in the Irish Annals of the same period.[8]

Some recent suggestions for the physical cause of the sun darkening over such a long period — which has been verified by the narrowed annual rings of oaks and other trees from the period — are that it was as a result of the widespread effects of a massive earthquake; or even more spectacularly a meteor break-up from a comet passing particularly close to the earth. The evidence for either hypothesis is not conclusive yet such scenarios for the demise of the Roman world and the beginning of the Dark Ages are but a variation of the many that have sought to explain the results of extensive tribal inroads into the Empire from the north and east amid the political upheavals at this time. The virility of the plague in Wales and Ireland may have been related to the extensive shipping links that western Britain enjoyed with the classical world, as has been suggested by early *chi-rho* monograms found on pottery vessels and also on one of the stone carvings at Penmachno church. At the same time the relative isolation of the Angles and Saxons along the eastern hinterlands at this time may have helped them escape the worst effects of an epidemic and allowed for their gradual expansion from eastern England without much resistance from the west. Even though it is only the saints and a king like Maelgwn that are mentioned in the Irish and Welsh Annals, one can infer that members of the leading secular families were equally affected. The memorial to Melus, as well as the other personalized inscribed stones throughout Gwynedd shows that its Romano-British society and institutions were still well established at this period.[9]

During the century preceding the departure of the Roman legions in AD 410 there seemed to have been a sense of expansion and prosperity in the western province, perhaps due to more settled economic conditions coupled with a wider embrace of Romanization by the native tribes. The confidence can be seen in the re-building of towns and forts; in the new country villas on the south coast such as at Llantwit Major; and in the religious buildings dedicated to Celtic gods, Sulis at Bath and Nodens in the healing temple at Lydney on the banks of the Severn. The layout of the precincts around it included a large guest house and a long building called the abation. It had small rooms for at least seven people to undergo the ritual incubation, known as 'temple-sleep' — a common practice in ancient Greece — whereby the sufferer would dream of the resident god for a cure to be a favourable one. Herbs and bathing were part of the therapy. In the excavations of the Lydney complex a great variety of votive offerings were found such as bracelets, pins and a bone plaque with an incised figure of an eagle on it. Six miniature dogs carved in stone and nine in a copper-alloy point to the particular Roman canine preference in small ritual offerings. The objects may symbolize or denote the religious sacrifice of actual live animals. Lead mining at some stage had been carried on underneath the building. 'Cursing' plaques of lead were common here. On one, Silvanus had lost a ring and was so sure that Senicianus had taken it, that he asked the god Nodens to ensure ill-health would follow all of that name until the ring was returned to him. [10]

Perhaps the popularity of the Nodens healing cult should be seen as a part of a neo-Celtic revival among the Romanized ruling families who would be unaware of the sudden withdrawal of the Roman legions at the end of that century and the possible demise of Empire. The gods would have been enshrined within the familiar urban model of bathhouses, games, offerings and healing by dream divinations. Whereas away from the towns and particularly among the tribes beyond the decaying networks of roads and old forts, the religion of the people and the indigenous ritual cults would be cruder, closer to nature and their old ancestral spirits. Excavations at Caerwent (Venta Silurum) revealed a shrine within a temple precinct that had a stone seated figure of a mother goddess with fruit and palm or conifer branches. There was also a sandstone head with wide bulging eyes that may have represented a god such as *Mars Ocelus*. The idea of a war god as a fighter against disease appears to have been a regular feature throughout the Roman world. The head may also have been a votive offering showing the part of the body in need of a cure. Within the extensive stone buildings of Wroxeter (originally in Powys but now in Shropshire) which was their third largest city in Britain, forty plaster eyes were found together in a heap. The average size was about five cm across. A representation of an eye made from sheet gold with the tear ducts and pupils emphasized was also found. The quantity of the votive offerings at this site suggests there may have been a temple here and possibly a well-shrine where cures for eye complaints were sought. An interesting die had been found near Wroxeter in 1808. A woodcut of its representation in sealing wax showed it to be roughly the size of a 50p coin. It had an abbreviated message written in small letters: 'The dialibanum (or eye salve) of Tiberius Claudius the physician, for all complaints of the eyes, to be used with egg'; a reminder to the patient that the contents should be mixed with the yolk of egg before use. A considerable number of such Roman medicine stamps have been found. It appears that in the smaller towns, rather than employ the expensive services of a doctor, people would go to the apothecary shop where potions and cures were on sale from Egypt, Greece and native sources. The stamps of a number of occultists have been found in excavations of other sites — Silvanus Tetricus in London; Vidacus Ariovistus near Hereford; and Julius Juvenis in St. Albans who had a myrrh antiseptic balm and egg salve. Gaius Vilerius Amandus in Bedford offered poppy ointment for inflammation, drops for dim sight and vinegar lotion for poor runny eyes.[11]

Perhaps the Julius Martinus from Chester, who sold a saffron salve for soreness of the eyes, may have been the father of Melus the Doctor, both of whom were named on the Langian memorial in the Lleyn peninsula. In an era bereft of historical data the stone is not only a marker to an individual uniquely honoured in the post-Roman period but at a time when the society of early Wales as we know it, was forming. The legions had departed a century or so earlier from their main towns in Wales — Moridunum (Carmarthen) in the south, Segontium (Caernarfon) in the northwest, Deva (Chester) in the northeast and Viriconium (Wroxeter) in the east but the remnants of the social order the military had instituted seem to have continued in some form. Pagan and Christian peoples no doubt maintained as best they could the world they had been born into. Historians were fond of a dynamic construct — based mainly on Christian writers like Gildas and Nennius — of the Romano-British society maintaining their familiar ordered world, as the conservative group in a Dark Age melting pot. Such peoples are seen as clinging

33

to the then outmoded social institutions and a body politic left behind in a provincial corner of a rapidly disintegrating Empire. It was a time when Mercian warriors were pushing in from England; the Irish Deisi and Laigan groups were occupying low lying areas of the southwest and the British people of northern Britain expelled from their ancient kingdoms in Lowland Scotland by the Angles, had settled in the mountainous sanctuary of Snowdonia. According to Nennius they then displaced the Irish from the fertile island of Anglesey and eventually consolidated what became known as the kingdom of Gwynedd.

The suggested connection between Martin the father of Mel and the Martin on the oculist's ointment stamp is possibly enhanced by the details of its archaeological finding. It was discovered in 1973 during an excavation situated below the Weights and Measures office carport in Gross Street, Chester. The report specifically states that it was found in a post-Roman context which would certainly help to bring the probable dates of Martinus of Chester and the father of Melus buried at Llangian closer together in the middle to late 6th century. The stamp was made of green mudstone and the four faces measure roughly thirty-nine by nine millimetres thick, the texts on each indicating the patent medicines were cut retrograde so that the prepared medicine would presumably be available in a small container to be stamped with the correct facet of the die. The medicines were *stractum* an unguentor ointment; *diapsoricum* an anti-irritant; *penicilli* referred to ointments; and *crododes ad aspiritudinem* a saffron salve for soreness (of the eyes).[12]

Curiously enough these, as well as the stamps found in France and Germany, are all medicines for the eyes indicating that such afflictions were prevalent at this time. Much later, the evidence from holy wells throughout Wales shows that it continued to be a common concern. According to Francis Jones in 1954, over a thousand holy wells had retained their reputation for healing up to modern times. The greater number of springs — apart from those that claimed to be able to cure all illness or those with a local reputation for unspecified healing — were the seventy-eight

34

beneficial for complaints of the eyes, including blindness, inflammation, stye and poor eyesight. Many 'eye' prescriptions that were to be found written in Welsh from later medieval manuscripts, and seemingly became fused into common oral lore, are often remarkably similar to those from the earlier Anglo-Saxon leech books.

The Classical Legacy in Britain.

It appears that after the departure of the legions in 410 their medical legacy was a combination of the practical and theoretical — an approach which found, in part, some expression in Anglo-Saxon literature. English medical practice has been considered as a mix of Teutonic charm magic, Roman herbal lore and Christian prayer. What have survived from their literature are magical 'curing charms' incorporating prayers and healing recipes. The distinctions between literature and medical writings may not have been as clear-cut as they are generally set down by modern scholars and overlaps between them were possibly more widespread than is appreciated now. The problem is one that bedevils the study of early medicine in Britain, and especially in Wales where vernacular manuscript evidence is only available from the 14th century. The Venerable Bede instances many examples of miracle cures that appear to have been influenced by biblical writings. His works exhibit hardly a mention of the heathenism of his forebears. As Charles Singer observes, almost without any indication that their imported German culture was a new element in Britain and one that was not welcomed by the Celtic peoples. In fact Bede appears more distraught that the British monks still retained their centuries old enmity against the Saxons. They would, he writes, refuse to sit and throw their food to the dogs rather than eat with them. He recounts the events around the story of the eight British bishops who refused to bow before Augustine who was sent by Pope Gregory in 596 or even to join with him in his mission to convert the pagan Anglians. So the lack of any continental influences on medicine or other arts among the kingdoms of the west is not surprising.[13]

Bede was informative about the practical aspects of medicine, especially blood-letting within the monastic orders of his day, and that there were lay physicians available at this early period. The *medicus* Cynifrid was called upon to perform a surgical operation during the fatal illness of Etheldrida an Anglian princess. Anglo-Saxon law ensured that noble women were well treated and if divorced, property was usually divided which was the case with Etheldrida who had refused to consummate her marriage to the pagan king Egfrid for twelve years because she was a devout Christian. She then founded a convent and as abbess became known for her saintly ways. After she died miracle cures were attributed to her. Sixteen years later her body was exhumed and found to be complete and not decayed. In fact the doctor was on hand to confirm that he had made a large incision in her neck to lance a swelling as a last ditch attempt to save the woman. This scar had healed over inside the coffin. The writer goes into detail at this point to show the sanctity of the nun and God's divine intercession preventing the natural physical processes after death. However in terms of medicine during the so-called Dark Age period, the fact that a leech or physician was attached to an ecclesiastical establishment and prepared to perform surgery in an emergency as well as attending to the exhumation of the body, indicates the status of the doctor and the range of medical treatment available to the early English nobility.

There is clear evidence from a number of later Anglo-Saxon manuscripts containing a Lorica or the charm prayer of Gildas, that the works of this Briton was esteemed. The *Lorica* was written in a form of Hisperic or the so-called Hibernian Latin that incorporated many Old Irish, Greek, Hebrew and other idioms. As an extended healing prayer it was probably chanted over the dying patient thereby describing all the parts of the body from the head downwards; a formula introduced into Britain by the Roman doctor Scribonius Largus. The term lorica was also used for the chain-mail

36

coat worn by Irish and English warriors in battle. A carving on the whalebone casket in the British Museum shows some fighting men of the early 8th century wearing them. The Franks Casket is an important relic from Northumbria and may show a symbolic connection with native healing. Wearing such a battle-coat made of leather was common in ancient times and the word was used in a religious sense as protection against the evils of this world. In the epistle of St. Paul to the Ephesians there are a number of exhortations to put on 'the armour of God against the wiles of the devil'; to put on 'the lorica of righteousness'; and take up 'the helmet of salvation'; a note that is repeated by Gildas with, 'on my head be a helmet of protection'. To add to the spiritual need of protecting the body against physical illness the lorica was usually linked in name with a powerful saint. The earliest surviving hymn is thought to be that of Saint Patrick. The protection that it elicits was from the incantations of pagan priests, and against the enemies that lay in ambush for his disciples and himself. Termed *feath fiada* or the 'cry of the deer', his *Lorica* was a plea for divine help against the actions of idolaters and the spells of women, smiths and druids. The second prologue relates all parts of the body that foul demons, as is their wont, may not hurt, beginning with a short list of the physical aspects .[14]

God the unconquerable guardian,

Defend me on every side by thy power.

Free thou all limbs of mine,

With thy shield protecting each,

So that the fell demons brandish not

Against my sides, as is their wont with darts.

Skull, head, hair and eyes,

Forehead, tongue, teeth and their covering,

Neck, breasts, side, bowels,

37

Waist, buttocks and both hands.

From the crown of my head with its hair,

Be thou the helmet of salvation on the head.

After all the individual parts of the head, face , mouth and teeth are enumerated he pleads to Christ invoking the nine orders of holy angels to be his *Lorica* and keep him safe from the invisible nails and stakes of his enemies.

Cover, therefore O God, with strong corslet,

Along with shoulder blades, shoulders and arms,

Cover elbows with elbow-joints and hands,

Fists, palms, fingers with their nails.

Cover backbone and ribs with their joints,

Hind parts, back, nerves and bones.

Cover surface, blood and kidneys,

Haunches, buttocks with the thighs.

Cover hams, calves, thighs,

Kneecaps, houghs and knees.

Cover ankles, shins and heels,

Legs, feet and the rest of the soles.

Cover the branches that grow ten together,

With the toes and the nails ten.

Cover chest, its join, the little breast,

Paps stomach, navel.

Cover belly, reins, genitals,

And pouch and vital parts also of the heart.

Cover the triangular liver and fat,

Spleen, armpits with hair covering.

Cover stomach, chest with the lungs,

Veins, sinews, gall-bladder.

Cover flesh, groin with the inner parts,

Spleen with the winding intestines.

Cover bladder, fat and all

The numberless orders of joints.

Cover hairs and the rest of my limbs,

Whose names, maybe I have passed by.

Cover me in all with my five senses,

And with the ten doors formed (for me)

So that, from the soles to the top of the head,

In no member, without within, may I be sick.

Some surviving Anglo-Saxon manuscripts written in English abbeys and presumably by monks in the centuries up to the Norman conquest, contain a definite substratum of old Germanic folk beliefs, medical remedies and the doctrines of elf dart and the 'venums'. Scholars have interpreted the main tenets of their magical lore as well as their medicine that was clearly considered important enough to be written down from an indigenous oral base incorporating social rituals, weather lore, charm medicine and even Christianized beliefs. To a committed Christian, many of the rituals, the magical incantations and pagan rites to the old gods; as well as the divination's, the casting of lots or *tan* and charm-medicine would be deemed to be detrimental to the new faith; although heroes and gods like Wotan fitted easily into an omnipotent omniscient God. The major part of the Leech Book of Bald contains the Herbarium of Apeleius Platonius which scholars believe may have been written in

Africa for many of its herbs originate there. The other part of this work is the *Lacnunga* or *Home Remedies*; it is a curious uneven mixture of cures, Irish incantations, Christian prayers (against elves), charms against flying venum, elfshot, miscarriages and pestilence. It describes how diseases arose in the world.[15]

The *Lay of the Nine Herbs* is a remarkable example that illustrates the old Teutonic magic of the northern forests. It contains the main elements of their folk-medicine and includes the doctrines of 'specific venums'; of the 'nines'; and of the worm; although a more common one of 'elf-dart' or 'elf-shot' is not named in the Lay. The elves were of a supernatural kind of beings who mainly clustered in wild uncultivated swampy areas from where they would shoot their foul darts at people, to pass on diseases commonly associated with such dank places. Songs to counteract their effects usually called on the powers of the earth to bury the darts.

Dha genam woden	Then took Woden
VIIII wuldortanas	Nine magic lots
sloh dha tha naeddran	Smote then that serpent
thaet heo on VIIII tofleah.	That she flew apart in nine bits.

Woden smiting the worm is a common northern myth and the god Woden or Odin as victor was also a harbinger of good fortune and good health. The following lines show how diseases, as a result, arose from the fragments of the reptile.

na magon that VIIII wyrta	Now these nine herbs avail
width nygon wuldorgeflogenum	Against nine spirits of evil,
widh VIIII attrum	Against nine venoms
widh mygon onflygnum	And against nine winged onsets

A description of their powers follows this introduction, as against the *red venom*, the *white venom*, the *purple venom*, the *yellow venom*, the *green venom*, the *livid venom*, *the blue venom*, the *brown venom* and the *crimson venom*. After the nine poisons come the nine diseases that they produce, although only six are listed in the *Lacnunga* manuscript. The *worm blaed, water blaed, thorn blaed, thistle blaed, ice blaed, venom blaed. Blaed* was a term for breath or spirit so disease was considered as emanating from animal, vegetable or mineral elements. Next are the *flying venoms* although the wind or agent that produced the disease is not a visible entity. They are called from the four quarters of heaven.

If any venom   Flying from the east   Or flying from the south

      Or any from the north   Or any from the west

          Come nigh   Over the world of men

The final passage is obscure suggesting that disease can be washed off by water in its curative aspect and to be completely blown away by the power of incantation. The respect given to breath and the shamanic action of blowing away disease or physical discomfort is still a popular form of medicine with Amerindian shaman healers.[16]

      We know   The running streams   And the nine serpents

      Now behold   All weeds must now   Fall among herbs

      Seas must desolve   All salt water

      When I this venum   From thee blow

Like much of what has survived of written Anglo-Saxon medical lore, incorporating different aspects of their native indigenous folklore, the example above was probably originally written in the form of old chants to be sung aloud. In some instances the services of a mass priest is advised to make a cure more effective though more usually absolute silence is stressed while a healing rite is performed. Not much is known about the chanted rites or even the leeches who attended them. Dun and Oxa are the two other healers beside Bald that were mentioned in the *Leech Book*. Perhaps in the manner of Anglo-Saxon poetry with its stressed beat in the centre of each line. Such chants would doubtless have been sung in a repetitive contrapuntal voice. *Gaeldor* was a common word for the magical song which is well rendered by the more familiar enchantment, although in its original sense of the Latin *incantatio.*

For many of their charms it would seem that the power of sympathetic transference was at work, especially those related to legendary heroes who suffered likewise or who were cured of a disease, quite different to the matter in hand. A curious remedy for the ague was by laying the fourth book of the Illiad under the patient's pillow. The reason given was that in it Homer relates how a milkmaid used the milk tooth of a child as an amulet under her head at night to affect a cure. The 3rd century Roman who recorded the cure for ague suggested that for the severest kind (of shivering fevers), the formula be written down as ABRACADABRA in a magic square and then applied to the sufferer as a healing amulet. The transference of a disorder was also equally brought about with some animal, vegetable, mineral object; or even to the earth itself. The power of a carved rune was used for seizure. The ritual instructions were of the simplest and had to be done alone and in silence: 'Take a hazel stick. Cut they rune (name) within in. Fill the rune with blood. Throw it over your shoulder into running water'.[17]

The translations of early Christian texts and those from Greek and Roman herbals is a fair indication of the intellectual acumen and thirst for knowledge of the Anglo-Saxons towards the end of the first millennium AD. The medical writings of the Dark Ages available to the English, according to Singer, were the translations from Greek into Latin of Galen, Dioscorides, Alexander of Tralles and Paul of Aegina whose works were probably available from the 8th century. There were also some treatises borrowed from the Greek but written in Latin from different parts of the Empire. The commentaries of Bede himself; and of Alcuin (735-804) on the Natural History of Pliny; and the works of Isidore of Seville (560-636) were summarized early in the 11th century by Byrhferth of Ramsey from the writings of the above on different aspects of healing. This had established the groundwork for English medicine in terms of the philosophical basis of the Four Humours and the Four Elements especially as transliterations from the Latin into the European vernaculars elsewhere were not generally done until centuries later. So using such classical knowledge as was available they created a synthesis within their own cultural milieu to incorporate sympathetic and contagion magic as a means of diagnosis and healing. It would appear from their descriptions that cold venum may relate to our ideas of a virus and that the flying, active, agitated or hot venum spread disease and caused epidemics. There were also illnesses created by red venum, white venum, wind venum and a range of other coloured poisons whose particular meanings or resonance within early English medicine remains obscure. We know that the spread of cholera, smallpox or the plague was by an entity so small that it could only be imagined prior to magnification by the microscope in the late 17th century. With the hindsight of neurological medicine and diseases caused by anti-immune deficiency it is perhaps easier to be sympathetic to their descriptions of disease in terms of flying venums, rather than those earlier commentators who tended to dismiss it as ill considered gibberish or poetic formulations by scribes who had no idea of what they were writing about. It may have been so, but their attempts to describe in words a range of essentially indescribable intrusions of diseases into the human body, should not be dismissed out of hand. Much of what has been written about old English medicine is tinged with the late 19th century superiority of western science as a panacea for every complaint and illness. Perhaps we are becoming more accustomed now to accept, according to medical science, new and strange viruses in the form of social epidemics as HIV or Aids and even that fatal strains of animal and avian diseases can and do enter the human food chain. The periodic discussions on television and media news show we seem to be as willing as any people in the past to explain disease away with words; rather than coping with human causality or the necessary radical changes to lifestyles that may herald some evolution of human consciousness.

Chapter 2. Riders of the Apocalypse

The recording of *plague* and its vile attendant *pestilence* was commonplace throughout the centuries between the Justinian pandemic of the 6th and the Black Death in the middle years of the 14th century; so much so that the constant repetition in the early chronicles dulls our responses to such periodic outbreaks of disease. Descriptions are general. Details of peoples' actual suffering are left to the imagination. We wonder at the resilience of the human condition and how they survived such maladies! High born or lowly bred, no one seemed to be immune; yet life carried on. A diseased saint or noble man might well symbolize the sacred and secular institutions that were at risk. Both being blighted — in so far as plague touched the inner soul and pest the outer physical body — gave people insight and perhaps a mite of grace into a world beyond the reality of suffering. The *mea culpa*, the public recriminations of the sinner, the self flagellants laying bare the shame of health and beauty were a means of bonding (to use a current term) with the leper and diseased outcasts of society. There are numerous references to monks and holy women licking their vile sores. To be as one with the diseased leprous condition, like the disabled, the sterile and the mad who were deemed to be in a far superior position to gain spirituality from their visible physical torments. This meeting of souls and the spiritual barter between the healthy and the diseased, mirrored that of the ordinary sinner needing guidance from a priest as well as the sick seeking help from healers of all kinds; doctors, wise women and quacks. It was the accepted reality behind the terse formulaic words — plague and pestilence — that recur frequently in Welsh, Irish and English chronicles.[18]

The early records began with different base-dates and were probably written down from older accounts and then recalculated backwards so the dates given for particular events should be seen as a rough guide to conditions of the time. However they often dovetail within a year or two to provide a general idea of a widespread

45

epidemic as written out by monkish scribes to highlight the events of a previous year. The words 'famine and severe mortality' carried the same informative weight and local interest as the crowning of a king, death of a bishop or outcome of a battle. However a writer like Bede often added some human dimension to the more common brief scribal detail as when forty or fifty starving people joined hands on a cliff top to leap onto the rocks and seas below. From a historical perspective we may ponder on such stark statistics of disease down the centuries, although medical historians have often argued about their causes and effects.

The earliest text — *St. David's Chronicle* — of the *Annales Cambriae* edited by Rev. John Williams in the 1860 Rolls edition, records the events and happenings in Wales between the 5th and 10th centuries, although they are thought to have been composed during the middle of that period. The first epidemic recorded in it was said to have occurred in the year 526. It was copied from the *Vita Brioccil* whose original source is believed to date from the 9th century and written in the form of a plea from the faithful in Ceredigion asking Saint Brioc to sail back from Brittany to save them. A *llan* dedication on the north bank of the river Teifi at Llandyfriog bears his name. The region had been overwhelmed by a great catastrophe and the saint was their final hope of escaping so great a peril. Plague or famine could equally have been the result of a major coastal inundation of the sea that has periodically helped shape the present wide arms of Cardigan Bay. The Irish *Annals* — *of Inisfallen, of the Four Masters, of Tigernach, of Boyle* and *of Ulster* — were written over long periods, by many hands in different monasteries. Each would have had their own abbots and clans or septs with diverse political aspirations. The Anglo-Saxon Chronicles began as a result of the academic revival in the Wessex court of Alfred and were originally commissioned by him as a historical account from the beginning of the world to his own time toward the end of the 9th century. They were to be sent out to the English monasteries, and as completed in segments of years up to 1018. The early entries are brief such as 'a general famine and severe mortality in England' for the year 793, and written in English rather than in Latin. However details become gradually expansive and flowery, even including verse and with political and religious overtones. The Chronicles survive in seven manuscripts and in some fragments.

The Plague Years

They could be said to have begun at the grim battle of Camlan in which Arthur and Modred both died. It was recorded in the *Annales Cambriae* for the year 537 after which there was a 'great mortality' in Britain. The chronicler of a different version stated that plague occurred in Ireland as well. A great mortality prevailed there in the year 545, written in the *Annals of the Four Masters* as *buidhe connaill* or yellow fever and that a great number of the saints of Ireland died of it. The *Annals of Tigernach* for the same year used the word *bleded*, referring to bubonic(?) plague. For the following year an entry in the *Annales Cambriae* states there was a great mortality in which Maelgwn king of North Wales died; an event 'predicted' by Gildas in his 6th century work usually known as *The Ruin and Conquest of Britain*. It survives in a 10th century Canterbury manuscript although extracts of it were quoted in earlier works. The *Life of St. Teilo*, written in the 12th century *Liber Landavensis* (The Book of Llandaff) enlarges on the plague. It was called a yellow pestilence because all the people who were seized by it became yellow and (were) without blood. If anyone tried to apply a remedy to a sick person, not only had medicines no effect but it brought the physician together with the sick person to death. It had seized Maelgwn the king of North Wales and destroyed his country. In the *Life of Oudoceous* from the same manuscript, the epidemic is called, *y dylyt melen* and that, 'after a long time the yellow pestilence came to Greater Britain which was called yellow because it occasioned all persons who were seized by it to be yellow and pallid'. Geraldus Cambrensis described it as the disorder called the

47

yellow plague or by physicians, the 'icteric passion' (jaundice) by which people died in great numbers throughout Wales.[19]

Adomnan, in his *Life of St. Columba*, writes of a huge rain cloud that dropped pestiferous water on Ireland, producing festering sores on people and the udders of animals. It is thought to have been a form of cow pox. Reports of the great plague of 664-666 put the death toll at a third of population. The pious attributed it to the hand of God who however did not spare either the religious or the men of blood who then ruled society. The death of Cadwaler, the son of Cadwallon ap Cadfan, a prince of Gwynedd was recorded in the same year as that of St. Cuthbert. According to the Venerable Bede he died of a tumour in femore, a swelling of the thigh. An interesting shift in administration of the Irish church is discernible from the large numbers of bishops who died in the plague of 546 but with very few abbots mentioned. In the epidemic of a century later, the position was reversed with the greater mortality of abbots who were thought worthy of mention in comparison to deaths of bishops. According to the *Law* of Eimmin Ban, the kings of Leinster approached the abbot, both as patients and penitents. They were prepared to sacrifice themselves to the monastic life in order to prevent further deaths from the plague. After they had consulted him, the abbot fasted and prayed all night. He then informed them that one monk would die for each of the kings. Such were the desperate measures needed to stave off the plague. However to prevent dishonour to the monks willing to sacrifice themselves for the people of Leinster, the over-king would have to free the monastery from all rents and dues. His lineage would prosper and his family would be buried in the cemetery of the saints. If he revoked his promise the other monks would use Eimmin's holy bell in the form of a ritual curse against the king and his reign.[20]

A general 'famine and severe mortality' in England was recorded in the Anglo-Saxon Chronicle in 793 and an epidemic in the year 829 struck the monastery of Christ Church at Canterbury. All the monks save five died of the pestilence. The *Annals of Ulster* record famine in 965 and in the *Annals of Inishfallen* for 1116, a famine so severe that fathers sold their sons and daughters (as slaves) for food. During the reign of Macedydd of Dyfed (983-994), Pembroke suffered from the Saxon pest or sweating sickness and also from the murrain in cattle and from famine. In the years between the expulsion of the Danes in 1005 when Henry of Huntington wrote of a desolation throughout the land, to the wasting of Yorkshire by William's son in 1069 (as noted by Simon of Durham) the *Anglo-Saxon Chronicle* records five separate famines and 'great mortalities' of men and cattle. In the following century seven famines were recorded, including the direst famine in all England for the year 1125. A famine occurred in Wales in 1315 and caused great hardship during the following four years.[21]

The Black Death is thought to have been responsible for the death of nearly a third of the population of Europe within months of its first outbreak in 1348. The particular strain of bubonic plague is thought to have been spread by the fleas of infected rats from an original source in China. It took almost two years to reach the most westerly ports of Europe. Moving at the speed of knots from port to port disgorging its carriers as well as its human infestation, it moved rapidly inland from the sea ports. It reached southern England and then by the middle of the year 1348 the first major outbreak occurred in Wales. One account relates how the bishop of Hereford forbade the acting of theatrical plays and such 'interlude*s'* in the town churches. Instead he ordered the shrine of St. Thomas of Cantaloupe to be carried in solemn procession around the town. It was then claimed that it and the bones of the former bishop of Hereford had checked the plague through divine intercession. Earlier in the 14th century, at the church inquiries leading to his canonization, a papal commission visited the shrine of St. Thomas. They had noted that it was filled with thousands of wax bodies, limbs and bones with an untold number of eyes, breasts, teeth and ears as well as limbs encased in silver. However by the end of 1348 the so-called miracle was merely a lull to be followed by yet another devastating outbreak in the following year. There were further spasmodic outbreaks of the plague throughout Britain during the twelve years that followed.[22]

'The Bubo is the Arrow of Death'

The tales of the Decameron were related by young people who had fled to the hills to escape the Black Death. It had swept through Florence killing a hundred thousand of the inhabitants in three months. As Boccaccio noted, they took the only sensible course on offer 'to flee early, flee far and return late' to avoid both the ravages of disease and the barbarity of the survivors towards the sick. As in the other European cities bodies were dumped in ditches outside the walls and just covered over with some earth for people could not be found to bury the dead in the usual ritual manner, for God, for love nor money.

The *pasteurilla pestis* or great pestilence as it was known seemingly began in China but it was in the Crimea when the Tartars were besieging a group of Italian merchants that it was first chronicled in 1346. In fact the Tartar warriors withdrawing from the siege catapulted their own diseased victims into the citadel where the Christians had taken refuge. The Genoese galleys returning home probably carried the rats whose fleas created the most disastrous pandemic in European history. However, many of these long accepted ideas have been questioned in recent publications. The bodies of plague victims are apparently not infectious, so the cause of its initial spread by the Mongol armies seems to be a myth. Other suggestions that the so-called Black Death was a form of anthrax and that rats did not thrive in northern Europe are countered by equally scholarly views. Within the general mindset and religious beliefs of the time it spread by the will of God. However since mass prayer and demonstrations of hysterical piety were seemingly of no avail, the consensus of the writers point to strategies of containment that eventually worked and would be part of the medical management of such widespread infections up to the present day.[23]

Bubonic plague was caused by the transmission of the bacillus *Yersinia pestis* entering the body through the bite of the infested carrier.   Once a person became seriously afflicted, seemingly without cause or reason, death followed quickly which, given the circumstances, was probably a relief to the sufferer. It swept across continental Europe with such speed and without regard to class or gender that ancient images of the *Grim Reaper* and the *Riders of the Apocalypse* took on a horrifying reality to scar the European cultural imagination for centuries. There was then no medicinal defence against the plague. In fact it was the natural predators of the infected rats that were often blamed and cats were slaughtered so allowing the real carriers of the infected fleas to multiply in and around the houses, villages and towns of the sick. Thomas Phaer of Pembrokeshire, two centuries later restated the medieval view of the causes of plague in his *Treatise of the Pestilence.* These were the will of God; baleful influences of the conjunction of Saturn and Mars; the 'stinche and filthy savours' that corrupt the air; and finally peoples' immoderation in diet and living. If a doctor took the strictly religious view that it was an affliction sent by God to cleanse the soul, then a quick death whether by plague or other cause should be welcome. If however it were viewed in terms of the then current university medical teaching whereby disease was due to constitutional imbalance of the four humours, the blackened blotched body was in such a poor state of health that it was unlikely to recover any of its former vigor; therefore the patient would probably die. Nothing in the pharmaceutical medical chest seemed to make a difference to such an outcome especially as the physician was more likely than others suddenly to have the swellings under the armpits and in the groin that were the definite initial signs of possible fatal contagion.

During the year after its first recorded outbreak in the Crimea, the plague was brought into the ports along the south coast of England and was rife throughout the country by Christmas 1347. It seems to have moved into Wales along the border counties by the following spring and in through the western ports of Carmarthen, Pembroke, Haverfordwest and Cardigan, probably directly from their trading links with Bristol, where over a third of that port-city's inhabitants were believed to have died. Friar Clyn of Kilkenny wrote that fourteen thousand people died in Dublin. The pestilence was so contagious, he observed, that those who touched the dead or persons sick from it died from boils or ulcers and the running sores which grew on the legs and beneath the armpits. Others suffered pains in the head and went into frenzy whilst many spat out blood. The final words he put down in his journal before he too died were that he had left the parchment for others to carry on the work of recording its effects, 'if perchance any may survive or be able to escape this pestilence'.[24]

The effect of the plague on the rural Welsh people clustered around the moors and upland valleys is unknown. However modern estimates of the previous vast numbers dying of it such as 'half of the people of Wales' or 'two parts of the Welsh people', have been somewhat revised. There was a lack of complete records at that time and the ratio of numbers was based on inquisitions of the ruling elite. The decrease in rents and disruption in trade among the crowded towns along the coastal regions indicate the numbers of the poorer classes whose uncounted dead bodies were probably dumped into massed graves at the edge of villages or towns. It has also been realized that the upland areas of northern England and Scotland contained large pockets where the disease did not penetrate. The plague seemed to have had a marked preference for young people rather than the aged; for the poor rather than the rich; and for those clustered within town walls rather than living in the open; for poets like Daffydd Namor, and Tudor Aled 'whom God had marked like the plague' or in the cywydd of Gwilym ap Sefnyn on the loss of seven sons and three daughters; or for Greuydd ap Ievan ap Llywelyn Fychan of St. Asaph mourning the loss of his daughter whom he had buried, he wrote: *Gwenwyn ymirbel ydelo. Saith y farwolaeth ym fo.* 'The bubo is poison wherever it comes. It is the arrow of death'. It was equally swift and deadly for the poet himself died of *y Farvolaeth Fawr* not long after. Another poet, Ieuan Gethin of Baglan, who lost his sons, likened the buboes to a shower of peas: 'The early ornaments of death. Cinders of the cockle weed'. Perhaps it reminded Madoc ap Dafydd a century later when he described the manner of the earlier poet's passing: 'The deadly shilling in the depths of the armpit; grinds like little onions as dangerous as hot embers; black rash that seeds like black peas'. This was a graphically accurate pen picture of the second stage of the terminal illness. Often, after a six-day incubation with chest pains, vomiting of blood and internal bleeding, the small black lumps and blotches appeared that gave the plague its common name. After the hard lymph nodes called buboes began to swell in the armpits, the groin, around the neck or behind the ears the unfortunate victim became delirious. Coma and release from further suffering usually followed soon after. It needed the skill of the poets' artifice to try to grapple with the horror of such unbeknown and unwelcome malignancies erupting on fair skins. And to remind any contemporary survivors that such contagion had actually occurred within and around them. It was as though an invisible war had been waged inside the body whose odious effects were all too visible and too unbearable for those who died of it. The end of the first virulent phase was in the autumn of 1349 when the plague everywhere appeared to have abated. General relief was short-lived for during the following year the great pestilence wrecked even worse havoc among all social groups.[25]

In contrast to the words of the poets and to chroniclers in England, Ireland and especially in Europe, the few extant contemporary Welsh accounts were muted. The Ruthin Court Rolls refers to it running through the Lordship, accounting for seventy-seven deaths amongst the inhabitants of Ruthin itself. Many reports had less to say about the physical effects of the epidemic than about the inconveniences it caused to their accustomed way of life such as the lack of tenants in Cardigan. 'There are now only seven and there used to be 104 called gabularii who left this year because of the pestilence'. Most of the complaint from the lowland and English border counties seems as callous as the effect of the plague on their tenants and feudal serfs. They instance claims for remission of rents; the lack of servants and tenants to do the daily work; that their mills were standing idle; that parishioners were unable to support the livings of the priests; that the bridge over the river Dee was out of repair for months and that the surviving miners of the lead mines in Flintshire were unwilling to continue working, when so many of their friends and relatives were dead underground. It seemed as if the vast majority of the rent-paying tenants had died or fled. Helped by wars at home and abroad, the upheavals of the plague quickened the demise of the manorial feudal system in Wales. According to Philip Zieglar, its eclipse in a few short years contrasts with the better part of a century it took to fade out in England. He also noted that there had been harsh climatic changes with colder weather during the previous decades that had reduced many wheat growing areas. As a result a series of disastrous harvests were then followed by terrible famines when people ate dogs, cats, dung of doves and *even their own children,* so that the three years preceding the sudden onslaught of the plague would have seemed uniquely unfortunate in any other century.

Leprosy and Lazer-houses

There were two skin diseases in ancient times known as leprosy. The serious type of bone disintegration that resulted in the physical symptoms of scaling flesh and mutilated feet and hands is now known as Hanson's disease. It is a form of bacterial leprosy. Its cause was unknown and sufferers of it became outcasts from society. The biblical Job was a good and true man who was tested in his faith by God so thereby losing his family, friends, belongings to become a leper and an outcast. He was then deemed worthy of redemption. This particular kind of warped thinking became a model for Christian suffering, especially the most loathsome kind resulting from diseases of leprosy and the pox that the Crusaders brought back to Western Europe from the Middle East. Their deformities, due to loss of toes or fingers and damage to the upper legs, were physically obvious. Smallpox was so called to differentiate it from the great pox or syphilis. The earliest examples of the former from Egypt were to be seen in the disfigured face of Ramsees V around 1157 BC. The later ruler Elizabeth I had a coin cast to commemorate her recovery from it.

The Rite of Exclusion that was read out in church over the leper related to the dangers and control of the disease with the care or alms which others should extend to the sufferer. They were given a bell and a white stick to warn the faithful of their immediate presence. All their clothes, houses and effects were burnt to prevent further infestation and the leper was expected to remain in colonies within the vicinity of a hospice. Such buildings by the 12th century had became commonplace in Europe but by then leprosy was on the decrease. Descriptions of the disease were included in the *Canon of Medicine* by Avicenna (980 -1037) the great physician and scientist of the Moslem world. When it was translated into Latin, diagnosis and treatment of the disease was gradually left in the hands of the physicians rather than the domain of the clergy. By then over two-hundred hospices or lazer-houses — from Italian *lazaretto* — were built outside towns in England and Wales. After the Black Death, leprosy decreased dramatically so that by the 16th century it was no longer prevalent as a major affliction. Various reasons for such a dramatic change have been suggested. It may have been due to the stronger strain of the tuberculosis bacillus which is closely related to the leprosy bacillus; or the fact that the plague killed so many and in its aftermath leprosy gradually lessened its grip on the human mind, like other so-called social diseases since then.

The evidence for the disease in Wales is mainly historical and onomastic — based on place names with *claiwr* (leper) or *cleifion* (sick) attached to them — outside such towns as Caernarfon, Welshpool, Haverfordwest and Tenby also in Pembrokeshire. The Latin term *Terra Leprosorum* is found near Wrexham and in the vale of Glamorgan. A work by John Brooke of Maroddwy written in 1590 states that Owain Cyfeuliog who died in 1197 made benefactions to Strata Marcella Abbey, Clettrwd Bridge and to a *elyssendvv* (almshouse) for lepers. This was later burnt down because of the fornication, probably due to the women inhabitants whoring or having children in the lazor house. The site of the house (at Clettrwd Bridge) known as *diory cleifion* or the Lepers' Meadow was mentioned in some old wills in Welshpool. A *domus leprosorum* existed at Carnarfon during Edward III's time and a leper or lazar house at Camaes in Anglesey was called Clafdy or Clafrdy.[26]

In George Owen's *Description of Pembrokeshire* written around 1550, he states that Gilbert de Clare — the Earl of Pembroke from 1234-41 — 'gave certaine lands to the Mawdlers of Tenbye towardes the relieffe of the leepers there'. The name of the Maudlens which is misspelt in the text was correctly made in a footnote to mean hospitals of the poor. An account of the latter days of the Maudlens was given during a hearing in the Star Chamber in 1576. Thomas Browne of Tenby, aged 55, in a deposition claimed he had regularly served Sir John Churchman, a priest at mass in the Mauldens chapel forty years earlier. The only leper he could recall having been seen in the Maudlens was one called Alson Walter, who was there for the space of twelve years or thereabouts and was paid a groat a week, and some weeks two groats, and some weeks none, which was paid by the mayor or by the wardens. Owen also mentions a number of bridges over a small tributary of the Western Cleddau River that flows beneath the Maudlins Bridge then by Saint Margretís Chapple and under the Maudlens Denant and on to Haroldston Bridge. The inference here seems to have been that such bridges around the outskirts of Haverfordwest (part of the town boundaries) each had a leper house beyond, and the diseased were not allowed to cross. A chapel and leper house to the south of the town was dedicated to St. Mary Magdalene and went by the name of Madlens or Maudlins. The nearby river crossing was called Maudlins Bridge — later corrupted to the present-day Merlins

Bridge. In 1896 parts of an ancient building — a square chimney and some walling — could still be identified but by the 1920's they had disappeared. Further west on the Solva River a bridge was called *Pont Dwrty Clyvon* and near it *Duioery Cleifion* (Lepers Water) ran into St. Brides Bay. On the northeast coast, a bridge near Newport had a place name *Pont Rhivír Claf*. The word *claf* meaning sick or ill originally referred to a leper. A common speech habit in using such euphemisms was the fear that even naming the disease would infect the speaker. The Bridge of the Sick crossed a stream of the Teifi (by the medieval town of Cardigan) through *Territorium Leprosorum* or *Tir y Cleifion,* land given in 1160 to the Knights Hospitellers of St. John. There they built the Hospice for pilgrims visiting Our Lady's shrine in Cardigan, on the ancient pilgrimage route from Bardsey Island to St. David's.[27]

There is a singular reference to a leper and a stone in the *Tripartite Life of Patrick*, along with remarks that he healed leprosy. As the saint was leaving Britain a diseased person asked to be taken in the boat. However being a man of the people as well as a diplomat he gave the leper his pillar stone — often used as an altar by early saints — and it is said to have miraculously carried the man safely across the Irish Sea alongside the boat. Hence Patrick who is famous for ridding Ireland of its snakes and toads may have brought a far greater misery to the island. And curiously enough the only primary evidence for leprosy in the British Isles has been recently discovered in Ulster at an old church dedicated to the saint. Excavations in 1997 at the medieval St. Patrick's Church in Armoy, County Antrim revealed a pair of feet with bone lesions of the most severe form of the disease, lepromatous leprosy. The big toes had such significant bone destruction that the narrowed sharp slivers of the other toe bones had probably been destroyed, according to the palaeo-pathologist, as a consequence of the disease process. The severity of the bone changes in the feet suggest that the victim would have had the characteristic facial bone collapse; with a collapsed nose, missing upper front teeth, loss of eyebrows, and nodules. No other diseased bones were found amid the remains of fifty-six individual skeletons of all ages and sexes. A larger number of human remains were found in the upper layers inside the western end of the present church. However the remains from both upper and lower levels were considered to have lain outside the walls of the original medieval east/west structure which suggests that people had been burying their dead around it for a considerable time. A calibrated AMS radiocarbon date obtained for the feet indicate that the person had died sometime between the mid 15th and mid 17th centuries. In contrast to the large number of recorded lazar houses in the southern provinces of Ireland only four were built in Ulster and none of them near to the site at Armoy. Therefore the dating of the feet found amid other burials around an old medieval church would indicate that this was an isolated case, compatible with the (earlier) history of the disease.[28]

Medical research in Brittany would suggest that as in Ireland and in Wales, leprosy had disappeared by the 16th century. Place-name evidence relates to certain hamlets or villages of the unclean; they are remembered in names like La Madeleine — patron saint of leper chapels — La Maladrerie or in Le Clandy, from house of the sick. However in a recent study of Breton Ballads, and especially the gwerz (ballads) of *Iannik Kokard* in relation to love and leprosy, the author quotes a certain Doctor Aubry who wrote a paper to the effect that the disease still flourished there in the 1890's. Mary-Ann Constantine asks at what stage did the many variations of the Kokard gwarz become part of the singers' repertoire? Was it from the 19th century when folk collectors like Hersart de la Villemarqué became interested or were the gwerziou a verbatim reflection of a very distant past? She recounts from the comments of the singers themselves that a gwerz tells a true story; as an event that really happened; a long story that went on and on; an old tale that is sung; a very old song. The name *Kokard* can be traced back to the 16th century. The Breton word kakous and French caquins and cacous were generally associated with the leper and with the universal emblems of the disease such as the white stick; the leper-house or lazor-village; as well as the tasks associated with their people such as rope making and carving wooden utensils. All of which were important contextual elements in the many ballads of the *Iannik Kokard* gwarz.[29]

Chapter 3. Healing in the Age of the Saints

Patrick, a 5th century Briton who became known as the premier saint of Ireland, was born in a Roman province somewhere along the western coast. It was possibly around Carlisle, but lowland Scotland and south Wales have also been suggested as the place of his birth, although the former location at the head of the Solway Firth seems the most likely area where marauding pirates captured the youth and then sold him into slavery in Ireland. According to his own account his father had been a Roman deacon and his grandfather a priest. His traumatic experience among the pagan Irish and the lively retention of early memories based on a church within the first stirrings of an evangelical Christianity with Christ as the spiritual head of the community are thought to have formed the religious basis of his later mission in Ireland.

The *Confessio* is one of the few documents extant from this period. Written in a 6th century Latin and by a man who was not a scholar but conversant with the writings of the church Fathers, it records his spiritual path from a troubled youth looking after cattle in the mountains; the decision to flee his master after six years; finding a boat ready to set sail in a southern port; to the later doubts about his priestly calling; the shabby treatment he received from the church elders in west Britain; and finally as the summation of his mission bringing the true faith, in his own words, single-handedly to the island across the Irish Sea. Recent scholarship confines this work to the north and west provinces during the latter part of the 5th century. Prior to the general spread of monasticism around the 8th century with an abbot — often as both the religious and secular head of a mother church — Patrick had introduced a Roman diocesan form of ecclesiastical hierarchy that had been established in Wales, but according to Liam De Poar probably without the church reforms

59

that had been brought about in Britain from around the time of his captivity. In relation to sickness Patrick may have followed the dictates of Saint Jerome in so far as healing the physical body occurred when a priest treated the wounds of the soul. According to Holy Scriptures a person's physical infirmities could be cured by prayer healing and for any such extra-ordinary actions to occur, the saint would have been miraculously imbued with the divine spirit. The later schism of mind and body — from introspective distinctions between body and soul that added strength to personal asceticism — had helped to displace the Patrician church in Ireland. The Irish clergy gradually disregarded the Roman model of a hierarchy of bishops ruling over ever larger areas of physical territory with St. Peter's in Rome as it's symbolic and literal head here on earth. In a sense it gave birth to a Celtic church that was uniquely Irish and was transplanted to west Scotland and north-east Britain after Columba had settled on the island of Iona in the Inner Hebrides. [30]

The young prince had studied under Finnian of Clonard and Enda of Aran whose foundation on that island in Galway Bay had introduced the template of the monastic ideal into Ireland. This transmission was from his teacher Ninian of Galloway who had based his own strict system on that of St. Martin of Tours. Many of the early churches in the north traditionally founded by the saint such as Derry 'of the oak groves', are considered by scholars now to be of a much later date. However what is beyond dispute is that Colum Cille — his name meant Dove of the Church and Latinized as Columba — precipitated the battle of Cul Dreimne when his tuatha or 'people' of the northern Ui Neill fought the High King of Ireland and thousands were slaughtered. This led to a voluntary exile on Iona in 563 at the age of forty. A popular tradition is that the saint had secretly copied a text from a gospel book belonging to Finnian of Moville and was angry when the king judged against him, with the famous remark that, 'to every cow her calf, to every book its copy' one of the first known copyright dictums! A man of tremendous energy he continued his Machiavellian role in the

60

kingships of Pictland and Anglo-Saxon Northumbria. It was due to his personal influence as abbot that the Iona mission was able to penetrate so far south into pagan England during the following century. Bede, commenting on its aftermath and contrasting it with the fine English stone architecture, wrote that when the Irish monks left their monastery of Lindisfarne after the Synod of Whitby in 664, apart from the small church, not more than the bare requirements of a seemly dedicated way of life were visible there. When Abbot Adomnan — who wrote the *Life of Columba* on behalf of the Iona Community — had accepted the universal date for Easter; the cultural cross-fertilization between Iona and Northumbria, became evident in Ireland. Not only in such masterworks as the Book of Kells and the ringed high crosses in stone but in the extension of the insular life of prayer in larger monastic complexes with scriptoria, refectories, kitchen gardens and hospitality for the traveller, the poor and the needy. An early 9th century plan of St. Gall in Switzerland — originally founded by one of the disciples of another of the Irish peregrini, Columbanus of Bobbio in Italy — shows a basilica-type hospital building and herb garden along with lists of plants. The varieties to be grown included the radish, shallot, lettuce, parsnip, cabbage, fennel, cumin, lovage, coriander, sage, rosemary, mint and the opium poppy.[31]

In view of the lack of medical material for the pre-Norman period in Wales, an essay by the historian Dr. Wendy Davies on early Irish healing may add some insights into the conditions that prevailed on this side of the Celtic Sea. She compared the low proportion of miracle cures in the earliest *Lives* of the saints in Ireland with the much higher percentage of healing miracles in the miraculous incidents of the continental *Vitae* on which they were generally based. Medical cures formed a major component of the latter with the saint presented as a superior kind of magic doctor. They could outdo the leach, diagnose more accurately and recommend better cures. By contrast the healings in the 7th and 8th century *Lives of Patrick*, by Muirchu and Tirechan, were few in number. Of the one hundred and twenty extraordinary accounts in Adomnan's *Life of*

Columba, only eleven of the incidents relate to healing. And these mainly of monks in monasteries who were protected from disease and that the plague — which decimated Ireland and Wales — had never reached Scotland because the saint himself lived there. To religious zealots advocating self-discipline and mortification of the flesh, the unmistakable physical results of the yellow plague would appear as a heaven sent message. The idea of original sin that was so central to Christian belief, and so alien to the native soul, could now be illustrated by the liverish skins of suffering people. It was probably the first real test of faith — a holy martyrdom by proxy — for people who had become Christians through repetitive Latin prayers, psalm singing and learning the gospel stories of the life of a teacher in the distant east, by rote. It would appear that the transition in religious belief from a pagan to a Christian society occurred between the late 6th and 8th century. It did not detract, as Davies observed, from the importance of women healers in Ireland. Yet once the church was firmly established and under the influence of Rome, it is likely that the role of women in medicine became more marginal. Paradoxically a figure like Saint Brigid with so many stories of her healing miracles, took on the mantle of the old goddess as patron of the smith, the leech and the poet. However the early 7th century *Life of Brigid* by Cogitosis, had only three healing accounts out of thirty-three miracles but in the later 9th century version, forty per cent of her miracles related to healing the blind, the deaf, the paralytic and even leprosy.

Davies then looks at the position of a skilled craftsman known as the *liaig* or doctor in the laws of sick maintenance as a type of quasi-legal advocate in relation to injuries suffered. A situation very similar to the role of the Welsh mediciner in the law codes of Hywel Dda written down many centuries later. And finally she examined the vernacular material in which the art of magical healing seemed to be within the domain of women who also acted as sorcerers of peoples' fates. The treatment of the injured was still sustained by a gender separation even when women performed the health-care and food-serving functions of the *liaig*. She concluded that if there were a tradition of healing it was solely a magical one and that what we call medicine and the study of herbal lore were unknown in early Irish society. Alluding to this in a brief summary of the paper, a reviewer suggested a different interpretation of the data. The failure of Davies to acknowledge the high status of women as pagan healers during the early period when the Christian nuns probably lacked proper social recognition in Irish insular society would certainly reflect on the small number of healing miracles attributed to female saints. And given the later practice of Christianizing native deities once the new religion had gained legal recognition, there would be no anomaly between the earlier few and the later increase of miracle cures in the *Lives* of the Irish saints. The accounts of healing carried out in Wales seem to confirm the view of female provenance. The 12th century *Life of Gwenfrewi* and the subsequent manifestations at her healing spring at Holywell in Flintshire had more incidents of both a general character and of individual diseases than those attributed to all the male saints. Examples include the cure of blindness, deafness, dropsy, fevers, epilepsy, gall stones, insanity, muteness and even the raising of the dead.[32]

In his compendium of holy wells Francis Jones admits that the evidence relating to the conversion of insular paganism to Christianity is meagre in Wales. So he looks to the building of early chapels in the proximity of megalithic monuments, ancient trees and especially holy wells as at St. Non's chapel, built within the remains of a stone circle on St. David's Head in Pembrokeshire. The building was largely dismantled in 1820. At the south end (its main orientation) the early rude coarses are obvious below the later rebuilt stone walls. The tradition of the nearby well, known for its healing qualities and especially good for afflictions of the eyes, is that it sprang forth at David's birth in a storm and the future saint's head was laid on a stone which bears a ringed cross and is now inside the chapel. The old pilgrimage route along this stretch of the north Pembrokeshire coast was marked by many wells where pilgrims could rest from their journey. Also there are still a number of Bronze-Age tall standing stones near them, unlike the majority of the well-chapels or chapels-of-ease that have largely disappeared. Many were abandoned, had fallen into decay, were destroyed during and after the Reformation or later used for building materials. A number in a good state of preservation are situated at the extreme north-western coast such as Ffynnon Gybi in the Lleyn Peninsula and Ffynnon Seiriol in Anglesey near the Penmon Priory church. They have a small rectangular walled area in which water flows and a slightly larger dry-stone building alongside. At St Gybi's there was a pool with a paved walking area, which latter has been turned into the nave and chancel of the old chapel. In South Wales there are several well chapels that were the focus of saintly lore and healing indicated by the crutches hanging from an oak tree that were observed by John Aubrey; a photograph taken in 1906 shows votive rags hanging on the same tree. Also in Glamorgan there was a rag well at Coedaritydyglyn, on the side of the road to Peterton; it can be seen in an earlier drawing. These are very common still in Scotland and Ireland which may indicate that the above wells are very ancient. However Francis Jones points out that Edward Lhuyd recorded, often in detail, a large number of our holy wells, and he makes absolutely no mention of rags on nearby trees. The holy well has survived with its old rites and customs that were once part of the pagan and Christian religions, even into modern times. Wells were a necessary part of rural life in both the physical landscape and in peoples' spiritual or inner lives. It was the respect for holy wells and their actual or even supposed healing qualities that helped in promoting what later antiquarians called 'sacred fiction'. Well cults to saints old and new, local and foreign, helped to sanctify their stories in song, folk tale and medicine, thereby having a far greater influence on Welsh life than the actual Celtic and later historical Christian saints themselves ever had.[33]

There is one category of well dedications whose antecedents may go further back than even those of the Celtic saints; perhaps initially to a spirit or guardian of the sacred waters. There are over seventy named after Our Lady in various forms such as Mair (Fair), Mary, and Lady Wells. In many places with such a named well, the parish church is dedicated to Mary so that she was the patron of the Lady Well. The cult of Our Lady began in the 4th century and became widespread and popular. There are even traditions that she came to the shores of Kidwelly by Carmarthen Bay where there is a Ffynnon Fair. Obviously in the form of a mermaid, she asked a man to throw her back into the waves. He killed her instead. He and his family never prospered. It was also said she had come to Llanfair in Merionethshire where a church was dedicated to her. She walked to a small lake a few miles south of Harlech. Kneeling at the roadside to drink from a stream, the marks of her knees remained in the rock and a spring of pure water arose which had miraculous healing properties. At Ffynnon Fair by Aberdaron where the boat once left for Bardsey Island there is a rock with two impressions, one of Mary's hand; the other of a horse's hoof. In the oak tree above Ffynnon Fair Penrhys in Glamorgan, an image of the virgin appeared and pilgrimages to it were frequent. It became one of the most famous Mary shrines in South Wales. A statue of the Virgin appeared at the mouth of the Teifi. There was a child Jesus in her lap and a burning taper in her hand. According to legend the statue was moved four times to a church in Cardigan but it returned of its own accord to the original spot. Eventually St. Mary's church was built and she stayed there with the taper that burned for nine years until a swearing Welshman put it out. Gerald of Wales mentioned this legend and the many miracles that occurred around it but he did not go into detail. Its fame seemed to have encouraged John Bulton, the burgess of Haverford who in his will bequeathed an annual sum of 5s 8d for the 'sustenance of our Lady's taper, which was to burn before her perpetually'. His 1465 will also stipulated that the bells of St. Mary's Church should be rung on the feast day of St. Thomas. The candle burned for sixty-three years in the chapel dedicated to Our Lady above the vaulted charnel house in the corner of St. Mary's Churchyard. The taper came to the attention of Cromwell and it was extinguished by Bishop Barlow. The chapel was demolished in 1891.[34]

The Welsh Saints

In the many *Lives* of Welsh holy men it is hard to isolate instances of a particularly Christian type of soul-healing as would appear to have been the norm in the early Church. A rare occasion was when Gildas in Scotland healed a beggar (of leprosy?) who asked him for alms. What seems more evident in the later writings, especially as the founder saints were considered to have been active over half a millennium earlier, is the view of the saint as a local hero; one whose petty reactions in anger and cruelty towards others are often followed by a repenting miracle. As Gerald points out, the Welsh saints do appear to be of a more vindictive nature that fitted into the medieval world picture of absolute male authority rather than the personal example of the life of Christ. Illtud, who became the teacher of Saints' Gildas, Samson, Paulinus and David, was a soldier before he received a St. Paul type revelation to retire and live in a hut in a swampy area in the vale of Glamorgan. When an angel admonished him about his sanctity he sent his wife away, into the night and refused all future contact with her. Later when she returned to him, he blinded her. If that was not sufficient punishment for interrupting his prayers he disfigured her face so that even any remembered beauty would not tempt him; or any other man for that matter! Saint Tysillio, on the other hand, disfigured himself to avoid marriage. Brigid, plucked her own eye out for the same reason, but later miraculously replaced it within the empty eye-socket. A saint's holiness was characterized by how well personal chastity was maintained. Its enhancement by severe and austere practices to help them overcome temptations of the flesh emphasized their differences from other men in the society around them. Even in the womb 'God's holy presence' becomes manifest as part of the saint's story as when the mother of the future Dyfrig was washing her father's hair, he discovered she was pregnant. He had her thrown into the river. When she did not drown he put her on a funeral pyre and lit it. The following morning she was discovered alive in the ashes with the baby as the future saint in her lap.

The lineage of David is directly linked to the noble family of Ceredigion. As a child he healed the blind servant who held him at baptism and then later performed the same miracle for his teacher, thereby defining his own spiritual superiority. Such an act was usually a prelude to the journey out into the world as a builder of churches. In the 9th century *Life of St. Paul de Leon*, David is called the *waterman* because of his spiritual practice of spending long hours praying in the river with his arms akimbo — an iconic posture of the true Celtic saint. Bishop Asser in his written account of the life of King Alfred of Wessex, writes from personal experience of being educated and ordained at St. David's, so the tradition of stern asceticism and a strict adherence to monastic rule, may have been the cornerstone of the native church in west Wales. Yet David, in a later *Vitae,* reacts in a thoroughly egocentric manner when crossed in his determination to settle in the Vallis Rosina, the Vale of Roses. Although part of Boia's territory, he puts the Irish chieftain's men into a state of paralytic fever and kills his cattle. He then punishes his wife for having her maids parade naked before the monks, by sending the woman into a total delirium and her slaves insane. When she sacrifices and cuts off her step-daughter's head probably as a desperate ritual act, his biographer adds that this was clearly a manifestation of her madness; for on the ground where the blood was spilled a holy well then flowed. Boia within his hill top fort was burned by a group of Irish pirates on the following night. The verisimilitude of this account appears to be borne out by the evidence of fire found during the archaeological excavation of the nearby site now known as Clegyr Boia. David was thus freed to move inland to a more secluded place by the river Alun to the 'valley of the Little Marsh.' And build his monastery where he wanted it or as the text relates where it had been divinely chosen. The present cathedral church is thought to have been built on this site after the first Norman bishop was enthroned in 1115. Seven years later Pope Callixtus approved the saint's cult, conceding that two pilgrimages to St. David's would then be worth one journey to Rome itself.[35]

There are also certain examples of the physical retribution on those who confronted holy men but who were often miraculously healed later when the whim of a saint was satisfied; such as the withering of assailants arms; instantly burying them up to their necks in the earth and even the magical actions of one holy man on another. Pedrog mentally paralyses Samson who was intent on leaving for Wales before he himself had arrived in Brittany but later cured him after his arrival. Cadog fasts against David for excluding him from the synod of Llandewibrefi after the latter had spoken from a mound that had arisen by the power of the Lord so that he could be seen by the huge crowd. In Irish texts this kind of moral retribution was often performed by saints outside the forts of pagan chiefs who refused to give them the land they wanted. But Cadog's action had more than a touch of personal spite in being outwitted by a superior magician, whose church now stands on top of the hill. Gildas was struck dumb in the middle of a sermon when Non, carrying the infant David in her womb, entered the church. Bishop Ailbe who there 'became filled with the spirit of prophecy' explained that God wished those present to know that the baby inside her was to be the chosen one to be called David. Gildas was then cured when he realized that he had to leave his native Wales for one who was to be 'greater' than he. The same exile had already been ordained for Patrick many years previously and for the same reason, after being told by an angel to depart henceforth for Ireland. It is possible to write out a list of the diseases healed by (or associated with) saints, such as David and blindness or Beuno restoring decapitated heads and raising the dead; but many others seemingly had the same ability to cure the blind and raise the dead. A list of illnesses could also be set against those who cured others such as Carannog healing Tyrnog of leprosy. However such a straight forward approach would be misleading, for as in the above accounts, many of these episodic events were related to both the initial cause of a saint's chagrin and his subsequent healing of the disability. And that such healing when it did occur, primarily illustrated the supernatural powers *only* available to those Welsh saints favoured by God. The pedigree and birth; spiritual education and performing a miracle that defined their spirituality, were presented episodically in individual *Lives* but sequentially each have been defined as stages in which their sainthood was often elaborated. Miracle healing as such, is part of this hagiographic record, but is never given undue prominence in a medical sense and was more likely to show the supernatural power available for the saint-to-be to call upon.[36]

The next stage in the saint's life, as characterized by Elisa Henken in her study of their patterns and traditions, is when a seminal miracle — like David healing his teacher of blindness — shows a particular man's power to be greater than that of his mentor. And thereafter he is ready to venture out into the world. This becomes a period of founding churches when the saint travels abroad as a famed teacher; and then making a pilgrimage to Rome or the Holy Land. It is this stage of the saintly pattern which she describes as being universally recognised, when such divinely induced healing becomes commonplace. By this time the saint usually had his own disciples as travelling companions and often used such supernatural aids as the crosier and the bell. The magical aura of these powerful relics, associated with the cult of founder saints, became part of his iconic insignia. During the last years the final act of sainthood is often retiring from the monastery to a nearby island such as did Dyfrig, Gildas, Pedrog, Samson and Seiriol, or a quiet place in a cave for Carannog, Colleen and Illtud. Unlike their heroic counterparts in the Welsh literary tales; the actual demise of a major saint was usually peaceful and written up as the summation of a life on earth as embodied in the Christian ideal of an afterlife with God. The many uncommon manifestations were usually of angelic visitations, ethereal light and even emanations of the body like sweet smelling flowers. Or some extraordinary natural phenomena as when Gwenfrewi's buried remains were subsequently miraculously moved from Gwytherin in the Conwy valley where she was buried to Shrewsbury Abbey. After death a whole new cycle of divine healing often became manifested. The churches, holy wells and sites associated with the saint during the lifetime, as with the remains of

69

the physical body itself, become secondary conduits through which divine healing could be invoked. Three different churches claimed St.Teilo's body. By the power of God it had become triplicated so it could be buried at Penally where he was born, at his main monastic foundation of Llandeilo Fawr, and since he was bishop at the Cathedral church of Llandaff, 'where the sick are frequently healed of their disease, the blind revive their sight and the deaf hear'.

According to Geraldus Cambrensis who lived during the 12th century, the Welsh paid greater respect than any others to their churches; to men in holy orders; to the relics of saints; bishops crooks; bells; holy books and the cross itself. He was an Anglo-Norman cleric and writer, interested in church and state; his world view was entirely religious. Geraldus Cambrensis had been educated in London, had taught in Paris and was in frequent correspondence with the Pope and the higher clergy. His long-held ambition to be ordained Bishop of St. David's — in the sense of being Bishop of Wales rather than of a diocese of Canterbury — was never to be realized. A recent collection of his writings translated from their original Latin shows clearly his long struggle within the Canons of St. Davids against the devious Norman archbishop and his rather close relationship with the Pope who ultimately made his decision to pass Gerald over on political grounds. When he records his native peoples' devotion to holy relics and rituals, it is not merely to add strength to his claim to be bishop of St. David's for we can be reasonably sure that it was also from his Welsh up-bringing. In his written accounts of what essentially was the first topographic account of Wales and journey to Ireland as chaplain to Prince Henry, Gerald tended not to name his sources whether written or oral, ancient or contemporaneous. Yet his descriptions of spiritual healing and the Welsh peoples' faith in relics are a useful indicator of the beliefs of the period. He refers to the difficult places and incidents of the journey he made with Archbishop Baldwin in 1188 as a Welsh speaking deacon to encourage many young knights to join a third Crusade to the Holy Land. And he includes some memorable events of the past and from his own time as well as wonders of the natural world like the fossilized trees standing in the sands of Newgale. He even mentions the mythic accounts of Merlin and his prophecies. However, like his contemporary Geoffrey of Monmouth, who was denounced by William of Newborough as a reporter of mere fables about Arthur which he had from the Britons and elaborated according to his own devices, Gerald with a more mischievous put-down relates that when evil spirits were tormenting a certain Welshman called Melerius, they vanished if the gospel book of John was laid on his bosom. In contrast he claims that the devils would settle on Geoffrey's *Historia* in greater numbers, finding it a congenial resting-place. An 18th century Presbyterian writer more forcibly brackets Geoffrey with the 'inventors of evil things, forgers of lies and the pest of mankind'.[37]

As an ardent churchman and archdeacon of Brecon, Gerald mentions some of the more famous holy objects in the smaller churches of the area. In St. Harmans a few miles from Rhaeadr the staff of St. Curig was shaped in the form of a cross and covered on all sides with gold and silver ornaments. It was useful for removing swellings and inflammation of the thyroid gland. An offering of a penny would restore a sufferer to health. However it happened that if a person only gave half-a-penny he therefore had a relapse. Gerald was fond of moral homilies so in order to obtain divine pardon that person then had to give three pence to gain a complete cure. A bell called *Bangu* once belonged to St. David and was kept in a church at Glascwm. Such hand-bells were used on the day of a funeral from the house of the deceased to the church and rung loudly between the singing of psalms. The torque of St. Kynauc was shaped in the form of a collar with four metal parts covered in gold and joined in the middle by a clasp in the shape of a dog's head with fierce protruding teeth. It was said that those who swore to tell the truth with this relic around their neck would not dare tell a lie, in case they could not remove the torque afterwards. One man who tried to break it up for the sake of the gold was deprived of his eyesight for the remainder of his life. One of the saintly children of Brychan named Aled or Elued was associated with St. Almeda's church near Brecon. At the

71

beginning of August a thanksgiving feast was held there in her honour. People who were sick and diseased often came from great distances in order to be restored to health. The main part of the festival was a mime by a troupe of young people, imitating the gestures and occupations of those watching such as ploughing, tanning and weaving. However the troupe would suddenly appear to fall into a trance and jump about with frenzied gestures to show, in his words, the effects of any unlawful work on the Sabbath. The actors were carried into the church, and followed by the people, who would then be reminded in mime that when offerings were laid on the altar they were likely to be cured. In like manner, according to Gerald, many of the sick people on the feast days were healed. It has been suggested by one writer on medieval medicine that what was being described here was the condition known as St. Vitus Dance when people suffering internal agony were smitten with an uncontrollable urge to move and shake their limbs about.[38]

Cult of the Holy Well

There are a few distinct characteristics that Ffraid, Dwynwen, Gwenfrewi, Melangell and Non share in distinction to the majority of male Welsh saints. A women's sanctity was usually defined by chastity. As in the manner of the focus on the heroines of the Mabinogion it would appear that it was not until they had contact with men and with male sexuality that they emerged to exist in their own right as women. Cut off from their families, they did not partake of an active role in the social life of the time as the male saints clearly did. Women saints did not usually build churches or travel abroad but tended to settle in one place. Within such limitations as are presented in their written *Lives* and in the folklore that subsequently accrued around them, it is obvious that the activities of these holy women tended to reflect female restricted roles, and according to the accounts by Elissa Henken to 'have had (healing) characteristics associated with feminine qualities'. It is also apparent in the form of physical sites dedicated to them. Dwynwen

72

was the patron of lovers. Her well near the church ruins, on the small remote Llanddwyn isle off the southern tip of Anglesey, was the scene of an annual pilgrimage in the Middle Ages. Sick pilgrims carried lighted candles and offerings so as to be cured of their afflictions. A sacred fish or eel in the well indicated matrimonial prospects for the lovelorn. A local woman was said to have been able to read the omens of those people who had spread their scarves on the water for the fish to appear. Lovers also drank from the well or immersed themselves fully. If the waters bubbled it meant that love was true and a 'marriage' was performed over it. The location on a tiny remote isle and the ceremonial associations of pilgrimage with the holy well may indicate its antiquity and even the possibility of it being an early goddess site. Elis Gruffydd who wrote his *Chronicle* of the world up to 1552 recounts that on a journey to Calais in 1529 as part of the guard to Henry VIII, their boat was blown adrift with the force of a storm. Amid the chaos he lost his best clothes and everyone on board was praying to their patron saints. 'At that time my faith was as weak as that of any man so I promised to go by foot with a penny for Saint Dwynwen as soon as God and the saints would give me leave to place a foot on the soil of England'.[39]

St. Ffraid (Brigid), who is said to have been carried on a sod of earth over the sea, retained many of the healing attributes of her sister saint in Ireland. A church dedicated to her near an old pilgrim path that has now fallen into the sea, was unusually close to the church of Saint Non at Llannon, above Cardigan Bay. Local tradition asserts that St. David was born and lived his early life here rather than in Pembrokeshire where the twelfth century *Life* placed the scene of his birth on the cliffs by St. David's Head in the south-western peninsula. St. Non's chapel and her healing well that is still popularly visited, are located within the proximity of a group of old standing stones on the cliffs above St. Bride's Bay. Non's well, like that of Melangell's church in Powys, has been re-consecrated in recent years as a Catholic shrine and has become a focus for latter-day pilgrims. The church with Melangell's shrine is situated at the head of a remote valley of the Pennant by the side of a massive domed hill. It was a popular gathering for women pilgrims seeking personal comfort or cures. Monacella (Melangell) was the daughter of an Irish chief who fled from an arranged marriage and lived in a hermitage here for many years. The traditional story of this saint who attracted a community of nuns around her, is conflated with that of a prince of Powys chasing a hare and then finding it hiding under the skirts of a beautiful young woman at prayer, both being common goddess motifs. A church built about 1160 AD is thought to have contained her healing sanctuary called *cell-y-bedd*, or the room of the grave. Her relics were placed in a Romanesque shrine. The sanctuary was eventually broken up in the 16th century. There has been much rebuilding in the church since then and recently the shrine was reassembled in the chancel. The rock where she made her bed, carved with her name Monacella, is set in the apse floor. Melangel's hermitage with the community of nuns situated beneath the dome of a hill, Dywnwen oracle well-shrine on a small island, and Non's chapel among ancient standing stones all indicate the continuity of ancient goddess cult sites into the later Christian period.

It was very different from what prevailed at Gwenfrewi's holy well; the most famous well-shrine in medieval Wales. Visited by Richard I and III, it then became even more popular after an elaborate chapel was built by the favour of the mother of Henry Tudor, Lady Margaret Beaufort whose estates were nearby. Up to the time of the Reformation and afterwards when most of the other well-chapels and well-shrines were destroyed, English monarchs continued to visit it. In 1665 James II made the last of such royal pilgrimages. With the established church endorsement and particularly endowments by the English nobility from its very inception, it continued to be a popular shrine, with close comparisons to Walsingham shrine in Norfolk, up to the time of and even beyond the Reformation. The short *Life of St. Winifred* (Gwenfrewi) was written in Latin during the 12th century by Robert, the Prior of Shrewsbury. It contained the story of her sanctity — sitting at home after her parents had gone to church; the lustful prince; the chase; decapitation at the sanctuary door and her miraculous healing by Beuno — as well as numerous miracle cures at the healing well that sprung from the red rocks where her blood fell. After the beheading of Gwenfrewi, Beuno's actions are as succinctly described as those of a surgeon. He presses the head to the body, covers her completely with his cloak, tells the family to be quiet and proceeds to finish the mass that had been interrupted. Only then does he remove the cloak. When she sits up, a ring of raised skin is visible around her neck. Thus it becomes clear that the restoring of her head is a holy act whereby Gwenfrewi gained a new life in the sanctuary of mother church. The healing spring gushing up from the reddened stones where her blood fell became a permanent reminder of her sainthood. The visible weal around her neck — mentioned in all texts as a red or white ring — a sign of her slavery and an acknowledgment of her former shame. A woman's shame in law did not imply any sense of inner hurt; merely the degrading of her social worth. The mark left by the miracle healing of the saintly surgeon's hands could also be seen as a symbol of a new life in the service of God available to women outside the secular restrictions of feudal society. It may have been one of the reasons why this holy well, a consecrated Catholic healing shrine, retained its popularity among high born and low bred from the 12th. Century, almost without interruption to the present day.[40]

The Healing Skull

The natural aspects of a healing well such as the depth of water, the type of rock strata, the gravel or shale through which the water slips and the trace elements it carries to the surface may influence its taste, texture and smell. Yet there is some kind of *otherness* that makes a Lady Well *fair*. Some ancient veneration still attached to a saint's name or a Christian feast day that made it into a holy well; a benign super-normality that seems to bring peace of mind to a supplicant. Perhaps we acknowledge its divine intervention into the natural order of the world. The importance of the well cult lies not only in its great antiquity but in its survival to modern days. Rooted in paganism, 'converted' to Christian usage, condemned by Protestantism, 'explained' by folklorists, rationalized by modern education, the cult has survived and still wields an influence over the human mind. Drinking holy water from the skull of St. Teilo in Pembrokeshire was perhaps the closest that some religious Welsh folk would have acknowledged as being touched by the primitive feelings that Francis Jones tried to express on their behalf.

The saint's well is near the church of Llandeilo Llwydarth and was famed for healing respiratory diseases like tuberculosis and whooping cough. However for a cure to be effective the pilgrim had to drink the waters of the stone-lined spring from a rounded well worn human cup. The holy relic was known as *Penylog Teilo,* the skull of Teilo. The legend states that it was taken there by a servant who had attended the saint when he was dying. The man was told to remove the saint's head after death so the poor and needy might benefit from such a relic. This is reminiscent of the popular story of the triplication of the saint's dead body so that Penally (his birthplace), Llandeilo Fawr (his monastery) and Llandaff (where he became bishop) could each have an identical posthumous relic. In keeping with such belief a fourth skull would have presented no problem to the miracle worker. In 1840 a youth suffering from consumption made a visit here and returned home to Glamorgan without any apparent change in his condition. When his father found out that the lad had not actually drunk from the skull, he took him straight back to Ffynnon Deilo. The skull was filled with water from the well and then given to the youth by the guardian to be drunk to the last drop. After drinking from the relic in the correct ritual manner the boy was cured. The hereditary guardians of *Penylog Teilo* were the Melchior family. The well practice continued up to the First World War when many people came to drink from the skull hoping to secure an end to hostilities. In the last decade of the 19th century an account made by some members of the Cambrian Archaeological group indicates that its popularity was then on the wane.[41]

The farmhouse was invaded by members of the party curious about the relic. Mrs Melchior brought it down and her son placed it on the parlour table in his most pleasant manner, emphasizing as he did so *Penlog Sant Teilo yw homo,* 'this is the skull of Saint Teilo'. The mother in conversation said she did not know if there were many people who now believed there were any healing virtues in the relic but she herself remembered when everybody afflicted with certain diseases used to come and drink water from the well. In fact as a little girl she was taken to it and made to drink its waters when she suffered from whooping cough. She said that some people would come from the town of Haverfordwest (about ten miles away) and from even more distant places on horseback. Outside, her son had already asserted that many in the past came to drink from the skull but that he had no idea how far back the practice went. The nearby gravestone of his great-grandfather was the only way of telling but he did not know how many of his ancestors may have lived here before him. They were said to have descended from Melchior ap Ieuan ap Howell of Newport, Gwent, who died in 1591 and they came to Llandeilo Llwdiarth by marriage a century later. Edward Laws — author of 'The History of Little England beyond Wales' — had examined the relic and proclaimed on the basis of the sutures that it came from a young girl. The Cambrian correspondent ridiculed this assertion as even for a man's skull, the one at Llandeilo seemed to them (to be) rather thick and substantial. He also noted that its outside looked as if were artificially polished but that may have been from it being handled over the years.

In the neighbouring county of Carmarthenshire in the district of the saint's main foundation of Llandeilo Fawr is Ffynnon Llandyfaen (the well was called Ffynnon Gwyddfaen by Edward Lhuyd) that in the past was celebrated for its cures of paralytic afflictions, numbness and scurvy. Water from here was also drunk from a human cup but by 1815 the reputation of the skull was to a great degree apparently lost. After the Reformation, a Bill of Complaint in the Star Chamber was laid against a number of the local gentry for failing to suppress pilgrimages and idolatrous practices. The magistrate did admit that many poor sickly people had been brought before him and he discharged them. Over two-hundred were not apprehended but left by the well itself. Later the chapel was used as a centre of Baptist preaching. The well was the first to be so used to baptize new converts which had caused a great sensation at the time. A chapel called Soar was then erected nearby and according to the 19th century historian Richard Fenton, a small building with an unenclosed stone tank had steps going down to the waters. Many such unused outdoor pools are still to be found in Pembrokeshire [42]

The wooden bowl of Nanteos has a more esoteric association with healing. It is referred to as the *Grail Cup*. It has a legendary history that is longer lasting than any of the human skullcaps and its healing capacity has been well recorded during the past few hundred years. It was made from olive wood or wych elm and its present size of 12x12cm was once larger, for over the years it was nibbled by the large numbers of the sick who thought that chewing the wooden sides of the cup would entail a better cure. It is actually held together by wire staples and fits comfortably in one hand. It was lodged in a bank by the previous owners of Nanteos House. The story of the Grail Cup is that it was brought into Britain by Joseph of Arimathea. A follower of James the Apostle he carried the blood of Christ in a dish or bowl to Glastonbury where it was kept in the earliest Marion church built here. During the Dissolution of the abbeys the relic was entrusted to the monks and taken to Strata Florida Abbey in mid-Wales for safe keeping. The last of the seven monks carried it with him to Nanteos House near Aberystwyth, hence the name that the healing relic since acquired. This fits in neatly with the historical account when the ruined Cistercian abbey of Strata Florida became the possession of the Stedmans. John Stedman built Nanteos mansion from the ruins of one of the outbuildings. The house and the healing cup eventually passed to the

Powell family. Apparently the cup was kept locked in a cupboard in the library. There was said to have been an annual gathering on the front lawn when locals and others would come to drink from it, but more usually the curing ritual was a formal one for visitors inside the mansion when Margaret Powell was in charge during the mid-19th century. In the dining room, filled with holy water she would hand it individually to them to drink from it. There was also a curious custom of lending out the cup to sick neighbours who would leave a sovereign or an expensive token such as silver watch as a pledge that would be redeemed when the cup was returned. The author of a work on Strata Florida abbey visited the Powell mansion for a few days in November 1887. He asked to see the cup but was told that it was out in the neighbourhood curing the sick people. He was then shown a number of receipts setting out the dates taken and when it was returned, the sum of money or pledge, and the nature of the cures affected. He stated that if the accounts of the Powells and the local bishop from whom he first heard of the cup were true then the relic was a most pertinent example of the survival of medieval belief, even of such medieval healing practices down to the present day.[43]

There is an interesting verbatim account of the cup by John Roberts the famous Romani harper. Telymor Cymru was giving concerts in Aberystwyth and was asked to play at the Powell mansion. Roberts walked the five miles or so to Nanteos House. The butler had charge of the cup and during the evening performance the musician made some remarks in jest about it. He had heard of its supposed extraordinary healing powers especially in relation to female complaints but no doubt the gypsy for all his outward social graces — John Roberts had performed for Queen Victoria and many of the crowned heads of Europe — he was uncomfortable about its presence in the library where the concert was held. Later he walked back to Aberystwyth carrying his large double pedal harp in its canvas cover. However all that night he was plagued by the rude remarks he said and so first thing next morning he returned again to Nanteos House. The Powells were at breakfast. The Romani apologized for his offensive comments and asked if he could see the relic. He was taken into the library and given the cup to hold in private. When he left a short time later he gave them one of his handbills on which he had written his message: 'This cup was handled by John Roberts or Telymor Cymru on the morning of the 4th of May 1887. Mind completely at ease'. Not so with Bryon Rogers, a journalist who recently confirmed the existence of the cup and with mixed feeling held it in his own hands.[44]

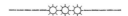

The medical legacy of Roman Britain; Christian miracle-working or soul healing; Anglo-Saxon charm medicine; and the cult of the holy well; are some of the major medical perspectives that inform any early history of medicine here. Each in their different ways modified earlier practices they encountered, in like manner that many of the intrusive cultures altered the dwellings and landscape of the native peoples. For us now the stone remains of Roman roads, towns and military fortifications; the modest communal monastic sites by accessible river valleys; the estuarial networks of Norman castles with associated medieval abbeys; and English manor houses are viewed as historical high water marks, useful for illustrating the changes in the lives of the ruling strata of Welsh society. What we might term schoolbook history! Yet they embody recognizable chronological hinges that give point to historical narrative when incorporating important Welsh contributions to pre-modern medicine such as the recognition of the doctor in the medieval laws of Wales and the early manuscripts associated with the Physicians of Myddfai. In conjunction with the influences of parallel European medical traditions, the above manuscripts highlight the native attitude to healing. Yet they often conjure a rather incoherent mosaic of influences for there is little of historical note until the renaissance of the Welsh Humanist physicians in the late 16th and mid 17th centuries. The medical and scientific works, the translations from Latin, and their related interests in other fields of intellectual

80

endeavour resulted in awareness that the new ideas of the Tudor era were different from the age-old superstitious forms of magic and healing that surrounded their forefathers in Wales. They seriously attempted to set down medically informed diagnoses, self-help applications and written accounts in Latin and occasionally in English, but rarely in Welsh. The introduction of such Humanist influences and the herbal cultivation of native and exotic botanical plants broadened the story of medicine here in Wales.

At the other end of the spectrum, traditional medicine or the folk healing from what has survived of herb cures, magic charms and the recorded anecdotes of antiquarians or churchmen may be a more accurate term than that of 'medicine' which was often used by the ordinary people when referring to plant recipes. Up to the recent past of a few hundred years ago, the largely conservative inward-looking culture of the rural Welsh shielded them from the language of progress in medicine which was first Latin and then English. Cut off from medical advances by the language barrier the majority of the monoglot population were also divorced by the more obvious class and social distinctions. Thus, they were enabled to maintain their oral traditions of home-healing, medicinal plant curing, magical charms, age-old beliefs or what were termed superstitions by churchmen in relation to countering the effects of nature, bad weather, and malicious and evil intentions of hags, conjurers and wizards on their homes, children and cattle. These beliefs and the extent of reliance on their own ethnic medicine were part of a social narrative that has largely been forgotten due to the massive population shifts into the shanty towns that fed the emerging industrial regimes of both north and south Wales. The fervour of the Methodist revivals among the poor working classes also contributed to what can only be described as a collective amnesia of the life that sustained them in their former rural surroundings.

Yet the central issue remains of identifying what would be acceptable as a quintessential Welsh medicine rather than as a minor and what is usually considered to have been an insignificant part of a mainly retrospective and generalized British overview. The historical account of what is termed pre-modern was generally compiled by cherry-picking the more obvious aspects that related to the Greek, Roman and post-Reformation scientific advances, leading up to changes in health care during the late 19th century. In terms of chronology this is, of necessity, the basis on which the next three chapters of *The Medicine Tree* are based. The final third part is devoted to the ethnic medicines of the traditional home healers; the actual practices from the healers' point of view; their encounters with the law of the land; and some of the more esoteric accounts in the recent transitions of modern medical practice in Wales.

PART TWO
CHIRUGIA THE WORK OF SKILLED HANDS

Chapter 4. Bloodletting, Bleeding and Ancient Pathology

Opening veins, pulling out teeth and minor amputations are all fairly common operations in all almost all societies the world over. One could add to the list trepanning or brain surgery, Caesarean birth — so named after the Julius Caesar who was said to have survived in this way — and the cutting of gall stones. A Vedic medicine compendium, *Sustrata Samhita,* from about the time of Christ describes the operation for the latter in an almost identical manner to how it would be performed by a modern surgeon. Cure of the stone was generally a specialist job and seems to be particularly prevalent in primitive societies. Such an operation is described by the Meddygon Myddfai of Carmarthenshire. Having bathed and fasted beforehand the patient was trussed-up like a chicken with legs tied around a pole within the bend of the knees and wrists tied over the nape of the neck. The patient was then laid on his back with some support under both thighs so that the calculus or stone can be cut on the left side of the urethra. After cleaning, the wound was dressed with flax and salt butter. Various herbal recipes were also suggested for dissolving gall stones. Most early medicine gave purgatives or emetics beforehand and used alcohol or a herbal sponge, a block of wood between the teeth or auto-hypnotic suggestion as forms of anaesthesia

Surgical operations that were described and written down generally determine the sophistication of techniques available to a particular society. However in the case of the Roman surgeon Celcus, his fine detailed dental work and facial surgery was lost to the profession in Europe for nearly a thousand years. His eight treatises — the last two on surgery — were rediscovered through Arabic medicine and translated back again into Latin. His was one of the first printed medical works by Caxton. So Roman medicine was not only judged on a small body of inferior writings but the reliance on them and such influences on healing up to the late medieval period in Europe was on a totally unwarranted authority. A perceptual shift of approach at the time can be seen when the church forbade its members to cut into the human body, thereby leaving the job to the secular barber-surgeons trained to do so. What may be shown from many later accounts is the difference in approach of how one doctor sees the patient as a human being with a pathological condition to be treated with the minimum of pain; while another using the empiric or rule-of-thumb approach of the field surgeon, may have to operate quickly surrounded by blood and gore on all sides in situations where there is not much time or scope for humanitarian treatment. A graphic episode from the time of the First Crusade in Mesopotamia shows up this difference in the cultural ethos of the period. It also conveys the brutal arrogance of the early European physician towards the sick and one that still unfortunately underpins the scientific materialism of surgical medicine. A knight with an abscess on his leg and a woman troubled by fever were brought into the tent. The native doctor applied a small poultice so the abscess opened and then it took a favourable turn. He lowered the woman's temperature and suggested that she did not eat certain foods. Eventually a Frankish doctor arrived and then announced that this other (man) could not possibly cure them. He asked the knight if he preferred to die with both his legs or live with a single one. When the patient made the choice to live the doctor ordered a strong man to bring an axe and to cut the leg off with a single blow. He then had the knight stretched out on a wooden block but unfortunately the first blow was misjudged and a second swing of the axe caused the marrow to flow from the bone. The man died not long afterwards. He then examined the woman and declared that a devil was in her head. So the physician ordered it to be shaved and that she be given garlic and mustard to eat. Her fever grew worse. He grabbed a razor and then cut into her scalp in the form of a cross. He rubbed the wound with salt and the woman expired.[2]

The human skull provides the earliest evidence for complex surgical procedures from as far back as the Stone Age. The smooth edges of small round holes left in the cranial cap indicate that the operation was successfully performed on living people and more important that they survived afterwards and long enough for the wound to heal over. Trepanning or trephining has been practiced in all regions of the world. The surgical procedure was clearly described by Hippocrates in the fifth century BC and deemed useful in alleviating conditions like epilepsy, migraine and serious head injuries. The Greeks were the first to use a small circular saw called a trephine. The instrument cut through a section of the bone that was then prised out from the skull. It was done without anaesthetics, though herbal relief may have been on hand as the persons scalp had to be cut and a flap of skin pulled back to reveal the area of bone to be sawn. A ring of small holes was sometimes drilled and the centre piece of bone scraped out. A few trephined skulls have been found in Ireland at the site of the abbey of Nendrum which was burned down by the Norsemen around 940; a cemetery at Collinstown, Co. Meath was excavated in 1935 and it contained the trephined skull of a thirteen year old child. The bones have been estimated to belong to the Iron Age or Early Christian period. Nine examples of trephination found from graves in medieval Ireland had used the scraping method. But one skull had it performed with a circular saw showing the semicircular grooves around the lip of the hole, indicating failure by the operator to get a good initial grip. Or perhaps it was due to the squirming patient. Yet smooth edges of the cut bone show that the healing was successful. Briciu — an ancient Irish scholar and surgeon — is said to have successfully removed a bone from the head of Cennfaeladh in an operation which was called, 'removing the brain of forgetfulness'. The Book of Leinster has an account of some such head operation. Conchubhar mac Nessa, a king of Ulster, was injured when a brain ball — a slingshot from a mixture of lime and the brains of an enemy — entered his skull. Finigin the physician said that if it were removed the king would die. However he could heal the head wound by stitching it over with gold thread so that no blemish would be outwardly visible. The same king was a participant in the first recorded Caesarian section. His sister who was pregnant by him fell into a river. She was rescued but fearing for the unborn child's safety, her side was cut so that the infant lived. A geis or curse laid on the king as a result of this incestuous union meant that in the time of greatest need his warriors would be subject to the pangs of labour and they would be as weak as a women in that condition. It was therefore left to Cuchulainn, the boy hero who was freed of the usual birthing process, to defend the province in a saga called Tain Bo Cuilgne otherwise known as the Irish Illiad.[3]

A skull recently found in the excavation of a medieval Anglo-Saxon site at Wharram Percy in Yorkshire showed that a man had been whacked on the head with a blunt instrument. According to the skeletal biologist from English Heritage, a successful operation was carried out by an unknown doctor a century before the Norman invasion of 1066. The resulting large depression on the brain was relieved and fractures to the bone were healed, allowing the patient to live for many years afterwards A current diagnosis of such an operation on what they term a plebeian (based on his diet) performed by an itinerant 'Dark-Age' doctor is presented as an extraordinary occurrence. However as shown in the first part of this study, the medical abilities of Anglo-Saxon physicians and the high level attainments of medicine in general, should warrant no such surprise. More to the point would be the lack of scientific medicinal examination of human remains by archaeologists on past occasional finds of paleo-pathology such as a cranial lesion in a skull recovered from what may have been the site of St. Cadoc's monastery at Llancarfan in Glamorgan. Other indications of early Welsh surgical know-how could be deduced from the miracle action performed by St. Beuno sewing-up the neck of the maiden Gwenfrewi after being gashed by a sword. It is clear from the medieval Welsh law codes that the three dangerous wounds to a person — a blow to the head cutting into the brain, to the body into the bowels and the smashing of a limb — 'breaking one of the four posts' — were all within the surgical capabilities of the physician. Treatment using a *goreth* or surgical drain, staunching major blood vessels, ointment, herbal medication and bloodletting were mentioned, each application having its own set fee. The Welsh mediciners used long monthly calendars on the best days to bleed a person and in relation to diseases that changed through the year from what they termed as strong to weak conditions. A summary in a sixteenth century manuscript attributed to Llywelyn Sion sets out the times of the 'good' days: the first day after the golden number in each month, before noon; the second day at noon; the third day in the forenoon and after; the fourth and fifth day early in the morning; the seventh in any part of the day; the eighth day at noon; the ninth day at all times; the eleventh day in the evening; the twelfth, the thirteenth and fourteenth days at all times; the sixteenth day in the morning; the eighteenth day at the third hour; the twentieth day after dusk; the twenty-fourth day at all times; and the twenty-eighth day in the evening. There were also lists of days in every month — usually termed the dog-days or Egyptian days — when it was dangerous for the physician to lance a vein.[4]

Bleeding along with purging had been the principal of medicine since the time of Hippocrates and continued to be so until fairly recently using leeches instead of venesection. The Greeks believed in nature's way of allowing the sick body to recover in its own way. However an equally persuasive school of thought maintained that the process needed to be helped along and if such methods worked gradually they might do better if applied vigorously and more often. So a universally important dictum relating to phlebotomy was the correct time of the month when it was appropriate and most effective. Blood taken from the basilic vein near the elbow was usual but whether it was actually appropriate to the condition of the sick person was a different matter. Bald the Anglo-Saxon leech wrote that if a sick man had to be bled he should be taken to a warm place and that it should not be overdone. Whether such a recommendation was respected is doubtful given the regularity and normality of the practice in monasteries as well as in sick rooms. In

87

the former bloodletting was part of a harsh regime to cleanse the body of lustful overheating and impurities of the blood while in the latter it was usually the first and probably also the last induction between doctor and patient. A Latin text by Bede of Jarrow states that if necessary, it can be done any time day or night. However if not for acute diseases then the best period was late spring to summer when the body's blood was undergoing increase. But afterwards note should be taken of the quality of the seasons and the course of the moon. The best times, in his estimation, were the fifth, tenth, twentieth, twenty-fifth and the thirtieth day of the moon. Bede also recounted a story about the Bishop of Hexham being asked to heal a young nun who had been bled in the arm but the wound had turned septic. When he was told that it had been done of the fourth day of the moon, he reprimanded the abbess that such a time was dangerous, *when the light of the moon and the tide of the ocean was increasing.* Needless to say the bishop healed the young nun. It was therefore vital for those like the abbess in charge of nuns or of monks, that such instruction be set out in an easy rendered form.

The most frequent method used in manuscripts was like a rebus with numbers, letters or ciphers written in and around a wheeled cross often with translations from Greek or Latin, and called *a sphere* and attributed to a famed personage. As a healing device that incorporated the use of magic numbers, it may have originated in Egypt. The *sphere*, on the one hand retained its ancient magical quality and it was also made acceptable by association with the name of a known saint or a famed thinker of antiquity. Such devices were attributed to Plato, Apulelius, Apollonius, Hippocrates, Pythagoras, Petosiris, Bede and Columba. Some written works referred to the device or sphere in order to ascertain an outcome concerning the sick. One early English text included in an eighth century Hispanic Latin manuscript stated that the day of the week be determined and the tide of the moon, according to the letters written below, and if added together and then divided by thirty, to consider the number that remained. If it were the same as those in the upper part of the circle, the patient would recover but if one of those below, he or she would not. An original Latin diagram drawn by Byrhtferth of Ramsey circa A.D.1000 and known as the *Sphere of Petosiris* reflects an elegant search for perfection in uniting heaven and earth. The macrocosm and microcosm are seen between the internal and external realms of man and nature. The four seasons of the year are connected with the four ages of man; the humours of the body with the four elements. The solstices and equinoxes were aligned with the cardinal points of the horizon whose letters make up the word ADAM around the centre circle. It in turn encloses the word MAN. Concentric rings hold the elaborate design in place. It includes astrological sun signs, the months of the year and the number of days in each month. Such devices are generally seen as part of an arcane language and 'obscure speeches' using numbers and enigmatic word pictures from alchemy and Christian mysticism. It is yet a further indication of the philosophic basis of English medicine that the Normans, like their Northmen forebears in a previous era, brutally hacked off root and branch from the ethnic Christian medicine tree.[5]

The Book of Holy Cures

Henry, the First Duke and later Earl of Lancaster, was born at Grosmont in Monmouthshire. When he re-organized the hospital in Leicester, founded by his father in 1330, he stipulated that patients should be on elevated beds in order to be able to see the altar during mass. He served in Flanders during the Hundred Years War. At the first major engagement in 1336, five thousand Welsh bowmen dressed in green played a decisive part in the Battle of Cre'cy. Throughout his military campaigns in Europe during the next two decades, Henry acquired sufficient medical experience and medicinal lore to write a treatise. Only two copies of *Le Livre des Seyntes Medicines* were known but parts of a third copy have recently been discovered in the National Library of Wales in Aberystwyth. Described as a typical literary effort of Anglo-Norman devotional literature *The Book of Holy Cures* is written in the form of a confession of his sins as an extended allegory. It begins by Henry liking himself to one of the poor and terminally sick in his own hospital and being so insignificant and so full of horrible poison and rotting filth that he is unable to show himself to Christ the Physician. Its metaphorical use of medical terminology is unusually dense as when he compares his heart to a foxhole and to a marketplace in which his many sins are entrenched. Or confessing himself to be mortally wounded in all the senses of the body and his soul; poisoned with the seven deadly sins; he then appeals to the divine physician for remedies to cure himself. Apparently the work contains vivid cameos of the sick room and the bodily afflictions of the wounded.[6]

Henry described the surgeons of Montpellier in Provence dissecting the dead bodies of criminals for the purpose of medical instruction. The treatise was written six years after the outbreak of the Black Death when he had retired from active service. He continued to write other works and died during the second occurrence of the plague in 1361. He had several doctors and surgeons in his employ who accompanied him on military expeditions. Among them was John of Arderne described as the foremost field surgeon in England who also served under John of Gaunt. He was one of the most distinguished specialists in the treatment of anal fistulas and produced a treatise on how to cut them from the anal duct. After his operations the bleeding was staunched by a hot sponge and the wound cared for by cleaning and daily enemas. For one such operation in 1370, he charged forty pounds in gold, a new suit of clothes and a yearly pension from his noble patron. He described women (nursing) practitioners as *ladies bountifull* since they charged no fee and he poured scorn on their slow methods of caring for the patients, who in his estimation took far too long to recover from the effects of such operations. Writers of surgical treatises like Arderne would inevitably have belonged to a social elite with no inhibitions in recording their own achievements. Few in his time were willing to undertake such delicate operations that were often regarded as incurable or to risk killing their patrons. His method of cutting fistulas was derived from that of an Arab surgeon, but Arderne's remarkable anatomical knowledge coupled with the restraint shown during post-operative care — by not frequently changing dressings or using aggressive applications to encourage suppuration — was unusual at the time. He made his own surgical probes and administered enemas of assorted herbs, soap and honey squirted gently into the anus through a greased pipe attached to a bag made from a pig's bladder in order to clean out the intestines. His recommendation of clysters for nutritional and general inner body toning has become part of a fashion in current complimentary medicine with a similar technique called colonic irrigation.[7]

The long drawn out Hundred Years War in Europe helped to bring about changes to medicine in general and surgery in particular; especially as the Lateran Church Council at the beginning of the previous century had forbidden anyone in higher orders to engage in it for fear of taking life unnecessarily. The medical hospital system of ancient Rome was first created by and administered within the army structure. So similarly within the English social hierarchy the need for experienced field surgeons brought about a more pragmatic approach in dealing with the sheer numbers of the wounded. English surgeons became more directly aware of the innovative practices of the doctors in the Universities of Bologna and Montpellier, as Henry Duke of Lancaster described them in his book. According to Dr. R.A. Griffiths, twenty-four English surgeons were known by name to be present at the battle of Agincourt, carefully organised in medical corps, while medical officers were equally important and included on the French side. In addition the 'spasmodic' war brought together the skills of the surgeon who did the knife work and the barbers, now known as barber-surgeons, who bled and took care of the patients. It helped differentiate their specialist knowledge and eventually was the basis of the medical Fellowships that became chartered from this period onwards. After the Company of Barbers had gained a charter in 1370, the Fellowship of Surgeons was established in London. Gilbert Kymer, a court physician helped organize the university-trained physicians, but many years were to elapse before the College of Physicians of London was founded in 1516. The physicians themselves were then allowed to regulate metropolitan practices. The apothecaries were the other important members of the medical quartet of the late Middle Ages. They began as wholesale merchants and spice importers. With the growth of the retail herb trade, their shops spread out of London into the provincial towns like the Port of Bristol. As part of Richard II's expeditions to Ireland in the 1390s, the king instructed William Bradewardine, a surgeon in his household, to buy medicines from the London apothecaries, 'for the body of the king and others in the household'. He spent over £66 on herbs and in 1399 twice as much again but there is no record of what afflictions they were to be used for; nor of the kind of medicines to be made. The Royal College of Physicians were always concerned about the financial power of the spice merchants and their growing influence among the rich and lower social classes. After the Worshipful Society of Apothecaries was formed early in the seventeenth century, they were brought under stern control by the restrictions on retail practice and only authorized to sell medications prescribed by a physician from those listed in the official London pharmacopoeia. It was this same work that Nicholas Culpeper translated from Latin into English and which he published in 1649 titled *A Physical Directory,* to bring down condemnation and abuse on him from all quarters of the medical establishment.[8]

Medieval Welsh Medicine Codes

Scholars have related the Laws of Hywel Dda to various disciplines from the legal to the mythological and to known medical practices; from the extant documentation of the late Middle Ages to the more extensive recorded later material, and especially the Brehon Laws. For instance in relation to healing, one Irish Law Tract poses a very important question. How do you estimate a wound, and then he proceeds to answer it as according to conscience, its colour and the doctor's verdict. The reference here was to the *Laws of Compensation* whereby the injured man was examined by a *liaig* (doctor in Old Irish) and the obligations of the defendant depended on his verdict. If seriously injured, the patient had to be cared for by the assailant and his retinue entertained. Thus sickness from injury seems to have been ritualized and healing was allowed to be a lengthy process.

The Welsh king Hywel ap Cadell, was overlord of the south, by marriage of the southwest, and then by conquest of Gwynedd in the northwest. He ruled a large portion of Wales for forty years; it was a period of peace and prosperity so that he became known as Howell the Good during the 10th century. The tradition of the original law codes of the king was given as a prologue in various legal texts. Hywel summoned twelve just men from every part of the kingdom to his house known as Ty Gwyn or the White House (now Whitland) on the river Taf, for the six week period of Lent. By examining the old laws or amending and enacting new ones, the twelve created the first formal legal basis of his kingdom, which was written down during the following centuries in a large number of legal manuscripts. These were essentially composed of individual treatises or tractates on particular aspects of the law and then gathered together as lawyers' textbooks. Many were subsequently collected by Aneurin Owen in the 19th century; he ordered them into three major Codes based on their place of origin — Gwynnedd, Dyfed and Deheubarth, — and published them with an English translation.[9]

These ancient laws were explicit about the duties of the court officials. Each had a title and an order of preference from the king downward at table but perhaps more important they became a symbolic yardstick of the family or territorial group with its own head and kin members. The twenty-four officers of the court were in order of importance after the King: the Captain of the Household, Priest, Steward, Chief Falconer, Court Judge, Chief Groom, Chamberlain, Bard of the Household, Usher, Chief Huntsman, Mead Brewer and Physician who was followed by the Butler, Doorkeeper,

Cook etc. The Welsh term *meddyg* was usually given for a physician or mediciner with the more general meaning of medical practitioner. Placed twelfth he was entitled to his land free, his horse in attendance, woollen clothes from the king and linen cloth from the queen. His position in the dining hall was by the base of the post near where the king sat. The physician lodged with the captain of the household and his protection was the *king's word* when asked to go to a wounded person inside or outside the court. His duties were defined as threefold. First was to the king and his officers; second to the queen and her household; third to the freedmen in society outside the court. In many respects the physician seems to have been an essential part of the secular legal apparatus. It was he who decided the extent of physical damage in any open disagreement. It was his judgment that could assertion the result of an attack on a husband by his wife or between members of different kin families. All of whom like himself had their legal due and social worth.

A dangerous wound or *arberygl* required a man's cut to be so severe as to leave the brain, the bowels or the bone marrow visible. For ascertaining its degree, the legal payment to the mediciner was four pence or eight pence in some texts. Any medication given, with herbs, but without obvious swelling was worth four pence. Equally so was the assurance given by relatives of an injured party which meant that the doctor would not be liable (to them) if he died under treatment. If the mediciner did not take the indemnity, he would have to pay them as a result of a death. Every medical action performed by the mediciner had a set price. Bloodletting was four pence. Food every night was three halfpence. Lighting cost a penny as did the pan he used for medication. Each separate part of the human body had its set monetary value. From the head and face — including eyes, lips, ears, nose, tongue and teeth — to each limb known as 'the four posts' — and each part of the body down to the toes if lost or mutilated; all had a special set price. Flowing blood, open wounds and physical scars also had a legal value. In a court of law judgement would determine the particular liabilities and costs incurred by all the parties. To the non-specialist, these ancient codes may be summed up as defining duties and compensations to and from each person with social standing or status in medieval Welsh society. In actual legal practice it would seem to have been that each side in law, or in legal dispute, had a right and a duty. Therefore judgement against an individual was generally not in terms of an absolute right or wrong as in English common law, but how far the event under consideration deviated from the written law codes. There were the laws that covered all aspects of social interaction and especially the trades represented by the king's officials; and the physician had equal legal standing as with all the recognized freedmen of society. Over and above the dues a physician might claim for his medical practice and implements, he had his *honor* or *face price* and his *sarrhaad* — which was described as a kind of worth compensation — to be paid to him for any insult or outrage whilst treating a patient.[10]

The duties of the medieval mediciner as laid down in the Welsh law codes were specifically related to the domain of the lord or tribal king. The accounts of healing in the *Vitae* or Lives of the Saints proclaim the power of God and the Roman Church. An implicit duality of the local and the universal, between an insular and European authority, is a characteristic focus from the earliest period of Welsh medicine. It was exemplified in the earliest known writings of the Meddygon Myddfai as in the social relationship between Rhys Grys (the hoarse) a prince of South Wales who, according to a colophon in manuscripts attributed to them, bestowed hereditary lands on the physician Rhiwallon and his sons. The manuscripts were written in Welsh. They combined translations of short classical medical treatises and recipes using herbal remedies; the former in a sense bestowing authority for the inclusion of indigenous plants and local healing lore.

In an academic paper published in 1975, M.E. Owen (of the Centre for Advanced Welsh and Celtic Studies) sets out the lists of contents of the manuscript works she ascribed to the Meddygon Myddfai. She suggests that they show a fluid and continuous tradition of medical writing in medieval Wales which compares with the fluidity of the Welsh law tracts from the same period. Not one of the forty law manuscripts written in Welsh and Latin, she asserts, was a direct and exact transcript of another and that (this) lack of uniformity was due to their being a kind of legal handbook (that was) composed for individuals from a variety of written and oral sources. And as such they had a direct correlation to the handbooks of practising physicians and, therefore, to the contemporary application of medical learning. The written works were generally of a small size and were probably in the nature of *aide memoirs*, for help with the examination of urine, blood-letting days and herbal mixtures. She has suggested a distinction be made between the medieval professional or orthodox physician and the hereditary healers who used a more traditional approach. Although the available written works by the latter from the Western Isles of Scotland and in Ireland are extensive; the problem here in Wales is that not much seems to be known of either group, apart from a few manuscripts. The former may well have been in touch with more intellectual developments and teachings of the first European medical school of Salerno. Their translations in manuscript suggests a philosophy of healing that had a firm grasp of the classical foundation of humoral medicine with its emphasis on diet exercise and hygiene. But whether the Welsh doctors or readers of the works would have then understood the constitutional basis of such an ancient tradition is uncertain. Each of its aspects had a complex unity and a body of instructive teaching behind it that stretched back to the Romano-Greek period; or even if they were aware at the time — as medical historians are now — of the extent of Arabic learning. It was by the Latin translations in the 12th century onwards, from their original works out of the ancient Greek of what had been to them virtually unknown medical practices, that gave fresh impetus by becoming part of the wider cultural horizons of the late Middle Ages.[11]

Owen asserted that the 1861 Welsh & English publication entitled *Meddygon Myddfai* was a good example of how folk-tale, tradition, and historical fact had become fused together. Although largely conjectural, due to the lack of historical material, she concentrates on the supposed origins of these hereditary physicians with a folk tale of 'the lady of the lake' theme that marries a mortal and thereafter bestows the gifts of medicine on her Welsh offspring. This introduction is followed by a copy of a genuine medieval extract from the much larger 14th century Red Book of Hergest. The text is said to have had an original colophon that states that Rhys Greg (the hoarse) gave Rhiwallon the physician and his three sons, land in the area of Myddfai in Carmarthenshire; thus bringing fact and fiction together in what she terms the 'popular writings' on the subject. She quotes the editor's spurious introduction to the 'history' of Welsh medicine, with a few references to Myddfai by Welsh antiquarians. And one might add even contemporary writings such as David Hoffmann's assertion that 'it was the physicians of Myddfai who collected the plants and put them in writing for the first time ... with a body of legends relating to the magical origins of their skill and knowledge', or Barbara Griggs stating that 'they were holistic in their approach and brilliantly studied and used by experts, as the traditional green pharmacy of the peasant'.[12]

Owen ignored the second larger collection of medical recipes from the above book, unlike many people who accept it as a real contribution towards understanding the traditional medicine of Wales. She suggests it is a work *fabricated by Iolo Morganwg* (my italics), otherwise known as the 18th century poet Edward Williams. She appears then to have followed the assertions of Professor G.L. Williams in claiming that 'like most of Iolo Morganwg's fabrications his text is a mixture of medieval fragments and his own additions'. In fact the Professor, who appears to have been the first Welsh academic to seriously study Iolo's works, suggested that this 'book' was merely his elaboration of a herbal originally complied by John Parry of Pontypool that he attributed to the Myddfai medieval physicians. Twenty years later in another paper Owen makes no mention of the so-called forgeries, but she sets out much the same material — in a reverse order — noting that the lack of historical evidence makes the medical vernacular literature important; and that it is 'inextricably bound up in the popular and written tradition of modern Wales, with the name of Meddygon Myddfai'. It may be unfair to single out a few sentences from her original work but she appears to be applying literary criteria to a collection of folk remedies that were translated into English by Dr John Pugh. However it would seem that the wayward genius of Iolo had access to many versions of such old works in his mammoth editing of nearly eight hundred medical recipes for a variety of human ills.

These remedies are not that far removed in content, style or even the flora that they are based on from those in earlier manuscripts written up to 1600. Quite apart from the upturn in Edward William's literary reputation, Iolo's singular contribution to Welsh manuscript culture during the late 18th century is at last being revalued. According to G.H. Jenkins he epitomises what historians like to call the 'invention of tradition', by offering a new vision of Welsh history and by "discovering and copying thousands of manuscripts which cluttered his tiny cottage at Flemington in the Vale of Glamorgan." In terms of traditional folk medicine, as an avid reader studying from a wide range of ancient Welsh texts, Iolo's editorial expertise almost single-handedly created that particular genre of folk medicine long before it became a popular concern during the Victorian era and especially in the late 20th century.

Of the three surviving manuscripts attributed to the Myddfai physicians the earliest is in the British Library (BM add.ms 14912). Written on vellum it consists of 180 small pages and is generally dated to the second half of the 14th century. The signatures on the manuscript are by Dafydd Nanmor, a 15th century bard, William Salesbury whose own unpublished Llysieulyfr or Herbal was written between 1566 and 1574, and Lewis Morris a scholar and antiquarian who indexed the contents; gave it a title page and may have added other material. One of many works that were part of his Welsh School collection that came to the British Library in 1843, Lewis claimed it to be the original ms of the Meddygon Myddfai. It is interesting to note that the three signatories were from north Wales and that the calendar of the holy feast days in the opening section includes three Saints — Dewi, Padarn and Derfel — associated with that region, rather than where the colophon places its origin in Carmarthenshire. It has not been translated, but the contents consist of short Latin medical treatises that dealt with urine, pulses, fevers, diet and blood-letting; and also some evidence of the influence of Arabic medicine from the late medieval period. Two later manuscripts that are in the British library are considered to be copies of the above and also of the Red Book in Jesus College, Oxford. A version of which was translated into English by John Pughe.[13]

There is one original ancient Welsh book that shows both the content of the written works as well as the family of healers that were conversant with its lineage. The medical manuscript of *Bened Feddyg* from Denbighshire now in the National Library of Wales is an interesting example of how some doctors from this western corner of Britain deemed it of sufficient importance to translate the European treatises into their native tongue. It shows an intellectual vigour that would become more evident in Wales after the Reformation, with the Humanist learnings and wide scientific interests of many eminent physicians during the mid 16th century. The manuscript refers to five generations of physicians from about 1420 to 1620. Bened ap Rhys was born around 1408 in the vale of Clywd and practiced there as a medical physician. He claimed descent from Marchwethian, the founder of one of the fifteen noble tribes of Gwynedd. He appears to have originated the book and scribed the main body of its material which has since been grouped into three broad sections. The first in the hand of Bened himself comprises his original compilation, with a list of contents. This could be viewed as a whole, as an example of an early fifteenth century doctors' handbook. After his death it passed to his son William who wrote his own name on two pages and inserted more material. He too was in all probability a physician. The second section consists of a number of medical works written by Tudor ap Elise. There are two treatises on Uroscopy, the longer in English with a partial translation in Welsh and the other in Welsh. There are tables, a rough sketch of a human hand and further medical anecdotal material. The third section is described as a broad miscellaneous assortment from the time of Bened's son William and his grandson Hugh. Included here are excerpts on the Four Elements; the Four Humours and the relationship with the seasons of the year, and a list of the *dog days* or the Egyptian days often noted in medical texts as unsatisfactory for phlebotomy or bleeding the patient.[14]

The original compilation by Bened Feddyg is a well ordered selection from many different medical sources. A content's list from the NLW ms Sotheby 3 includes the following:

-Treatise on the Four Humours that govern mans' *complexion*.
-Treatise on the nature and properties of food and drink as related to above.
-A discourse on the taking of pulses.
-A selection of the remedies in terms of ailments affecting parts of the body.
-Methods of preparation of ointments, poultices and plasters.
-A short version of a treatise on Uroscopy.
-A brief statement on the principles of bloodletting.
-Some general advice to a medical apprentice.
-A short treatise on the four parts of the body attributed to Aristotle.
-Treatise on Palmistry.
-A Christian charm.
-A copy of the Latin prelude to the Gospel of St. John.

The manuscript has some poems at the end, probably by Hugh who was a poet and an accomplished harpist. He wrote his signature in it with a note — the book of Huw ap William ap Bened after his father's name. He stated that he was a year old in 1523. Hugh's son John wrote his name on three separate pages stating that the book was among his possessions. Further evidence in the book confirms this and that he was sixty-seven in 1621 which means that this medical work remained in the same family for at least four generations after the death of Bened ap Rhys.[15]

Chapter 5. Welsh Humanists and the Renaissance.

The printed book had been a rather tentative first footing out of the private domain of the literate minority into a public realm where many copies of a written work became available to more people. And at the same time readers were able to assess the worth of its writing for themselves rather than rely on a chorus of medieval church middlemen trained to decipher ancient manuscripts. As the leather satchel with its quills, inks and folio leaves was the insignia of the old medievalism, the printed tome became a byword of the new Humanism. Welsh physicians and scholars professing Humanist ideals were in the forefront of change. Due to the innovation of the printing press and the ideals of the Renaissance with its commitment to publish in the vernacular languages outside Latin, doctors from north and south Wales were committed to spread both classical and new scientific knowledge to a wider social milieu. If the grandeur of their ideals was never quite realized in a poor principality inchoately aware of the outer trappings of European culture, the intellectual breath of the most prominent writers was remarkable, despite the general lack of patronage in Wales and without the rich surroundings of ornate palaces, grand cathedrals; or even a university of native learning.

One the earliest of the London based Welsh polymaths was known as Lewis of Caerleon in Monmouthshire. He had a breath of culture and learning that heralded the renaissance of the Humanist physicians of the following century. He was a mathematician, theologian, doctor of medicine, astronomer and teacher at Oxford and in Cambridge although in 1466 he was fined twenty shillings for failing to deliver the lectures in medicine required of him as regent there. Six works of astro-mathematics were attributed to his name. One of these which included calculations on solar eclipses he wrote when imprisoned in the Tower of London. While attending Lady Margaret Beaufort in 1483 he became a go-between for her while plotting to put her son on the throne. After the triumph of the king,

Henry VII promoted him to royal physician with a gift for life of forty marks. There was a second gift of twenty marks in 1486, when he was called the King's servant and as Doctor of Medicine he is recorded as such in the Calendar of Patient Rolls.

Within a relatively short time of Henry Tudor becoming king in 1485, a large number of his Welsh countrymen and supporters who stayed on in London had risen to the upper echelons of the court and the professions, especially the law. As an early ethnic London minority, the Welsh probably did not think of themselves as foreigners or look different, until they opened their mouths when asserting Cymric ancient origins and genealogy or as Gerald de Barri wrote, they carried their pedigree aloud with them; even to the popular jibe of St. Peter clearing them from heaven by opening the gates and shouting *Caws pobi*, or free toasted cheese. Their association with the leek, the harp and funny accent with its associative term Taffy was probably enjoyed by all groups, most of the time, as common urban banter. But it was during the following century with the influx of the Scots and the Irish, that the earlier privileges given by the Tudors to their Welsh supporters became an issue creating a sharper tone as in the well-known rhyme — Taffy was a Welshman / Taffy was a thief / Taffy came to my house and stole a slice of beef.

The popularity of the broadsheet made it an important public expression for political ideas, current news, scandal and popular opinion in London. For those from the earliest wave of native in-comers in the train of Henry Tudor, the tracts with such titles as *Crete wonders foretold by then Crete Prophet of Wales* — a Wenglish tract of 1647; and *The Welsh Doctor or the Welshman turned physitian* by Shon ap Morgan, Shentleman of Wales, Professor of her medical Arts and Sciences, were probably not merely the stereotypical view we might think now but rather more in terms of advertising their services as wizards fortune-tellers or conjurers. The origins of these popular characters from early woodcuts such as Shon ap Morgan and his son Sheffrey Morgan or Morgan ap Shons — whose *observations of the stars as he sat upon*

102

a mountain in Wale' — are lost in the obscurity of the period. *The fyrst boke of the Introduction of Knowledge* with a 'second chapitre treateth of Wales and of the naturall disposicion of Welshmen' was published in London in 1547. The most memorable remark by Andrew Boorde that Welsh wizards there go bare-legged, drink, 'tell prophyces wyche be not in ryme' and play the harp, is often quoted as an example of an early printed satire on the Welsh in London at the time. Boorde, a native of Sussex who had spent twenty years as a Carthusian monk before studying medicine in France and travelling between there and London, also remarked that he sought to teach Englishmen to speak some Welsh. Like the more scholarly Welsh-English dictionary by William Salesbury — the first book to be actually published in Wales — Boorde's work may have been an attempt to show the alterations in both the spoken and written Wenglish used in the capital. Roy Porter referring to the changes in society and medicine at this period points out that the dissolution of the monasteries resulted in the closure of almost all the medieval hospitals that had afforded shelter to the aged, sick and incapacitated. At the other end of the social register he mentions a book by Boorde called *Compendyous Regyment or a Dyetary of Healthe* which set out where to situate a house, organize the household, what to eat, drink, and exercise to take as well as more detailed methods of preserving health. One of the most important shrines in Wales was at Llandderfel church in Merionith: A large wooden sculpture with eyes and arms that could move mechanically. It was believed by the rural Welsh to be capable of saving condemned souls from hell and it was reported to the King that as many as six hundred people a day came to see the image of their favourite saint. Ellis Price wrote to Thomas Cromwell in 1538 that the people had so great a confidence in the saint that some would bring oxen and carts and even money, for there is a common saying that whoever will offer what they can to the image of Derfel Gadarn, will get out of hell if they are dammed. The king ordered that the large wooden idol of the saint be taken to Smithfield and burnt there at the stake alongside Friar Forest who opposed Henry VIII's divorce from Catherine of Aragon.[16]

The current gift-wrapping of the glories of the Celtic past is not a particularly modish practice. Sir John Prys, the King's Chancellor who had the singular honor of writing the first printed Welsh prayer book simply called *Yay Lhyvyr hwan* or *In this Book*; wrote a long and robust rebuttal of the scepticism expressed by Polydore Vergil that Brutus the son of Aeneas, was the noted ancestor of the British. The historian had been asked by Henry VIII to write a critique of the then accepted history of the early kings of the realm. The classical origins of British and later Welsh history, based on Geoffrey of Monmouth's fictional account, were considered as infallible as the Bible itself. It was thought to be beyond question until the Italian cast doubt on its authenticity. Prys was as incensed by the tenet of the 1534 *Angelica Historia* that Roman writers knew more about their ancient past than any Welshman could; as the assertion that their glorious genealogy was likely to be as bogus as Arthur himself. Perhaps the fact that he had — in his *English History* — 'namyd Lewys a Welshman born' who could come and go between the two women (Margaret Beaufort and Edward's daughter) as he pleased without arousing suspicion, and as a known jailed conspirator had also rankled Prys in his diatribe against the Italian. The longwinded detailed answer by him was published posthumously in 1573, together with *De Mona* a work by Humphrey Llwyd who was also a staunch defender of the ancient faith. William Camden in his *Archaeologia Britanica* had already turned to the Roman and Anglo-Saxon past while shedding most of the mythological gloss from British history. Yet writers like Thomas Twyne and David Powel who would rework Lhwyd's pseudo-historical books continued to ensure that their Welsh version of the distant past would became further entrenched between the twin peaks of a fabled Arthurian nationhood and a Hebrew-Christian creation story.

Robert Recorde was born on the south coast of Pembrokeshire at the *Maudlins*, which then was outside the walls of Tenby. It was formally a leper house before becoming a hospice for the poor.

Recorde graduated at Oxford and become a Fellow of All Souls College in 1531. He then taught mathematics and medicine at Cambridge, becoming a doctor of Medicine in 1545. Recorde taught both subjects there as well as arithmetic at Oxford. These, like the fledgling sciences of astronomy and anatomy as well as music and poetry were all within his province. Comparisons have been made between him and some of the Italian scholars like Cardono who was professor of mathematics at Pavia and medicine at Bologna. Robert Recorde was one of the first in England to champion the Copernican system. He popularized the use of plus and minus and actually invented the *equal* sign. He was probably in practice near London, for on the death of Henry VIII he was appointed court physician to the young king Edward VI (who died at sixteen) and his sister Mary. Recorde was made Comptroller of the Mint at Bristol and was later Surveyor of Mines in England and Ireland. His illustrious career ended in jail at the age of forty-six for in his will, it stated that he died in King's Bench Debtors prison in Southwark. Recorde wrote a treatise on anatomy, now lost, which may have been as he himself described it: *An exact book with goodly pictures aptly framed.* After the Reformation, the sons of the Protestant lesser gentry who could speak English began to study divinity and medicine at Oxford or law at the Inns of Court. It has been estimated that between 1540 and 1642 the majority of the two thousand Welsh students registered in English Universities, studied at Jesus College, Oxford. It was founded in 1570 by Dr. Hugh Price of Brecon. With an initial intake of twenty-five men it became in effect the only Welsh fraternity until the first University College in Wales opened at Aberystwyth three-hundred years later in 1872. One direct result of Welsh scholarship in the service of the Protestant faith was the translation of the Book of Common Prayer from the Greek by William Salesbury in 1567 and the Welsh Bible by William Morgan in 1586. [17]

Welsh physicians in the 16th century writing about contemporary medicine tended to ignore their own ancient folk traditions with the mingling of superstition, magic and anecdotal remedies; rejecting the charm-magic and the often bizarre recipes of the peasantry in favour of a more empiric Tudor medicine. Even here astrology held sway but it was related to the natural sciences and to a philosophy that strove to understand the laws of the universe as much as the physical imbalances of individual illness governed by the constellations of the heavens. The broad cultural outlook of Welsh doctors is evident in the contributions they made to intellectual fields outside of medicine as well as the medical works they wrote and translated from Latin which was the common lingua franca of intellectual expression throughout Europe.

The Art of Astrology

Probably the most infamous and well-known Welsh wizard of his time moved in the upper echelons of Tudor society. John Dee acclaimed mathematician and astrologer provided the young Elizabeth with the most favourable date for her coronation. A horoscope, he maintained, gave a clear indication of the likelihood or disposition to certain diseases so as well as the time of a patient's birth, the date when an illness first manifested was equally important in astrological healing. As the horoscope so used, was both a diagnostic tool and an essential indication of possible medical treatment it was therefore often unnecessary for such a doctor even to visit his patients. However Dr. John Dee grandly accompanied the Oxford Regius Professor of Physic to the bedside of the queen for a consultation.

Born in London in 1527, the son of an official at Court, he claimed descent from Rhodri Mawr on his father's side and also was related to contemporary Welsh historians. Educated at Cambridge, the University of Louvain and at the College of Reims in Paris; his earliest publication in Latin explored how the physical universe was governed by magical principles and properties of light. Known as the *Arch conjurer of England* Dee maintained relations with many of the leading nobility of the day who were accustomed to have a horoscope cast on the birth of their children so it was more or less unavoidable for them to (then) have recourse to doctors who used semi-astrological methods; as his biographer noted. The conjunction of the work of practicing magicians with the accepted intellectual ideas underpinning the natural world up to the 17th century included the additional cosmology elaborated by Cornelius Agrippa, an earlier transitional figure in the study of the black arts. The 15th century German's most influential work *Occult Philosophy* was translated into English in 1651. Equally important in the arcane conjunction of medicine and astrology was the Doctrine of Signatures. As suggested by Paracelsus — the Swiss hermetic physician and chemist T.B. von Hohenheim (1493-1541) — that those distinctive botanical forms were clearly natures' own guide to the healing power of plants. This notion was further elaborated upon by William Coles, author of *The Art of Simpling* in 1636, who wrote that God made herbs for the use and delight of mankind. He therefore had given them a distinct form and particular *signature* or shape so they would be as easy to read as a letter of the alphabet. Hounds Tongue would be useful to ease aching feet when walking because, according to Coles, not only do the leaves look like the aforesaid hanging tongues of dogs but tied (together) they would not bark at you! Heart trefoil is triangular as the heart of man (is) and because each leaf is flesh coloured and contains a perfectly shaped icon it is therefore good for heart complaints. Since the earth was considered at this period to be a living element and the airy heavens filled with innumerable spirit beings; so too were colours, letters and numbers endowed with active magical properties. Belief in divination of all kinds was rife whether in the cards, the crystal ball, scry glass or in palmistry. Foretelling the future; where to find hidden treasure, lost or stolen property; how to catch a thief; counteract an illness as well as casting astrological charts were all part of the diverse and profitable arts of the run-of-the-mill street charlatans as well as the society astrologer magicians. Yet those with higher magical aspirations and helped by the dubious arts or Faustian compact were feared. Such knowledge was popularly attributed to people like William Lilly who was known as the *glory of the black art* and to Dee himself on a number of occasions. He barely escaped imprisonment during the reign of Queen Mary when a London witch was found to be sticking pins into a doll-like replica of the queen. She claimed that it was Doctor Dee who had *told* her to do it. He was questioned by a number of bishops and acquitted with a warning to keep away from magical practices. Keith Thomas suggests that with his mathematical knowledge, Dee was a key figure in the Tudor revival of an art that previously had been considered a science and therefore beyond general scope or interest.[18]

Early in his public career John Dee dug into some ancient burial mounds of his native Radnorshire in search of buried treasure and petitioned Queen Mary, without success, for the mineral rights of all such monuments in Wales. He had edited Robert Recorde's *The Grounde of Artes* in 1561 and since Dr. Recorde was the royal surveyor of mines in England and Ireland who had died in a debtor's prison three years earlier, perhaps Dee saw a possibility for his own betterment. Another and probably more worthwhile scheme which also did not meet with royal approval was to buy up old manuscripts from the devolved abbeys and churches. He clearly believed that they held information that would give him access to much of the liturgical gold and silver plate that was popularly thought to have been secreted away by the Catholic clergy. In 1563 his household at Mortlake in West London — where a group of his fellow Welsh associates often met — was attacked, pillaged, and its extensive library burnt by the mob. He had left for Poland where he would spend seven years in Cracow conducting alchemical experiments in the search for gold and the Philosopher's Stone. John Dee, with the assistance of (or as been claimed under the influence of) the Irish alchemist Edward Kelly, was in thrall to the spirit world and its mediums whose visions as seen in the sacred *shew stone* with their mystical instructions and obscure symbols, were faithfully recorded in his diaries. Kelley (or Kelly) who arrived at his house in Mortlake in 1582 had received the transformative powder by accident while staying at an out-of-the-way inn in Wales. 'The landlord of the inn had an old manuscript and two little balls that he had stolen from a Catholic's bishop's grave. He had hoped that the learned scholar might be able to read the strange language. Kelly purchased the manuscript and balls that contained red and white powder respectively to be used (he hoped) to create the Philoshoper's Stone. The manuscript was of such technical alchemy that Kelly could not understand it. He contacted the famous hermetic and scientific scholar John Dee, and joined forces with him in a series of alchemical and erotic adventures that (in another sense than Shakespeare's) defined the outer limits of the late 16th century. It begins with an intellectual passion for the art of astrology and other forms of divinatory magic. Dee began to see himself as a magus or master magician; a cut above the street conjurers and almanac hawkers who proliferated in the London of this time.[19] The following text is from a notebook by John Dee, 1589:

> Ther is a body of a body
> And a soule and a Spirite
> With two bodies must be knit
>
> There be two earthes as i the tell
> And two waters with the(m) to dwell
> The one is whit the other red
> The quick the bodies that be ded
>
> And one fier in Nature y hidd
> And one ayer, w(hich) them doth y dede
> And all it cometh out of one kind
> Mark this well man i they mynde

A second or a more populist phase in the art of astrology was made fashionable by William Lilly, Nicholas Culpeper and others at this time in London. Lilly in *The Universal Medicine* describes his master Dr. John Evans from Merionith, with whom he studied astrology, as the most saturnine person his eyes (had) every beheld. Evans published Almanacs and Prophesies but it was after moving from Oxford to London — then the centre of politics, magical arts and medicine — that he gained high repute as a magician and astrologer. If Lilly's description of his teacher as beetle-brow'd, thick shouldered, flat nosed, full lipped, dark eyed, locked black curling stiff hair and splay-footed was not stereotypical enough of the wizard who plied his trade in the mid 17th century, the engraving of *this ill-favoured astrologer* a century later was certainly a caricature.[20]

From the little that is known of Culpeper's life, he seems to have been a kind of tragic figure, an idealist and an introspective. Yet he was prepared to promulgate a better life for the lowly poor in the London of the mid-1650's; a period of strife during the turmoil of the Civil War. *Culpeper's Herbal*, still his best known work, was a kind of common reader written in English of useful plant herbs to cure most complaints. Set out with astrological rather than their botanical aspects it was an important part of what he termed his Hermetic Philosophy. He described himself as a saturnine man 'with melancholy as the enemy within'. His father, a rector of Ockley in Surrey died in 1616, two weeks before he was born and so his mother had to vacate the vicarage and return to her family home in Sussex. Refusing to follow in his paternal footsteps, he decided at sixteen to study at Cambridge. However what appears to have been a turning point in Culpeper's life two years later was the sudden death of his young love. They had planned to elope and brazen out any parental misgivings later which seems to have been common in that established society, as John Donne likewise, at the beginning of the century, wrote to his new father-in-law hoping that he would accept him, even if his own expectations were not then of the highest. Nicholas's mother had given him two hundred pounds so the pair could marry and stay at Lewis in Sussex. While waiting with her jewels and maid in a coach during a storm to meet him, a bolt of lightning struck the girl and she died instantly. Months later his grandfather decided to set him up in London in an apprenticeship to an apothecary. After a number of setbacks Culpepper became an assistant to another one in Threadneedle Street. With his friend Leadbetter who had become a licensee of the Royal College of Physicians they took over the running of the shop after the sudden death of their master in 1639. The College issued a number of reprimands to Leadbetter over his unlicensed apprentice although with the Civil war imminent they became less concerned about such matters. Culpeper never bothered to become a master of the pestle; for he then seems to have begun to practice physick or medicine. Around this time, he was accused of bewitching a widow called Sarah Lynge. After spending a month in jail he was found not guilty and she who was 'languishing' quickly recovered. Not long afterwards he espoused a fifteen year old gentlewoman of good extraction who also brought him a considerable fortune thus enabling him to build his own house in Spitalfields. This area had been Church lands until the Reformation and then was used as an artillery firing ground. When Culpeper moved there it had already become a popular area for small tradesmen, back-room businesses and taverns where many so-called doctors conducted their work, and prescribed medicines, until the coffee houses became popular in the following century. During the following decade until his death in 1654 he devoted himself to the study of physick and the practice of astrology; as well as writing and translating such works as a *Treatise of the Rickets* and a *Guide for Women* or a *Directory for Midwives* (1651). It has been described as a blend of medical knowledge and commonsense on labour and nursing of children although since six of the seven Culpeper babies died at birth, one might wonder at its usefulness at this time when so little of the inner working of the female body was understood. In fact it was not long after William Harvey had shown in 1628 that the blood circulated constantly around the body, contrary to what had been the acceptable teaching of Galen and his theorists. So one can understand why once that bedrock of medicine had been undermined, especially at a time of revolution without the long established monarchy, many people

111

would accept any theoretical basis for the popularity of medical astrology; the revival of Paracelsus and hermeticism.[21]

The apothecaries could not compound any medicines other than those set by the College of Physicians and written down in Latin in their own *Pharmacopoeia*. It may have been from writing out such medicines into plain English for his fellow apothecaries that Culpeper may have been encouraged by them to do a full translation of the Latin list, known as the *London Dispensatory*. The fact that the work was printed in the same year as the execution of Charles 1, brought Nicholas Culpeper into the London political arena, He had already been wounded when fighting for the Parliamentarians against the king; so as far as the Royalists press was concerned such medicines were only safe in the hands of the physician and that his *cul-paper* was not fit to wipe one's arse with. The general noteriety he had gained increased when he became more outgoing with his call to disband the priests, physicians and lawyers, 'the three sorts of men who infringe the liberty of our Common-Wealth'. He also began to publish short discourses on astrological matters, allied to prophecy, divine providence and God's purpose on earth. He even addressed a pamphlet to one of his powerful rich relatives, Baronet Culpeper, warning of an immanent total eclipse of the sun on the 29th March 1652. This cosmic event became known as *Black Monday* which would herald the fall of Kings and Popes; with the Ages of the Saints and the establishment of a new era on earth. There were reports of people fleeing from London, hoarding in food and good water but the darkness was not total. It produced a pamphlet a few days later titled *Black Munday Turn'ed White*. Another was entitled *A Faire in Spitttle Fields where all the Knick Knacks of Astrology are exposed to open Sale.* [22]

By the time the second edition of the *Pharmacopoeia Londinensis* was published a year later, Culpeper was a very sick man with advanced consumption which may have originated from a musket wound in the chest during the Civil War. His own bedside admission of an over-accustomed use of tobacco and red wine would not have helped this condition when he died at the age of thirty-eight. Although many of his written works are thought to have been destroyed in the Great Fire of 1666, within a year or two the printer, who shared his radical views, brought out seventeen posthumous publications which included translations and a few of his works such as *Health for the Rich and Poor by Diet, without Physick,* and two books on bloodletting. A number of works were also published by another printer that included some by Alice Culpeper, all attempting to capitalize on his name. Perhaps the most controversial work was issued by his wife, as *Mr. Culpeper's Treatise of Aurum Potabile,* in 1656. This was claimed as a universal remedy for all disease, which would 'exhilarate the vital spirits and heart which supplies the microcosm as doth the Sun the macrocosm'. *Aurum Potabile* or 'drinkable gold' was reputed to be a cordial medicine containing pure gold. However it is uncertain if Culpeper knew enough about alchemy to have had the skill to produce it or if he merely put his name to the concoction made by Dr. Freeman, who lived nearby and whose name appears on the advertisement for *Aurum Potabile,* issued just days before Culpeper died. A promised treatise published by his wife appeared in the following year, with the knowledge necessary to the study of Hermetic philosophy, faithfully written by him during his lifetime. Her preface emphasised that that it is the most precious of all medicines and worth its weight in gold, although there were no practical indications for the preparation of such a remedy. An anonymous pamphlet with the title of *Culpeper Revived from the Grave,* called her a silly woman selling a fraudulent mixture of mercury, vinegar, sal ammoniac and tartar, a combination destructive to the human body. At this time there were a host of elixirs on sale in London with wonderful names like the Golden Elixir and medicines made from Beams of Light, Sun Beams and of the course Mercury or Quicksilver. In 1683 a pamphlet by a William Cooper was published showing how to make *Aurum Potabile.* It was a young Englishman named Francis Anthony who seems to have perfected this process for 'drinkable gold'. He had graduated with a Master of Arts degree in Cambridge and then studied medicine in

Hamburg. He may have been involved with alchemy and learnt the above process or perhaps translated it from the ten volumes of Paracelsus that were collected and published in Basel in 1598, nearly half a century after his death. It is likely that Anthony had the alchemical process before he returned to London to practice. However the College of Physicians fined and jailed him for doing so without their licence. He was released in 1602 and then continued to practice for a decade until some churchman on his death bed 'complained that the *Aurum Potobile* had killed him'. In his defence he was forced to reveal the recipe for his elixir but the process was kept a secret until Cooper printed it. Apparently there was such a demand for the remedy that Anthony's son continued to sell it after his death.[23]

Hermetical Physick

Henry Vaughan is often described as the last of the Welsh Humanists with his classical translations, his metaphysical poetry, knowledge of European languages and his late practice of medicine. Even though he described himself as MD, a Doctor of Medicine, and had it carved on his tombstone, the many biographers of his life and works have not been able to find an official degree recorded in any centre of learning. Perhaps the combination of the lofty ideals of his own unique worth in the divine order of the universe and the Hermetical Physick he practiced meant that his claim to be a (spiritual) doctor was far above that of the ordinary physician of the seventeenth century. Certainly he had nothing good to say about the qualified practitioners of his day seeing himself 'as the true Physician (and) created so by the light of Nature' while his twin brother Thomas, more down-to-earth, called them 'quacks and piss-pot doctors'.

Born at Llnansantffraed by the river Usk in 1621 the twins Henry and Thomas were the grandsons of William Vaughan of Tretower Court in Breconshire. They were educated locally by the rector of

Llangattock Church. At the age of seventeen both enrolled at Oxford. Henry left two years later without a degree and was then sent to London to study Law. However his education was cut short by the start of the Civil War. He returned home and appears to have seen some battle action as a Royalist. The growing influence of George Herbert's *The Temple* on his poetry began to reflect on what has been described as a sense of his own 'transfigured despair of wandering alone in nature'. The death of his younger brother William in 1648 and the execution of king Charles I in the following year seemed to have had an enormous effect on Henry Vaughan; a mood pervading the volume of work containing over a hundred of his sacred poems with the title *Silex Scintillans* (with a meaning of 'flashing flint' or 'sparkling rock'). The engraving on the title page shows a dripping heart pierced by a divine thunderbolt. Such emblematic language scattered through many of the poems often makes their hidden meanings even more obscurely arcane. If this first volume was a spiritual high, the second, five years later, with an added supplement of rather mediocre verse has been described as its nadir. In the new preface Vaughan refers to a terrible illness (a dark night of the soul perhaps!) which changed his life. It appears to have been from this period on that the Silurgist in his mid-thirties began to dedicate himself in a practical way to helping others as a gentleman physician.[24]

Among his prose treatises were translations of Plutarch's *Of the Diseases of the Mind and Body*; and of a Greek sophist work by Maximus of Tyre — equating the soul as a king over-lording the physical body as its subject. This was in effect the manner in which the poet himself, at the height of his creative powers, viewed human spiritual dependence on the spirit of God in nature. As an Anglican poet and ultra Royalist, he had extolled the English king as the head of what he termed the *British Church*. His translation of a medical treatise by Henry Nollius with the title of *Hermetical Physick* that was published in 1655 (the same year as his second volume of the Silex poems) may have pointed the way forward, especially with its subtitle; *the right way to preserve and to restore health*. The interaction between doctor and patient was probably holistic, involving spiritual, physical and emotional aspects in the work of healing. Together, he would have prayed with the patient; spending *quality time* on the illness rather than merely dispensing mineral medicines to the afflicted person. Henry and his brother Thomas followed the professional insistence of Nollius that the true knowledge of alchemy was not magical, but was based on empiricism. All the prescriptions of his *supreme universal medicine* should be, he insisted, adapted to the specific needs of the patient and with any actual medical interference by the (spiritual) doctor kept to a minimum. Nollius appears to have adopted the Paracelsian chemical prescriptions of medicine but based on a Hippocratic or natural balance of healing, without the need for violent purging, blooding and stomach-turning mineral remedies that were such a feature of current medicine at this time.[25]

Thomas Vaughan after taking his degree at Oxford was appointed rector of Llansantffraed but probably did not see much of his twin brother as he continued his studies. However the Propagation Act of 1650 meant that he, like many other ministers of the Church of England, was extruded from the livings at Llansantffraed by the commissioners for sequestration in the county of Brecon. After this he seems to have lived in London and was singularly engaged in experimental work of alchemy and medicine alongside his wife Rebecca, as both their initials were often written together in his notebook during this period. After the restoration of Charles II, he began to associate with Sir Robert Moray, 'a great patron of the Rosie-Crucians' who was close to the king and so Vaughan for the last five years of his life worked for the Crown. At the time of the Great Fire in London, Eugenius Philalethes was staying at the home of the rector of Albury when, 'as twere suddenly he was operating strong mercurie, some of which by chance getting up his nose marched him off'. Given the circumstances of his death and the year 1666 there seems to have been some confusion regarding it, for even his brother Henry Vaughan got the name of the place wrong and the

116

above account only appeared in the 1721 edition of Athenae Oxonienses by Anthony Wood.[26]

'He was a great Chymist, a noted son of the fire, and experimental Philosopher, a zealous brother of the Rosie-Crucian fraternity, an understander of some of the oriental languages and a tolerably good English and Latin Poet'. Although Wood's description places him among the Rosicrucians, Thomas Vaughan's relationship with the secret and magical fraternity is thought to have been an ambiguous one. Yet under the poetic nomen Eugenius Philalethes he dedicated his first book to the Brotherhood, claiming 'to stand in the vestibule of the Temple, nor is my offering placed on the altar but laid in modesty at the threshold'. In each of his subsequent publications from 1648 to 1665, his association with them seems to have become more pronounced. But still in his *History and Confession of the Fraternity,* 'which I have here adventured to publish, I have for my own part no Relation to them, neither do I much desire their Acquaintance... but their Doctrine I am not so much a stranger to'. Of course such a disclaimer was usual among the Rosiecrucians, who had become known in Germany from the beginning of the century. He had declared himself a disciple of Cornelius Agrippa and included his portrait and a poem to him called 'Glorious Agrippa'. In terms of the then current interest in alchemy, Vaughan also quotes from the works attributed to Hermes Trismegistus and from Paracelsus, Lull and Robert Fludd. His *Lumen de Lumine* can be described as a poetically obscure Rosiecrucian tract.[27]

Henry Vaughan's poems also have allusions from similar works, whether through Thomas' influence or books which he no doubt would have read. But the brothers, as twins, appeared to be very close in many ways, even to the extent that their important publications were written during the same period between 1650 and 1655. For Henry and probably most of the population of England at that time, the death of Charles I; the Civil War; its effects and aftermath up to the end of the 17th century, brought about quite a different social order. One from which he quietly retired! Even though when he had turned to the study of hermetical medicine, unlike John Dee an earlier exponent of magic and astrology, he appeared to have incorporated it into his *natural* healing as a rural doctor in the Usk valley where he had been born and stayed most of his life. Henry lived on to a ripe age unlike many of the earlier Humanist physicians. Although embroiled in legal tangles with his two families — after his wife died he married her sister — he seems to have enjoyed the remunerative work and spiritual help he was able to give others in his rural medical practice.

Arise Evans (1607-1660's) was a colourful character among many other prophets in London during the Civil War. Evans Rhys acquired his nickname as a tailor's apprentice in Wrexham. He usually had to be called upon or more probably shouted at *to arise from his dreams* every morning. Eventually he was so taken by the sound of the word 'arise' wafting in his sleep he came to believe fervently that there was a special message for him in every verse of scripture that included it. His dreams grew even more accentuated when the former private prognostications became part of his public prophetic utterances. He was driven to go to London in 1649 in order to warn King Charles of his impending fate. Like numerous other seers with similar messages he failed to gain an audience with the king but apparently did so with Thomas Cromwell, Earl of Essex, telling him of his future role. Arise was naturally attracted to many of the millenarian sects that came into being during this troubled period, especially the *Fifth Monarchists.* For many Puritans from 1651 onwards, the downfall of the king heralded 'a collapse of nations' and subsequent establishment of a more just society under the compassionate leadership of the *Fifth Monarchy*. People looked forward to the *Age of the Saints* when humble folk would not have to work, suffer hunger or an early death. Such an era was thought to be akin to the reign of Christ as foretold in the Book of Daniel. A time when biblical and individual prophecy was so allied to the *Fate of Nations* that pamphleteers of every imaginable persuasion felt driven to express their hopes and anger or to denounce the views of others they disagreed with, as false prophets. The narrative thrust of Arise Evans' *Voices from Heaven and Echoes of these Voices,* was

118

certainly not out of the ordinary for its time and place. It was a mixed bag or *pot pouri* of omens and warnings of God's purpose on earth; with many millenarian prognostications and references to forthcoming events after Cromwell's death in 1658. One scholar who actually read the work, noted that his spellings of Welsh place names were as appalling as his dreams and visions.[28]

It is not known when Rhys died but he was still alive after 1660 to be able to accost the new king in St. James's Park. Charles II did not need much persuasion that his subjects still believed in the royal touch as the best cure for scrofula — a painful neck swelling of the lymph glands known in England as the King's Evil. It was more usually treated by the powder ground from a deer's horn and often kept in the house for such a purpose. Another cure was said to be the blood of a wrens' brood — nine or twelve chicks — which was called the King's Blood for the wren was considered to be the king of the birds. However the cure of the King's Evil by the royal touch was thought to have been granted by God to Edward the Confessor. Numerous kings and queens of the realm continued the ceremony of actually touching the necks of queues of sufferers. However in the ensuing crush in St. James's Park, dozens of people died and Arise Evans was said to have reported that the king's glove had healed a large abnormal growth on his nose. Perhaps a third and more general phase in the widespread use of magic occurred in the following centuries as it moved out into the corners of the kingdom. With the translation of *Culpeper's British Herbal* into Welsh in 1818, its astrology and magical recipes began to be used as part of the staple diet of Home Herbals and Almanacs as well as the outlandish costumes worn by the *dyn hysbys* or conjurers with their magic signs and iconic symbols. Equally impressive was the locked tome *the Magic Book* that became the stock-in-trade of many of the later Welsh wizards such as Dr. John Harries of Cwrt y Cadno.

Humanists of North and South Wales

In 1928 Dr. Roland Williams MA of Maenclochog in Pembrokeshire read a paper on the most eminent of these doctors, at the Annual Meeting of the British Medical Association in Cardiff. He pointed out that in the 16th century there were two distinct medical traditions. One old and hoary embedded in the soil and the peasantry while the other was of a recent scholarly origin — nurtured in the universities of Western Europe — and imbued with the spirit of the new learning. Relating the former to its origins in ancient folk belief and superstition he mentioned the Welsh preoccupations with pig grease or cow dung poultices and 'the sheer filthy ordure as theraputic agents'; as well as the charms and spells in the writings of the Physicians of Myddfai; and that in the previous year, a mouse had been roasted, pulverized and administered in food to a sick person on the advice of a *wise woman* in Cardigionshire. The point Dr. Williams was making was that since such deep-rooted traditional survivals were still practiced in his day, how much more so they would have been four hundred years previously and how profoundly the new Humanist learning had influenced the practice of Welsh medicine. The broad cultural outlook of these doctors was evident in contributions they made in intellectual fields outside of medicine as well as the medical works they wrote and translated.[29]

Robert Recorde (1510-1556) was a mathematician and astrologer who popularized the discoveries of Copernicus. He wrote a treatise on anatomy, now lost, which may have been as he himself described it: *An exact book with goodly pictures aptly framed.* However his *Urinal of Physick* (1548) still exists. It was dedicated to the Wardens and Company of the Surgeons in London and intended for them so that they might not often confound medicine with the *knife;* and for lay people so that they may be better able to describe their urinary symptoms when consulting the physician. Like Thomas Phaer, Recorde was forthright in asking men not to hide their nervousness by jesting or mocking the doctor when asked for a sample of their water; and especially the habit of bringing in the stale piss of a beast or their own as their wives'. He stressed that urine alone was not enough in coming to a diagnosis but that the case itself and the general observation of the patient were of equal importance. The classical views of uroscopy from Hippocrates, Galen, Pliny and others inform Recorde's little book. His books such as *The Pathway to Knowledge* (1551) on geometry and *The Treasure of Knowledge* (1557) on algebra are now lost. *The Grounds of Artes* was later edited by John Dee in 1561. *The Castle of Knowledge* (1556) dealt with astronomy and was written in the form of a dialogue between a master and pupil. The title page shows a female figure of knowledge holding the sphere of destiny and measuring the stars on the left side of the castle; and on the right is a blindfolded man of ignorance playing the wheel of fortune linked to the moon above. The work is prefaced with a striking quatrain.

> If reasons reache transcendee the skye
> Why should it then to Earth be bound?
> The witte is wronged and leadde awrye,
> If mynde be married to the Grounde.

Thomas Phaer (1510-1560) though not born in Wales lived most of his adult life in Pembrokeshire and is usually included in the group of Humanist physicians. He had studied law before becoming a doctor. His ideas in taking care of the very young, as set out in his *Boke of Childryn,* were so advanced for the period that Dr. Phaer is considered to be the father of paediatrics. He translated Virgil's Aeneid, finishing the Ninth Book of the epic on his deathbed. Sion Dafydd Rhys (1534-1609) had published a number of works in Italian as well as the *Grammar* by which he became known. William Salesbury (1520-1584?) a philologist and theologian, helped translate the Bible into Welsh. His *Herbal* — the only such compilation written in the native tongue at this time — unfortunately remained unpublished. Humphrey Lhwyd (1527-1566) was a many-sided genius who wrote an extra-ordinary range of works that included astrology, ancient history, topography, cartography as well as medicine.

In the manner that this representative group of physicians sought to extend the boundaries of learning to make it more accessible *to those in ignorance,* there were others who made important incursions into the domain of medicine. Elis Gruffydd (1490-1552?) who was called *the Soldier of Calais* — as one of the personal guards in France to the Tudor king at the *field of the cloth of gold,* — wrote and translated a number of important manuscripts. His works include *The Chronicle of the World* (to the year 1552) and a miscellaneous collection of Welsh poetry, prose and genealogies. He translated into Welsh such established medical texts as Sir Thomas Elyot's *The Castel of Health* and Thomas Phaer's English version of *The Regimen of Life.* Thomas ap Wiliems (1543-1622?) curate of Trefriw probably did not complete a medical degree. He had a considerable reputation in north Wales as a healer and practitioner. One of his patrons Sir John Wynn, Baronet of Gwydir, had more than twenty medical treatises in his library as a catalogue of the Wynn papers now in the National Library of Wales shows. They also include several of Wiliems' medical prescriptions written in English and Welsh.

Humphrey Lhwyd was born in Denbigh which is probably where he received his early education. He gained a B.A. at Oxford (1547) and M.A. (1551), being a commoner at Brasenose College. He then went on to study medicine and became private physician to Henry Fitzalan, Lord Arundel. Lhwyd remained in his service for fifteen years and helped his patron collect books and manuscripts, becoming part of a closely-knit circle at the palace of Nonsuch in Susssex. It included Arundel's son, Lord Lumley who became Humphrey's brother-in law after he married his sister. Lumley's library, when he died, was bought by James I and is now part of the British Library collection. In 1563 Humphrey Lhwyd returned to Wales and sat for the Borough of Denbigh until his death five years later at the age of forty-one. Lhwyd's first publication was a treatise on astrology of which only its extended title is known: *An Almanack* and *Kalender, containing the Day, Hour, Minute of the change of the Moon for ever and the Sign that she is in for these Years, with the Natures of the Signs and Planets, with divers other things.* His *De Mona Druidism Insula* was printed by Abraham Ortelius of Antwerp and then included in *The Atlas of the World* (1570) and as an appendix to Sir John Prys's *Historia Brytannica Defensio* (1573). On the day before he died Lhwyd sent his maps to Antwerp with a letter to Ortelius stating that the map had *auncient names of rivers, people and places*, as well as the ordinary English names. Like his (other) map of England and Wales it included place names mentioned by Ptolmey, Pliny, Antoine and others. His Welsh map was not superceeded until 1741. At least two of his medical writings have survived. However since the spellings of his own name include Llyd, Llwyd, Lloyd and Lloyde, some scholars maintain that these were written by a Humphrey Lloyd of Leighton. At the request of the Earl of Stafford, Lhwyd of Denbigh compiled a book entitled *The Treasury of Healthe*. It contained a popular collection from the Latin of the writings of Hippocrates, Galen and Avicenna, as well as his discourse on *the causes and signs of every disease*. It was addressed to the *gentilhearted reader* who was asked not to despise this simple work because it was not decked out in the gay painted sentences of those who *maintain the fifthy lucre*. It was for people who needed to know about the signs and causes of disease when no physician was on hand and how to go about the practice (of medicine) for themselves. Medical books and other texts were written in Latin but translations into English such as Phaer's *Boke of Children* were becoming popular. Yet paradoxically as professed Humanists with a deep love of the classics, very few of such works were translated into Welsh. The past they strove to bring to the people was that of ancient Britain rather than the glories of Greece or Rome. The ideals of the native scholars were fired, first and foremost by service to the divine and thereafter to refining the Welsh language as an instrument of religious learning.[30]

According to an early 19th century account of his life, Lhwyd being now a well-esteemed gentleman returned to Denbigh to practice his faculty of medicine and that of his music for diversions sake. The town stands in the centre of the fertile valley of Clywd; a part of north Wales that had been rich in patrons and poets of the classic bardic tradition during the 15th century. In the 16th it was the home of many of the men of the new learning. Lloyd was acquainted with William Salesbury and Gruffudd Hiraethog, a notable poet who wrote a poem of praise to the physician extolling his learning, his knowledge of Ptolemaic astronomy, mathematics and music. Humphrey Lhwyd and his works were well known to George Owen of Pembrokeshire and others in Wales and England such as John Leland and William Camden who referred to him as *a learned Briton.* Proverbs enjoyed enormous popularity during this period and so epigrams and published proverbial sayings sold well in England and Europe. In his preface to a collection entitled *Oil Symmayr pen Kembero*, William Salesbury paid tribute to the well-known model of the genre, the *Adagio* of the classicist Erasmus and dedicated the published work to Humphrey Lhwyd his contemporary as one 'who can claim precedence over all on account of completeness and worthiness in all manner of true learning and natural gentility'.

Salesbury was considered to be the most learned scholar of his day conversant with Latin, Greek, Hebrew and some European languages. His great achievement was the translation of the New Testament from the original Greek into Welsh. Early in the reign of Elizabeth I a law was passed to allow the Church services to be conducted in the native tongue and he was invited to assist Bishop Richard Davies of St. David's in the translations of the bible. The New Testamount and the Book of Common Prayer were completed and published by 1567. Twenty years earlier, his Welsh-English dictionary — aimed at helping Welsh people learn English — was probably the first book to be actually published in Wales, rather than in London or Oxford. Henry VIII signed a licence granting Salesbury sole copyright to the dictionary and to all the books translated by him. A copy of this document was printed at the end of his *Epistles and Gospels* (1551). Up this period he had written seven

124

books and a Latin treatise on rhetoric that remained in manuscript form. His insistence on people learning in their native language is well known, for otherwise, he said, "they would become worse than animals". However the monoglot rural population — then estimated to be a few hundred thousand people — could barely write in Welsh let alone read Latin or English. However for him and his fellow theologians, the wider knowledge of Welsh was in the service of God and the Protestant religion. They were mostly Protestant from the stock of the lesser gentry and the professional classes, although there were some notable recusants (who refused to recognise Elizabeth as the head of the Church) like Thomas ap Wiliems, Sion Dafydd Rhys, and Thomas Thomas, author of a Latin-English dictionary published in 1561. Thomas declared that he had written it to do his utmost; "for my county and my mother's natural tongue and my loving kin throughout Wales".[31]

An important Dictionary that Wiliems compiled remained in manuscript form. It was through his interests in medicine and philology that William Salesbury's Herbal has survived. The curate passed on the ms to his younger contemporary Roger Morris, a scholar and translator, who made a copy of it. Wiliems own transcriptions of the native tales and bardic grammars such as his *Dictionary* were never published in printed form. He appears to have spent many years engaged on the work and it was probably completed after Wynn had expressed an interest in publishing it. The framework of the dictionary was a Latin/English one by Thomas but using the Welsh translations of the Latin headwords. John Davies (1567-1644) the Rector of Mallwyd in Merionith took up the cause of getting it into print after Wiliems died. Wynn procrastinated when it came to actual financial help. The correspondence over the years with him and his successor at Gwydir, in relation to printers' costs and possible returns on the venture were to no avail. An abridged and edited version was included in Davies's own *Dictionarium Duplex* which he paid to be printed in 1632. Little is known of his early life except that he was educated at Oxford but he is considered one of the great native scholars, assisting in the translations of the Welsh Bible and the Book of Common Prayer.

Sion Dafydd Rhys was born at Llananfaethliu, Anglesey. He studied at Oxford but did not graduate for he left England at the age of twenty-one perhaps because of his religious beliefs. Unlike many of his scholarly contemporaries he remained a Catholic. His travels eventually took him to the heartland of the Renaissance. He studied medicine at the University of Sienna and graduated there as a Doctor of Physic. He became moderator of a school at Pistola. With excellent Italian he wrote three important treatises that were published in Padua. The first was a grammatical work, an introduction to the study of Latin; the second a Greek grammar; and the third was a guide to the pronunciation of Italian that became a favoured book for later English visitors to Italy. When he returned to north Wales he took the oath of loyalty to the Queen as Head of the Church of England and in 1571 became headmaster of a school in Bangor. Eventually he resigned to help his cousin Richard Davies with his biblical translations into Welsh. He stayed with him at the Bishop's Palace in Aberqwili outside Carmarthen until 1581 when he apparently set up a medical practice in Cardiff. It was around this time that he began to write his best known work, a treatise on Welsh grammar and prosody which was completed at his retreat in the Breconshire Beacons. It was published in 1592 with the financial help of Sir Edward Strading of St. Donats in the Vale of Glamorgan. The *Grammar* was written in Latin for Rhys maintained it would reveal some of the magnificence of the Welsh language to the rest of Europe, especially the art of its poetry. He did admit however that the latter half of the work was inadequate in this respect due to the reluctance of poets to be open about their ancient craft and that the Welsh gentry were not keen to publish such native literature, unlike patrons elsewhere who were generously supporting poetry and art. The patronage of Bishop Davies and Edward Strading was important in attracting scholars such as Rhys and Salesbury to south Wales. They could live in comfort and work in congenial literary surroundings with collections of Welsh manuscripts, English books and Latin treatises to hand. The differences in religion between some of them did not detract from the common bond of the love of Wales and the Welsh language. William Salesbury's sojourn at Aberqwili and his collaboration with Richard Davies ended due to some scholarly disagreement. His translated work was eventually incorporated into the William Morgan bible of 1588. The Bishop's Palace and the Castle at St. Donats, like the home of John Wynn of Gwydir, were important meeting places for a wide cross-section of the literate society, motivated by or aspiring to the ideals of Humanism. [32]

Thomas Phaer was of Flemish descent and his family lived in Norfolk. There was a large enclave of Flemings, as Gerald noted, in south Pembrokeshire which may have influenced his choice of abode after being appointed Solicitor to the Council of the Marches. He settled at Cilgerran by the river Teifi and was buried in the churchyard at the age of fifty. He had been educated at Oxford and studied law at Lincolns Inn. It has been said that "he changed his studies from Common Law to Physic" when he returned to Oxford in 1552 and there gained his Bachelor of Medicine degree. During his long practice at Cilgerran he had been experimenting with poisons and their antidotes, not an uncommon study at this period especially as mithridates were part of the regular antidote in use against the plague. He also became a custom's officer at Milford Haven which was a centre of shipping between Wales, the West of England and Ireland. The vast estuary that penetrates deeply into the south western peninsula was a favoured haunt of smugglers. Phaer edited many legal texts and his translation into English of the *Regimen Sanitatis* and a treatise of the plague in 1543 along with the *Boke of Children* shows his concerns in medicine. His translation of a French version of the *Regimen of Health* into English was turned into Welsh by Elis Gruffydd, one of the very popular books in most European languages, with editions in Irish and Highland Gaelic. Obstetrics was a subject that interested Thomas Phaer. Midwifery, the delivery and care of the young child, as well as the early diseases they were prone to suffer from were all included in his

Boke of Children. With such a common sense approach to childrens' illnesses, their physical defects and methods of dealing with them, he is considered as one of the pioneers of paediatrics. Phaer's philosophy of making such works available in English to ordinary people is spelt out a number of times. "My purpose here is to do them good that most need, that is to say children and to show the remedies that God created for their use." And blasting against the snobbery of the medical profession of his time he asks: "of physic into plain English why do they begrudge the translation". This work — "composed by Thomas Phaer studiouse in Philosophie and Physicke" — with his translation of the *Regimen of Life*, of another French treatise on the Pestilence and a manual on bloodletting were all included in the 1543 edition. A decade later it was reissued with a title page which stated the *Boke of Children to be newly corrected and enlarged.*[33]

The Boke of Children

It was not the only medical text book on paediatrics available in the sixteenth century but it was the first one written by a British physician and one of the earliest medical works to be printed in the English language. As well as the earlier classical treatises on diseases of childhood there had been a few books published in Europe especially one by Rhodin or Rosslin, the city physician of Frankfurt. It appeared in various English editions during the middle of the century under the title *The Boke of Women.* Divided into four sections, it dealt with general anatomy and physiology; practice of midwifery; infant care; feeding and diseases; and finally with fertility. However Thomas Phaer's book published in 1543 was devoted entirely to children's diseases and since it went through many editions it appeared to be an important contribution towards understanding the nature of the ills that can affect everyone at the threshold of life. Written in English rather than Latin it meant that those in Tudor society who were concerned with the health of their young families could benefit from it. Phaer acknowledges this sentiment of home medicine himself a number of times in the book. At the end he refers to his little treatise on the cure of children which if thoughtfully received he would have done his studies, "to the honor of God and the general good of the people". The book of fifty-four pages was corrected and enlarged by the author in 1553. Thomas Phaer set out clearly his approach in the opening words of the book: "To begin a treatise on the cure of children, it should be expedient that we should declare somewhat of the principles, as of the germination, the beginning in the womb, the time of the proceeding, the manner of the birth, the binding of the navel, etc, which would take a volume. I intend in this book to let them all pass and to treat only of the things necessary so as to remove the sickness wherewith the tender babes are often times afflicted". He describes about forty of the common ailments with their physical effects on children, with a summary of each condition and its cures.

Major and minor ills include swellings and scabs of the head; terrible dreams; the falling evil or epilepsy; the palsy; croup (angina); stiffness of the limbs; bloodshot watering eyes; itch; pain in the ears; in the gums; canker in the mouth; quinsy; cough; wind, colic, troublesome stomach; vomiting; worms; swelling of the navel; bladder stone; pissing in bed; bursting (hernia); chaffing of the skin; smallpox; measles; fevers; shingles; burns; scalds; lameness and goggle eyes. Phaer's language was direct, to the point and clinical. Many of his physiological insights would not be out of place in modern baby care. The best way of adjusting a squint since it cannot be healed and medicines were useless, he advises to turn the cradle so that the baby would look at the light in one direction only. Or failing that, a child with 'goggle eyes' could be blinkered to look only to the front. Pissing in the bed and nightmares or what he calls night terrors that keep children wide awake, were to be dealt with sympathetically. He also remarked that milk from the mother's breast was best! "It is necessary and comely for the mother to nurse her own child" but if a foster nurse had to be used, her milk should be examined for quality, colour and consistency. His remedy for increasing the supply of milk was a mixture of parsnip and fennel root soaked in chicken broth and eaten with a little fresh butter. Unusual for his time, he distinguished between measles and smallpox stating that they were frequently grouped together by classical writers as exanthemata. Hernia he terms *bursting;* it was to be treated medically rather than by the castration method commonly done by itinerant healers. He suggests that the patient should be laid on his back and to take and reduce the bowels with your hand into their due place. Afterwards make a plaster of *rosin fransynesnce mastyke cumyne pouder of osmunde roots*, to be laid upon the coddes and then bind with a lace around the back. Epilepsy would be difficult to cure if it were passed on by the parents whereas the other variety due to bad diet was curable. Its cold and moist humours produced in the brain could be alleviated by the peony.

In relation to the problem of urinary calculus, he stated that this is the most feared, among many diseases, of all those that (can) affect children of a tender age. The stone is a pitiful disease, "ever the more increasing in days, the more rebelling to the cure of physick". Phaer points out that quinsy is a dangerous sickness both in young and old and that the signs or symptoms are apparent by a swelling of the neck "and that the child cannot cry, nor swallow down his meat and drink without pain". Sometimes it settles in the throat upon the windpipe and can stop the breath and strangle the child. If Phaer's clinical descriptions and awareness of the patients' suffering point to a better understanding in the general practice of Tudor medicine, especially in relation to children, the remedies he suggests were the perennial folk recipes and those of the classical authorities. In a sense any other kind of prescriptions would have been unusual at this period and could have detracted from his stated intentions of making such medical awareness more acceptable and available to ordinary people.

The second book on this subject written in English was by a physician with the very Welsh name of Jones. If Phaer is considered Welsh by adoption having spent his adult life living at Cilgerran in Pembrokeshire then, according to the medical bibliographer John

Cule, the writer of the 1579 publication was almost certainly born in Wales although he was not able to establish Jones' medical qualifications. The title of *The Preservation of Bodie and Soule* seems needlessly obscure and suggests religion rather than medicine. There is only the briefest hint in the full title that parents might find the volume of interest. And although it is very different from Phaer's book in that it does not specifically cover actual illnesses that affected children, nor are there any cures or remedies included; it appears to be a verbose exposition on the care of the infant and the upbringing of children. The first part is devoted to nursing and the needs of the nurse, of which John Jones himself seems to have had strong memories and obvious fascinations. The latter parts are on to how children, "eyerye ways are to bee ordered", with their social and religious education. Jones' writing seems to be expansive, outgoing and opinionated with his personal preferences meshed into a colloquial style. He says that he had studied at both Oxford and Cambridge and had practiced medicine at Bath and in the Midlands. Two of his books deal with the benefits "of the bathes of Bathes ayde and Buckstones" and the first one certainly relates to springs at Bath. He had read Thomas Raynold's *The birth of mankynde, otherwise named the woman's book,* and Phaer whom he thought showed better judgement on how children could be affected by too much "pampering or pyning, dandling or dulling, cockering or clowning". Jones had also read Thomas Elyot's works, especially *The Governor* which dealt with their moral upbringing. He also knew the *Urinal of Physick* by Robert Recorde of Tenby.[34]

Jones may have been exaggerating slightly when admitting that since his mother was fifty-two and upwards when he was born so he was able to suckle at the breasts of his nurse longer than a child of a younger mother should. He adds that he does not advise everyone to suck as long when he could even carry the stool for her to sit on. Since he speaks from experience he has many recommendations for the choice of a good nurse and although he would have preferred the milk of the natural mother there are many good reasons why a woman cannot feed her own child. He says that a nurse should have the right colour and be without squint or ugliness. Her breasts should not be overlarge or too small; the first because of too much milk the latter because of too little. And even the way she should feed the baby with her fingers above and below the nipple. And if the child has to grow happy and contented so too should the nurse so he suggests a small glass of wine during dinner would not go amiss. And that shutting her away from the temptations of the flesh might be too extreme for not only would it change the goodness of the milk but would also dull the girl's spirits. Both of which would be bad for the baby. Jones suggests that the best nurses are the trim and skilful Welsh women who can sing pretty sonnets in their own tongue to the child. However he did not care for the lascivious ditties or wanton lullabies of the English. Along with diets and natural food he advises the nurse to steer clear of any of the Paracelsian remedies if she herself should feel poorly.

Emerging as a pleasant commonsense doctor who loved life and children, John Cule suggests that his published work expresses the accepted beliefs of Tudor times. If John Jones' book illustrates some of the current notions of conservative medicine it would appear that Thomas Phaer's *Boke of Children* was closer to those laying the foundations of later medical science but whose work may not have contributed significantly to clinical practice at that time.

A short account of a plague in Haverfordwest

The widespread bad harvests recorded for the years 1629, 1645, 1649 and from 1656 to 1660, affected the majority of the poor and very often resulted in starvation or general illness throughout the following year. If food was in short supply, the price of available basics was high and the inevitable cycle of malnutrition among the lower classes added to the likelihood of disease. Their general unhygienic conditions in small overcrowded dwellings, unwashed bodies and lack of even rudimentary sanitary arrangements meant that those close to starvation were more susceptible to illness.

Primitive medical knowledge and the lack of understanding of the nature of disease and how to combat it, added to the sum of human misery. Fire was an equally feared and fearsome hazard. Usually from lightning but just as often a carelessly lit candle could result in instant destruction of cottages, houses and barns where grain was stored.

The plague periodically returned to ravage Welsh and English towns after the Black Death so that some writers viewed its cycles as a pandemic ending with the Great Plague of London in 1660. With its virulence, often re-erupting in a particular town, and the resulting physical debilitation of the victims followed by many deaths, it had the hallmark of an apocalypse to which it was so likened. In 1593 all but three of the inhabitants of the small town of Presteigne in Radnorshire died. And almost forty years later the plague again annihilated many of the town's inhabitants almost overnight. It then spread to neighbouring areas in mid-Wales such as Llanidloes and Newtown; and as far west as the coastal town of Machynlleth and then to Tenby and Haverfordwest on the south coast of Pembrokeshire in the early 1650's. The wealthy usually fled the towns to the surrounduing countryside, as soon as they were to be closed in an attempt to limit the spread of the disease. However once a towns' regular market was curtailed it not only deprived more fortunate citizens who were not affected, of essential food, but also adversely, the livings of the outlying farmers who were dependent on such local markets to sell their produce.

The town of Haverfordwest was the largest in the County with a population of nearly three-thousand people and it had a crippling tax burden from the Civil War. A plague outbreak soon afterwards added to its social and financial troubles. A hundred people died during the six months epidemic. However its effects were minutely recorded and many of the above characteristics and attempts to limit the disease were observed. The mayor and leading citizens left so a later collection from the surrounding region went directly to the poor to buy provisions, to pay two barber surgeons and the *tar-coats* whose job it was to disinfect public buildings and bury the dead.

The disease seemed to have originated from a Spanish ship docking at Galway in September 1651 and over a thousand Irish are thought to have died in the first week. It then spread to Bristol and by February of the following year some of the houses in Haverfordwest were under surveillance of the *sick watch*. By the end of the month four people had died of it. Suspected families were immediately locked in their homes while medical relief and food was distributed, but as more became affected they were all taken to the castle tower which had been turned into a pest house. The afflicted inside were enjoined by the clergy to work more closely with God and to avoid all occurrences for sin, swearing, Sabbath breaking, lying and drunkenness! As soon as people recovered they were sent home but often many had to return with fatal results. In all about twenty-four people were treated in April and the monthly total of patients increased, peaking at seventy-two in August, to drop back to just one sick person by late November.

The poignancy of the fate of the Bayliffe family stands out amid named lists and official records. John Bayliffe a labourer lived in Quay Street. His daughter was brought to the pest house on Wednesday 1st of September. Before Saturday she was dead. Her father was brought in that day with another child. Before Tuesday he had died. The child remained there. The same day on which its death was recorded, the mother appeared on the list. On Saturday the 16th she was added to the sick list while another daughter appeared on the recovery list. On the next page the mother and both children are dead. These were the last deaths on the official list. The two barber surgeons were commended for their sterling work with a women helper who was not named, only described as a *strange woman*. The medicines used in the *pesthouse* for that year and the beginning of 1653 were listed as mithridate — the universal electuary used against all kinds of infectious diseases, and diascordium which was an electuary prepared with dried leaves of water-germander mixed with honey or sugar, cordial waters, syrup of violets, lemons, roses and coltsfoot; conserve or roses, plaistre, salve, pills of refus?, salad oil, oil of chamomile, of lilies, of ginger; autumn vitae sack and burnt sack or mulled wine.[35]

Chapter 6. The Physic Garden

Wynken de Worde printed the first English herbal at Westminster, a translation of a 13th century Latin treatise on herbs from one of the nineteen books in the *De proprietatibus rerum* by Bartholomew Anglicus. It was described as a compendium of wonders in the tradition of Pliny's great *Natural History*. De Worde, whose name comically personifies the sly emergence of the new medium of movable type in London, had been an assistant to William Caxton. By their very nature herbal books were worked up from field notes, observations, borrowings, readings, hints and plagiarism from earlier writers, colleagues and friends. Most of the classic English herbals were in fact translations from the Latin *turn'd into English* but with additions of empirical observations from the writers' own gardens. William Turner, for instance, cultivated the plants he wrote about in his garden at Kew (the site of the now famous botanical garden) and also in Germany when the religious political climate turned unfavourable. Henry Lyte worked in the grounds of his Lytes Cary manor house in Somerset. Gerard's London garden was in Fetters Lane and John Parkinson's in Long Acre. William Salesbury too alludes to the plants growing in his garden at Llanrwst, Conwy; even admitting to removing a radish he found in an old monastery plot of Aberconwy, to his own. He observed where to find plants; their growing seasons; and their medicinal uses — such as wood sorrel with its tiny leaves that grew in damp places and was therefore good for sores of the mouth. The entries in his Herbal often follow the same order of Latin, English and Welsh variants. 'Spinicia in Latin, Spynache in English and let the Welshman choose what he may, either conforming with the Greeks by calling it Spinach or with the Latinists by calling it Spinac'. In this he was following Turner's method evident from the subtitle of his first *Herball* wherein *are conteyned the names of Herbs in Greke, Latin, English, Duch, Frenche'.*

The original manuscript of a medicinal herbal written in Welsh by William Salesbury between 1566 and 1578 no longer exists but a transcription by Roger Morris in 1597 has recently been re-discovered. In the meantime an inaccurate copy by Evan Thomas of Bala in the 18th century was eventually edited by Stanton Roberts and then published under its present title *Llysieulyfr* or Herbal, in 1916. The Welsh text, with an introduction in English, had 205 separate entries. Salesbury's descriptions of 133 plants were, according to the editor, taken wholly or in part from Leonhard Fuch's famous herbal and that his Welsh translations made no attempt to identify the plants or say if they were grown in Wales. He adds that the contents of the manuscript show the intellectual awakening of the period but they cannot be taken as evidence for the existence of a spirit of scientific research and experiment in Wales at that time; a point that few botanists would dispute. However the rediscovery of the Roger Morris copy has led modern scholars to assess its originality and sources. The extent of the Humanist's borrowings from contemporary herbals, especially from that of William Turner in 1568, is generally accepted; but the description of it as a first draft of a work, simply of transcription and translation is a harsh literary one. From a horticultural or even a botanical viewpoint the creative reworking by the Welsh author and his subsequent influence on later lexical writers should not be undervalued. William Salesbury certainly cast his net wide during the decade he was working on the herbal. It was unfortunate that his attempt to rewrite the medical botanical knowledge of the period into Welsh was not completed or even published then. It has been described by Iwan Edgar as, the first modern scientific work written in the native vernacular. Brindley Jones also of Aberystywth University, was of the opinion that contemporary criticism of Salesbury's other works, mainly written twenty years previously, and the lack of financial support prevented him from taking his unfinished *Llysieulyer* eventually to press. He even cites his poor spelling as a reason although, as the editor of *A Welsh Leech Book* points out, the author himself complains several times in his *Herbal* that he was unable to find Welsh names for many plants and that he was constrained to translate Latin names. Had Salesbury taken his book to press it may have sparked the interest of native gardeners and growers in the manner that he did the minds of later lexigraphers 'many of whom rashly expressed their wonder at the large number of Welsh words for plants, but the native Welsh names as distinguished from the translations from Latin and English are disappointingly few'.[36]

Published in three parts in 1551, 1562 and 1568, *A New Herbal* has been described by Mrs. M. Grieve as the only original work of its time on botany written by an Englishman, for both Lyte's and the popular Gerard herbals were translations from the French. Turner, at one time physician to the Duke of Somerset, is considered to have been the main influence on the Welshman. Another work was Henry Lyte's *A New Herball* issued in 1578 which was based on a French edition of D. Rembert Dodoens *Historie of Plantes* but originally written in Latin. The important text for Salesbury was probably the *De Historia Stirpium* (1541) by Leonhard Fuchs whose name is remembered in the sweet smelling fuchia. John Cule — a Welsh medical historian and bibliographer — asserts that the great German botanist set the standard for its scientific study thereby making possible medical botany and that, in the decade of the 1540's, his was one of the three works that revolutionized medical thought. The other two were Andreas Vesalius on anatomy and Nicholas Copernicus's *De revolutionibus orbium celestiun*, both published in 1543. Cule in fact used a direct reference to the conclusion by Charles Singer at the end of his chapter on *Early Herbals* thereby setting the high-water mark of the Renaissance when modern science was dawning. The woodcuts that illustrate Fuchs' work 'are of extraordinary beauty and truth, and based on a first-hand study of the habits and structure of plants'.[37]

A copy in the Chelsea Physic Garden library has a page of portraits of the artist drawing a flower and the block cutter actually at work along with the 'sculptor' or printer of the book. Singer also points out that although the herbal tradition is extremely ancient, with a few Palaeolithic scratched leaves, what is remarkable is how long it took people to observe plants closely, in the sense of drawing or recording them for posterity. Egypt too had some diagrammatical representations; the early connection with medicine is evident from the *Egyptian Papyrus Ebers* manuscript found near Thebes in 1872 but written about the time of Moses and before the exodus of the Israelites from Egypt. It was the early Greeks who incorporated the arts of medicine to provide the main themes of the herbal. While the campaigns of Alexander were underway, Aristotle wrote a treatise on plants. This has disappeared but it was his pupil Theophrastus who set out the first extant system of plants known in Europe. It was through him we learn of the class of traditional herbalists called rhizotomists who used plants mixed with magic rituals in the treatment of diseases. They were the forerunners of those mediaeval rural healers that Parcelcus esteemed above the learned doctors of medicine. When they gathered at the University of Basle in their rich furs and robes to hear his words of wisdom, as he let it be known he would reveal the secret of medicine, he held up a dish of hot steaming ordure for all to see and flee from the hall in disgust. The later herb hags of Ireland; the cunning men of England; and even the Welsh home healers and *dyn hysbys* or conjurers can be related to the same root-gathering tradition.[38]

A short dialogue appears in a number of publications on herbal gardens as a verbatim exchange between the Holy Roman Emperor and his gardener or advisor asking the question: 'what is a herb'? Charlemagne replied, 'the friend of the physician and the praise of cooks'. This was simplicity itself, especially given the numerous and complex definitions that have been written and rewritten in volumes of books since the *Enquiry into Plants* by the botanic Greek scholar Theophrastus around the 3rd century BC. He classified plants as herbs, shrubs or trees. It was over a thousand years later when the king of the Franks is said to have made a list of seventy herbs and fruit bearing trees to be planted in the garden of his villa. A copy of the *Capitulare de Villis Imperialibus* was written out 58 years after Charlemagne's death in 814, with the heading that 'we desire that they have in the garden all the herbs, namely, the lily'... followed by roses, in a three column list of plants, fruits and what are now called vegetables. Alcuin, the English abbot of St. Martin's monastery at Tours, has been suggested as the Emperor's advisor on the useful plants for the kitchen garden. The Benedictine monk had travelled widely seeking out plants, gardens and manuscripts. He had stayed at Charlemagne's court but died ten years before the Emperor. Some chroniclers attribute the list to Benedict an abbot and known gardener at the monastery of Anine but equally likely is Walafrid Strabo or squint-eyed, author of *The Little Garden* or *Hortulus* an exceptional Latin poem in 440 hexameters. At the age of twenty he was tutor to the son of Charlemange's successor and at thirty became Bishop of Richenau; but he died by drowning at forty. His poem written a few years earlier in 842, tells of the seasons and the peace of the monastic garden with its herbs and plants. The manuscript lay hidden for six hundred years at the monastery of St. Gall in Switzerland where Walafrid was a monk. It was first printed in Venice in 1510 and an English translation was published here in 1924.[39]

An equally fortuitous account of the layout of the gardens and buildings of St. Gall's exists for what may be an idealized monastic plan as there is no evidence that the actual gardens were ever built. It has been suggested that the *herbularius* depicted had been given as the literary embodiment of Walafrid's *Hortulus*. The plan was found among the papers of Alcuin, addressed to Abbot Gozbert and dated a few years after the Emperor's death but it is thought to have been done by Haito, another keen gardener and abbot of Richenau. This was an island monastery and not a great distance from St. Gall. So although the actual connections between Charlemange's list of plants and the possible garden advisors who may have helped in its composition is open to conjecture; it shows a new interest in growing herbs and food plants at both the court and among the leading monastic officials during the early decades of the 9th century. A simplified version of the plan of St. Gall shows the entrance to the monastery from the east and at the western end is a chapel surrounded by the infirmary, the physic garden and a house for bloodletting. At the south end there was a cemetery and the herb garden with a house designated for the gardener. To the side of the monastery was a calefactory — a warming area for the monks — a secluded cloister adjoining the refectory, a cellar and a building for giving out alms. Beyond these were a series of workshops, barns, bakery, and stables for the animals. Very little was left to chance as the names of the vegetable plants are given for each of eighteen plots to be reserved for: onions, leeks, celery, coriander, dill, poppy, radish, chard, garlic, shallots, parsley, lettuce, parsnip, cabbage and fennel, etc while in the medicinal garden rose, watercress, cumin, tansy, sage, rue, peppermint and rosemary are among the plants.

In England the connections between food, plant cultivation and medicinal herbs can be traced back through the Tudor planted gardens to the Norman monastery pleasure gardens to the Anglo-Saxon abbey gardens. An old Greek manuscript copied onto vellum at Bury St. Edmonds in Suffolk had parts of the *Materia Medica* by Dioscorides alongside some drawings of plants by an unknown Byzantine artist with a few drawn in a more naturalistic manner probably by one of the monks at the abbey. The text probably written out first had the spaces left for illustrations. In London and many large English town markets there was a thriving nursery trade in seeds and also by itinerant seeds-men moving around the country with their pack-horses filled with leek, hemp, mustard, colewort, onion seeds and sets as well as other plants and small trees for the cottage gardener too busy or lazy to collect his own. From the Middle Ages onwards this horticultural trade and interest in gardens also found a direct expression in literature. The well known prologue to Chaucer's Canterbury Tales in the passage beginning: with us there was a Doctor of Physic described in his Middle-English as, 'a parfait practisour...ful redy hadde he his apothecaries/to send him drogges and his lectuaries.../wel knew he th'olde Esculapius / and Deiscorides'.

During the Tudor era herbs and roots of useful plants were collected in the countryside of England by wandering *green men and women* — descendants of the root gatherers of ancient Greece — and then sold to the apothecaries, who over time had begun to prepare and compound drugs. The Worshipful Society of Apothecaries was set up in London early in the 17th century and at the same time a law was passed forbidding the grocers — with whom they had been professionally linked for over three hundred years — and the surgeons from selling medicines, but allowing them to dispense and attend to patients. Earlier in 1586 the College of Physicians were allowed to plant their own physic garden following the European practice by which most cities then had a garden associated with the medical school of the university, for the study of plants. The first was in Padua in 1545 where botany and medicine began to be taught separately rather than formally as one subject. Other towns in Italy followed the trend at Florence, Rome and Bologna; in Germany, the Netherlands, and France at Montpellier and Paris. The Oxford Botanic garden was followed by the Chelsea Physic garden in 1673 and two years later Sir Robert Sibbald with the surgeon Andrew Balfour created a physic garden in Edinburgh. They had became acquainted with James Sutherland who was professor of botany at the University with a personal collection of nearly 900 plants so they moved from the initial small garden plot to a larger site, now occupied by the Waverley railway station, where the Botanic Garden was established. The divisions between the teaching of medicine, botany and herbalism that had set in at this period became further marked when the system of plant classification created by Carl Linnaeus had become widely established. The herbal tradition went into decline and medicine and botany became two separate fields of study, using botanical Latin rather than the mix of formal and vernacular languages that had been general, so that each plant had a generic (first) name and a (second) name of the individual species that distinguished it from all others within a class, Linnaeus made it possible for plants to be studied scientifically and allowed trained botanists to avoid the previous confusions in identifying plants and a host of misconceptions — in relation to their formal and vernacular names — that had increased with the popularity of the herbals from the middle of the 16th century.[40]

Wales was in general bereft of such abundance of information although some such publications were no doubt available to scholars in the house-libraries of the gentry. There were exceptions to the general Welsh laissez-faire. Sir Edward Stradling (1529-1609) who made improvements to the castle buildings and gardens at St. Donats wrote a treatise on the Norman conquest of Glamorgan. It was included in David Powel's Historia Cambria. He was a known patron of poets, physicians and scholars like John Dafydd Rees and William Salesbury. John Stradling, an adopted kinsman who inherited the estate, wrote a poem on the beauties of its landscaped gardens. Written in Latin hexameters, the thirty-five line poem is addressed to Sir Edward, invoking his garden and beginning with the well-known opening words of the Roman poet Virgil when introducing a pastoral scene. *Est locus* — a place there is. The final seven lines, translated by Ceri Davies, direct our senses to the herbs growing in the garden that are medically useful, were good for the dinner table and so wonderfully scented.[41]

> Here Spring continues uninterrupted,
>
> Here the earth bountifully bestows a rich crop of flowers
>
> And among the blades of grass the ground puts forwards
>
> > pale violets
>
> And white lilies in honour of the Nymphs
>
> And produces plants pleasing to mortals.
>
> These the royal table of a king does not spurn;
>
> Apollo, inventor of medicine does not avoid them as if they
>
> > were hurtful;
>
> Nor does Cytherean Venus disdain their delighhtful scent'.

Plant Hunters of Snowdonia

Probably the most renowned plant-hunter of the 17th century was John Ray, a Cambridge lecturer and prolific author. On his first journey through Wales in 1658 he failed to get to the summit of Snowdon due to bad weather. He did climb Cadair Idris to discover a new flowering plant called the Globe-flower. Four years later he returned again but discovered no new plants although on his travels he found the Welsh Poppy and the small White Orchid which is now quite rare. His *Synopsis*, a major work published in 1690, reflected Ray's particular interests in the study of plants — their botany rather than medicinal properties — and it was probably the most influential work for many generations of botanists. In the second edition of 1698, Ray included over forty unknown plants from the upland regions that had been recorded nearly two decades previously by Edward Lhuyd, particularly the still rare alpine Snowdon Lily that was named *Lloydia serotina,* after him. In its circumpolar distribution it is scarce and only found in the Alps, Siberia, the Himalayas, China and the Rocky Mountains. Unknown in the rest of Britain, the small number now in Wales are probably a relict of pre-glacial flora. These are now located in clefts of the high north facing slopes like Cwm Idwal below the great cleft of Glyder Fawr known as the Devils Kitchen. However due to global warming and the fact that the existing plant bulbs cannot climb higher in order to maintain their adoption to extreme cold when dormant, it is likely the delicate cream flower with pink streaks that open in June may soon become extinct here.

Due to debts incurred in the Royalist cause Edward Lloyd lost his 'estate of medium size' in 1676 when young Edward was sixteen. Illegitimate, he seems to have been brought up by a nurse until he became a boarder at Oswestry Grammar School. He was familiar with the hills of north Wales and in the early months of 1682 before going up to study at Jesus College Oxford, he made a note of the plants he had collected in the mountains. Under the heading 'on travailing our hills' he sent the list of thirty-seven of the most interesting and where he located them, in a letter to his kinsman

144

David Lloyd. He also then changed his surname, one of the oldest along the Welsh borders, to Lhuyd. After he became Keeper of the Ashmolean Museum in Oxford he began a correspondence with John Ray, for his main interest was then in fossils or what he called 'his formed or figured stones'. He was aware of the links and the importance between buried fossils and geological rock strata for the biblical flood and the age of the earth were avidly disputed by many of his contemporaries interested in the new sciences. In fact it was to be Sir Charles Lyell in the middle of the 19th century who finely set out the scientific principles of geology stating that the fossils of animals, as well as the sedimentary rocks they were found in, pointed to the ever expanding and far reaching antiquity of the earth.[42]

Lhuyd's father had been a keen gardener and employed Edward Morgan who had been superintendent of the Westminster Physic Gardens before it closed in 1687. Since Morgan lived near Llandudno, it may have been he who helped to familiarize the young Lloyd with the mountain plants of Snowdonia. The twenty-year old Morgan was one of the botanical companions of Thomas Johnson, the London apothecary, when he visited Snowdon in 1639 searching for rare species. It had taken twelve days for Johnson and his companions to arrive at Glenllifan on Anglesey, the home of Thomas Glynne, an MP and a keen botanist. With the help of local guides, the party attempted to reach the summit but mist prevented any observations of rare flora. However among the plants found 'upon the moyst rockes at Snowdon' were the Dwarf Willow, Mountain Sorrel, and *Saxifraga sellaris*. Johnson had revised John Gerard's *Herbal*; and included in it the first list of names in Welsh — from those that had been supplied to him by an antiquarian, Robert Davyes — when he published the corrected edition in 1633. Among others who had assisted him in reworking the herbal, was John Goodyer who had translated the *Materia Medica* of Dioscorides from the original Greek into English. Both texts were eventually published on facing pages in the 1933 edition by Robert T. Gunter of Oxford.

The author Dewi Jones has extensively researched this close network of botanists, plant-hunters and guides throughout Snowdonia during the centuries up to the mad Victorian fern craze that almost exterminated the plant entirely. According to him the names of the Snowdon Lily — *brwyndddail y mynydd* or the rush-leafed mountain plant and *y bryfedog* a loose translation of the English word spiderwort — were the first Welsh names of that plant, to be written down by William Morris in the margin of his copy of the Thomas Richard's 1753 Dictionary. Like his brothers Lewis and Richard, William was a compulsive letter writer and avid collector. He previously had copied out the printed list of rare plants from Edward Lhuyd's 1696 edition of Camden's Britannia. However in 1741 when he went 'a simpling' to the top of Snowdon on June 17th he recorded the plants he found there but the name of the *Lhoydia serotina* does not appear on the list. Morris' main preoccupation was botany of which he had a fair knowledge, for his notes on the local flora of Anglesey were later used by Hugh Davies in his *Welsh Botanology*. This was a modified medical herbal based on the Myddfai material, Culpeper's Herbal as well as Morris' own field work. Rhys Price of Cwmllynfell in 1840 published a similar work using varied and earlier source material.[43]

Known to his friends as Gwilym y garddwr or William the gardener, he wrote a work that bears comparison with the English husbandry manuals. Its title *The Kitchen Fruit and Flower Gardens* states clearly what it dealt with. Published in Dublin around the time of his death in 1763, the book seems to have dropped out of circulation for even the standard biography on the Morris brothers makes no mention of such a work. The book recently came to light and seems to be a genuine work by him for his signature and the year of publication is written on the title page of the copy now in the National Library of Wales. As stated in his subtitle, it is an extract carefully examined and compiled from all the best authors who have written on the subject. Set down in four parts it contains everything that is useful in the way of gardening. *It containeth the best culture for upwards of three thousand two hundred trees, shrubs, plants, roots and flowers.* A detailed list of the first part begins with, a table of the pot herbs, salled herbs, physic herbs, plants and roots. It is well written and packed full of sound advice on a wide horticultural basis in the manner of the period. Had it been available then it would have made a valuable contribution to garden literature which is notable by the absence of Welsh authors. Morris was said to have been keen to produce a detailed *Gardening Calendar,* perhaps inspired by the manuscript of another Welshman Sir Thomas Hanmer who had lived in England. His *Garden Book* (1659) contained a calendar entitled *rememberences of what is to be done in a garden every month of the year and what plants are usually in fflower.* Yet it too never saw the light of day until it was published in 1933.[44]

The earliest English herbal to be translated into Welsh was the 1816 edition of Culpeper, under the title *British Herbal: neu,Lysieu-Lyfr Britannaidd. Yr ail ran.* Published by L. E. Jones of Caernarfon and reprinted seven times up to 1828, with some later editions to the final years of that century. The book therefore had an importance that is not generally appreciated. Simply laid out in alphabetical order with the common rather than the botanical plant names, it described hundreds of herbs and the grounds where they grew best; the times for seeding and flowering; and most notable as regards folk medicine the astrological importance of each plant in relation to their healing qualities. Perhaps it was this magical curative aspect that appealed to the Welsh reader. It was especially popular in publications like the almanacs and such that appended astrological material in their yearly editions. There were also the charm healers and magicians who used the signs of the zodiac and the attributes of astrology as the basis of their doubtful healing arts. The proliferation of Home Herbals at this time in Welsh society — that included magical remedies, ancient medical lore, healing recipes and astrological information — was clearly a potent combination appealing to a growing literate population eager for esoteric herbal knowledge in a popular readable form.[45]

147

Often overlooked in general medical works or included under the odd or unlikely practices in folklore surveys, toothache remains a common complaint. However prior to the use of the x-ray in modern dental care and apart from violent extraction, toothache with the attended diseases of the gums and mouth could be relieved by a bewildering series of remedies. A selection here is included from the wide range of plant cures hopefully suggested by Welsh healers and writers with an extraordinary diversity of herbal recipes recommended to ease this perennial intrusion of facial pain. The value of a front tooth in the Laws of Hywel Dda was set at 24 pence; double if a back molar were smashed. The late 14th century medical compilation from the *Red Book of Hergest* and copied as the first part of the 1861 edition of *The Physicians of Myddfai*, suggested rubbing the inside of the ears as you washed to prevent toothache. And also wrapping self heal in a dock leaf, to be put under the tooth. Bruised birth wort or thorn apple coated well, to be applied at night. Mustard was good and another hot cure was to have a candle of sheep suet mixed with eringo seeds to be burnt on or as near the troubling tooth as possible. A bowl of cold water under the candle was advised to catch the worms as they tried to escape the heat of the flame! The slightly later Havod 16 manuscript has recipes for dirty teeth, bad breath, toothache and abscess. Fire ash and burnt cinders for cleaning and wheat husks or the bark of a dry hazel to be used for whitening them. The juice of rue and a sprig of mint up the nose were useful to counteract foul breath. For toothache the resin made from rue and wormwood boiled in white linen to be used; also the seeds of holly and leek. Sea holly with fennel mixed in fresh wax could be applied.[46]

William Salesbury in his sixteenth century unpublished *Herbal* included nearly thirty recipes for complaints of the mouth, tongue, teeth and gums noting that the plantain was good for aching jaws, for molars that bleed and for vomiting of blood. In the following century, the *Receipt Book* of Dr Samson Jones of Bettws had dried ginger powder to be blown up the nose or a clove of garlic pricked with holes, dipped in honey, wrapped in linen and placed in the mouth. A rich cocktail for a sore mouth was composed of a quarter pint of white wine vinegar, red sage, two penny-worth of mercury, rosemary, woodbine leaves and four spoonfuls of honey. The *Prescription Book* of Dr. Daniel Lewis suggested a fig to be boiled in milk until tender, then split and laid on the affected tooth.

The translation into Welsh of John Wesley's 1759 edition of *Primitive Physic* by John Evans of Bala included many recipes collected from around Britain by the preacher's followers. Asparagus and mugwort were good for toothache. Gargle with the juice of wood sage to be rid of mouth sores or half an ounce of the spirit of lavender mixed with the juice of cinquefoil. Fresh ivy leaves made into a broth would take away pains whereas a ground nutmeg and alum in a quart of milk could be distilled and (a poultice of it) placed around the neck. Garlic or boiled apple could be placed on a tooth; betony leaves pushed up the nose, and the ultimate cure for toothache was to warm your feet in hot tar water, rub well with a cloth and go to bed. The various Welsh editions of Nicholas Culpeper's *British Herbal* translated between 1816 and 1828 included many recipes: The inner rind of the elder with a dash of pepper made into balls to be placed between the aching teeth. For cleaning them dip a piece of cloth in the vinegar of quinces and rub the teeth and gums to sweeten the breath as well. Culpeper was also included in the 1881 *Herb Book* written by Dr. D. T. Jones of Llanllyfni. He suggested a mixture of alum powder, myrrh and bay to be rubbed on the gums and sore teeth. Boiled mint and rosemary was good for bad breath as was powdered smallage seeds mixed with honey or boiled in water.

The Welsh text of Iolo Morganwg's *Book of Howel* was collated around 1800 and both it and its English translation were published in 1861 as the second part of *The Physicians of Myddfai*. With over 700 individual healing recipes, charms and simples, it included numerous plant cures for toothache. To extract teeth without pain, blow ants' powder through a quill onto the affected tooth. Another method was to make a pulp of nightshade root pounded in goats' milk and then add the black berries separately; macerate in vinegar trice for three days, decant and dry the sediment in the sun or near a fire. Then place the powder on the tooth and it will come out painlessly. A powder of ivy gum and leaves mixed with the juice of the petty spurge into a paste may be used to fill a painful cavity. Inhale the vapour of holly leaves boiled in spring water or make three small balls from the bruised root of pellitory of Spain. Keep the first ball inside the mouth against the tooth and walk for a mile, then walk home with the second ball in the mouth and repeat again with the third. Afterwards lie in bed and keep warm. To keep your teeth white rub them with baked balls of powdered sage leaves and salt. In *Everyone's Book of Everything* a mouth wash could be made from half-an-ounce of myrrh and two of oil of almonds in a pint of water, to be used every morning. Elias Owen in his 1887 *Welsh Folklore* quoted the use of a burnt branch of rosemary placed in a linen cloth to be rubbed on the afflicted tooth. In the *Family Herb Book* pennyroyal was good for toothache as was a decocation of young apples or gentian root. In the *Commonplace Book* of Philip Phillips, henbane seeds were to be soaked in water and then placed on the tooth. In a recently published article by Ann Jones on home remedies recorded from Welsh speakers living in West Wales, it was suggested that the buds of elder flowers were used for toothache.

Apart from the various manuscripts from the 15th century onwards associated with the *Meddygon Myddfai* that contain remedies and plant lists as well as those in an early sixteenth century *Havod 16* manuscript by David ap Griffith, not much else has survived in early Welsh literature directly related to botanical interests. Their actual influence in relation to popular medicine or herbal practice is harder to determine due to a lack of contemporary commentary although over the centuries many such plant recipes appear to have been commingled with and were passed on as part of a popular oral tradition relating to folk healing, to the extent that it is often impossible to separate the two elements.

Flora Myddfai

Whatever scientific distinctions botanists make in relation to plants it is well to remember that the earth's flora preceeded *Homo sapiens* and that, like many other so-called quaint aspects of pre-modern medicine, the widespread reliance by the poor on herbs and herb-lore was regularly scoffed at by university trained physicians. Since then the extract of salicin from willow bark, used for rheumatism, and digitais from the foxglove for heart diseases have been proved scientifically and shown to be effective. Distillation of St. John's Wort when its golden flowers blossom at midsummer, to ease pain and as a muscle relaxant has also been chemically verified in that it stimulates the endorphins, so helps our bodies to combat ache and pain naturally. Stramonium as an extract from the thorn apple — a species of datura that looks like a conker with spines — contains a mixture of family alkaloids that has been shown to be useful for asthma sufferers.

Birthwort — an aborfacial — has been so named because its funnel-shaped yellow flowers surrounded with large green leaves had a faint resemblance to the female uterus. It was generally used by midwives to bring on the birthing process. Herbal remedies for abortion or to offset barrenness in women and impotence in men seem always to have been in demand. An infusion of birch in water and then later drunk was an old cure for sterility. A variation of the *split wittan* charm cure for men involved splitting a young ash tree and then pegging it apart after fastening it at the top. Into this symbolic vulva the impotent male would introduce his recalcitrant member. The split tree was then bound up to enable it to grow anew while hopefully a man's own potency would do likewise.[47]

The physicians of Myddfai advised a brew of St. John's wort, yew, agrimony, amphibious persicaria, creeping cinquefoil, mountain club moss, orpine and pimpernell for men and women unable to conceive. To bring on a period, their recipe was to pound rue to express the juice but to let it stand before drinking. The recipe for a heavy menstruation was to mix together reddish bastard balm, small burdock, orphine, stinking goose foot, pimpernell and water avens with the ashes of burnt harts horn and then boil in red wine; after straining use as a daily drink until the mixture was finished. The rationale behind such a cure was that when restrained by this potion the menstrual blood would then be habitually diverted to the woman's thighs and ankles. Juniper was widely used to produce abortions. *Juniperus ammunis,* formally known as the saffron, saffren and savin tree was carefully preserved in Wales and it was considered unlucky to cut it down. It was usually allowed to die of its own accord. A recipe suggested boiling some sprigs of saffron and when cold straining through muslin and drinking a wine glass full of the juice for four consecutive mornings. If a woman missed a period, a sprig of saffron could be placed in each of her shoes or clogs for nine days. Parsley and pennyroyal were sometimes used in a similar fashion. An interesting use of the liberty cap or *magic mushroom* to prevent conception was prevalent in the Preseli Hills of Pembrokeshire. The tiny fungi were gathered in late autumn and stored away until Christmas. They were then made into an infusion and drunk during and after the festivities. The immediate effect made the men and women more amorous and loving toward each other with the added benefit to both that the women were highly unlikely to conceive afterwards. A similar effect is thought to have been produced when the Celtic druids ritually used the mistletoe drink or *soma* during their midwinter festivals.

The 1861 Welsh texts and English translations, edited by the Rev. John Williams and published for the Welsh MSS Society as the *Physicans of Myddfai* describe fairly similar remedies using common garden plants, in two separate 'books'. It is from this mid-19th century publication that the tradition of the native physician and his physic garden was related back to the hereditary healers of early Wales. The doctor is not only enjoined to keep himself in a professional manner but that he should cultivate a garden of trees and herbs. Especially those that do not grow naturally in Wales for the physician should be as knowledgeable about the garden herbs as was the herbalist and apothecary.[48]

Plants from the Red Book of Hergest.

Where specified in the manuscript they have been grouped in terms of roots, leaves, bark, fruit and juices. One fungus named morella is presumably the morel mushroom of the genus Morchella. The majority of the plants are unspecified as to what parts are to be used in the recipes or the time of the year they are to be picked. Occasionally alternative ones are named for a cure of a particular ailment, if the first is not available. Or as in the cure for pneumonia (no. 11) a Galen-type cocktail mixed in white or red wine was to be composed of madder, sharp dock, anise, agrimony, daisy, round birth wort, meadow sweet, yellow goats' beard, heath, water avens, woodruff, crakeberry or blackcrow, corn cockle, caraway and that 'other herbs as (may) seem good to the physician (could) be added'. The numbers after the examples below refer to the times that such plants are mentioned in relation to particular cures or specific remedies.

agrimony (8)	meadowsweet (3)
anise	mountain moss (2)
amphibious persicaria (3)	motherwort
apple sorrel	mugwort (11)
asarabaca	mustard cress
bastard balm - red (2)	nettle
betonica (2)	orpine (3)
betony (6)	purple dead nettle (2)
burdock (2)	parsley
butcher's broom (3)	pepper
caraway (3)	perppermint
celadine (2)	plantain (7)
celery (2)	poppy
centuary (2)	privet

153

columbine
comfrey
coriander
corncockle
creeping cinquefoil
daisy (4)
dandelion (4)
dittany (3)
duckweed (2)
dwarf elder (2)
fennel (3)
field southweed
field scabious (2)
field southernwood
foxglove
fumitory
garlic (3)
greater plantain
gromwell
ground ivy (5)
harts marrow
harts tongue
herb robert
hemlock
hemp (3)
knapweed (2)
laurel
leek
lesser celendine
lettuce
liverwort (2)
littlefield madder
madder (2)
male speedwell
mallow (5)

radish (2),
red cabbage,
red nettle (2)
river starlip (2)
round birthwort (6)
rue (5)
saffron (3)
sage
saxifrage
sharp pointed dock
shepherd's purse
shepherd's needle
speedwell
stinking goosefoot
stinking hellibore
st. johns wort (5)
sweetgale
tarragon
turnip
tutsan — a species of St. Johns
wort (4)
violet (4)
vipers garlic
water avens (4)
water pimpernell (7)
wild chamomile (2)
wild clary
wood betony (2)
wood sorrel (2)
woody nightshade
wormwood (5)
woodruff
yellow goats beard (2)
yew

Roots: comfrey, cornbell flower, dock, fennel, fern, mugwort, red nettle, small thistles, tulsan, valerian, white lily, yellow goat's beard. Leaves: bay, dock, earth nut (2), honeysuckle, lily. — Fruits: blackberry, crakeberry, figs. Bark of birch, blackthorn, elder (2), elder below ground (2), ivy, kegindrew, peach, stinking goosefoot, thorn apples (2). Trees: walnut, white thorn, willow, yew. Ashes of balm, fern, heath, ivy, smallage, hartshorn. Juice of elder, fennel root, primrose, strawberry, turnip.

In terms of the times that plants were to be used, mugwort in eleven recipes seems to have been the most useful. St. John's wort and tutsan were listed nine times. Plantain and agrimony in eight recipes; water pimpernell in seven; betony, milfoil or yarrow, round birth wort were listed six times and rue in five recipes.

Plants from Havod 16 ms.

A slightly later medieval manuscript known as Havod 16, with a hundred pages of medical matter was once part of a larger religious collection of works known as the Book of Talgarth. The list of plants below may have been originally cultivated in the physic garden of Llantony Abbey.

agrimony (2)
alexanders
anise (2)
asphodel
asarabacca (2) (an acrid plant
used in the preparation of snuffs
for catarrh)
avens (5)
bears foot (setterwort)
betony
bilberry (4)
birdsfoot trefoil

hollyhock
horse chestnut
horse mint (3)
horse trefoil (2)
house leek (4)
knapweed
knotgrass
lavender (2)
lettuce (2)
lily
liquorice
lovage (2)

blackcrow
broad leaved garlic
broad leaved peppermint
broad leaved pondwort (2)
burdock (3)
chestnut
chickweed
cinnamon
cinquefoil (3)
clary
clove pink
common borage
common broom
common cudweed
common dandelion.(2)
common feverfew
common fumitory
common harts tongue (3)
common hounds tongue
common maidenhair
common mustard
common meliot
common navelwort (2)
common primrose
common privet
common polypody fern (3)
common tansy (2)
common vervain
common white bone hound
cow parsnip
cranberry
crowsfoot
cucumber
cumin
dandelion (2)

madder (4)
malespedwell
meadowsweet
mint
motherwort
nettle
poeny
pennyroyal
pepper
pellitory (2)
periwinkle
poppy
purple foxglove
purple grass
purslane
radish
red bartista
reed
reedgrass
ribwort plantain (2)
rice
round birthwort
rue (4)
rush
sage
savine (juniper)
saxifrage
sea holly
sea lavendar
seawort
sedicer
sharp dock
snakeweed
soapwort
spinkeared

devils bit scabious
dittany
dock,
dogrose hips
dwarf elder (3)
dyer's greenweed
elder
fennel (2)
fern
field scabious (4)
field southernwood
filopetunia
gentian
gorse
great mullein
greater plantain(5)
gromwell (3)
ground ivy
herb bennet
hemp
hemp agrimony
hemlock

splurge
stinking cranesbill /herb robert
(3)
stinking helibore
stitchwort
strawberry (tree & leaves)
st johns wort
thistle
tormentil
trefoil   tufted vetch
turnip (2)
violet (3)
vipers garlic
water hemlock (water cowbane)
water pimpernell
wild chamomile (4)
wild English clary
wildwood sanile (2)
wood sorrel(2)
woody nightshade
woody reed grass
woody wormwood

St. John's wort, wild chamomile, rue, leek, madder and field scabious were listed four times; water avens, devils bit scabious and plantain five times each. No roots are mentioned. The berries include crakeberry, cranberry, rosehips, strawberry and bilberry four times. The trees named were chestnut, elder, strawberry and yew.

In contrast to the manuscript copy from the Red Book of Hergest above, the Book of Howel the Physician is a very much larger compilation of medical remedies. Many of the recipes have specific instructions as to how they should be processed including which part of the plant is to be used. Juices are very prevalent. Since this form of application was not generally common until the 17th century

— as recommended in some English herbals — it would appear that a portion of the work was copied from material later than claimed. On the other hand an ancient recipe for sophoric sponge and some old magic herbal charms are listed. There are also a series of remedies using animal parts. Mineral elements are included, perhaps from Paracelsus but more probably from the publications of the 17th century Hermetic healers of the Usk valley.

Plant list of Howell the Physician

acorns (2)
agrimony (6)
aloes (6)
angelica
anise seed (9)
apple pulp (5)
ash keys & bark (7)
avens (6)
barley (2)
barberry (3)
bay leaves
betony (35)
birthwort (2)
bitter nightshade
blackberry (4)
black cameleon thistle
blackthorn bark
borage
bramble (2)
briar
brookweed
broom (17)
bruisewort (14)
buckbean
buckthorn (3)

lily root (5)
lime twigs
livergreen
liverwort (2)
lovage
madder
maidenhair (2)
mallows (17)
mandrake
marigold (2)
marjoram
marshmallows (3)
marsh pennywort (5)
meliot
milfoil (5)
mint (3)
mistletoe (3)
mugwort (13) mustard seed (2)
nettle root (10)
nighshade (2)
oak bark
oak leaves
onion oliveoil (7)
opium poppy (3)
orange

bugle (3)
burdock (3)
butterwort
canella bark (white cinnamon) (3)
caraway
carrot
camphor oil(2)
celandine
celery (5)
centuary(11)
chamomile (6)
chickweed (3)
cinquefoil (4)
cleavers (4)
cloves
cloudberry
coltsfoot
columbine
cornpoppy
cowslips (3)
cumin (7)
daisy (7)
dandeloin
demask rose
dill (2)
dittany
dock root (6)
dwarf elder root (4)
elder leaves and bark (7)
elecampagne root (11)
elm bark (3)
eryngo seed (11)
eyebright (2)
fennel (20)
fern (7)

orpine (2)
paradise (4)
parsley juice (2)
parsley seed (13)
pear
pellitory
pennyroyal(3)
pennywort (2)
pepper seeds (9))
periwinkle
plantain (33)
plums (2)
primrose (6)
puffball mushroom
radish (2)
raspberry (3)
red alder (2)
red cabbage (3)
red dock root (3)
red fennel (18)
red fennel root (2)
red mint (2)
red onion (3)
red nettle (3)
riverstar tip
rosemary (11)
rue (49)
saffron (4)
sage (39)
saxifrage (3)
scurvy grass
seabeet
seaweed
shepherds purse (2)
sloes

feverfew (10)
field mint
field scabious (3)
figs (4)
foxglove (6)
fumitory
galingale
garlic (15)
ginger
gorse
great fern root
great oxeye daisy
greater plantain
ground ivy juice (13)
groundsel
hartshorn (2)
harts tongue fern (2)
haws
heath shiedfern
hemlock (6)
hemp
henbane
herb bennet
honeysuckle (9)
honeywort
holly bark (5)
horse mint (2)
house leeks (3)
hyacinth (2)
hyssup (7)
ivy leaves (3)
Juniper
knapweed (6)
leeks root (11)
lettuce

smallage (5)
spearmint
spurge
sorrel juice (2)
southernwood (6)
sweetberries (5)
stinking iris
tansy (15)
thistle (3)
thyme (5)
trefoil
turnip (2
tutson (4)
valerian
vervain (16)
violet (3)
vipers bugloss
walnut
water chickweed (2)
watercress
water hemlock (2)
water lily
water pimpernel (9)
wheat bran
white borehound
white bryony
white roses (3
wild campion
wild carrot (2)
wild rape (2)
wood sage (5)
wood sorrel
wormwood (3)
yarrow
yew

The trees named were the apple, bay, briar, elder, elm, ivy, juniper, oak and yew. Two toadstools, the boleta and the puffball are included as well as some seaweeds.

The plant list above is extracted from about 700 recipes in total, so therefore the number of individual remedies listed in brackets is much higher than in the other examples. For instance the top five are rue used 49 times; fennel 40; sage 39; plantain 37; and betony on 30 occasions. The next groupings were celandines 20; broome 17; vervain 16; garlic, pansy and tansey 15; bruisewort 14; ground ivy and mugwort 13; rosemary, elecampane, leek and centuary 11; nettle, feverfew, and eryngo seeds 10 times. The remainder of the 164 plants were used fewer than 10 times

Yet there is a surprising correspondence between the majorities of the common plants from all three groups. Of the most popular plants used in the third list, the plantain and rue are high in the second; and in the first list are plantain, betony and mugwort. The overall groups show that the ancient Welsh herbalists relied on and were clearly conversant with the healing properties of an extremely wide range of the wild and cultivated native flora. A few toxins are listed in the Havod 16 ms. In the final list are hemp, henbane, hemlock, nightshade and mandrake (root). See the appendix for a facsimile of the list of plants given in Welsh/Latin in the *Physicians of Myddfai.*

Probably the most recent and detailed study of the plants used in folk medicine was undertaken by scholars and staff of the Welsh Folk Museum in Cardiff. The information is at present stored in extensive files, in special questionnaires and on unpublished tape recordings. Anne E Williams (nee Jones) when formerly with the Museum, during the period of 1977 to 1989, interviewed about sixty native speakers of West Wales from the old counties of Caernarfon, Merioneth, Ceredigion and Pembrokeshire about the remedies and folk-medicines they were conversant with at present, or at least those used in recent memory. A majority of the remedies recorded were herbal and in a published report the results for both human and animal applications were briefly set out in terms of herbs, weeds and flowers, wild plants, trees, fruit and vegetables. The herbs she

161

quoted as the basis for remedies were rosemary, groundsel, rue, parsley, wormwood and tansy. The flowering plants were pennyworth, ivy, houseleek, stonecrop or wall pepper, dandelion, dock and daisies. Wild plants like wood sage, buckbean, plantain, coltsfoot, cinquefoil and gorse were also included. A few other categories such as human urine; animal, bird and fowl products; vermin and reptiles; fish and miscellaneous remedies were indebted to the old literary sources she quoted from, for it is almost impossible to ascertain the original source of the oral tradition which is still extant. And a considerable amount of printed material has in turn become orally transmitted. Yet much of this record, apart from diffusions of herbal teas, appears to refer to past medications, what used to be done, rather than at the present time. Any actual healing that was involved remains unclear as does the individual sources of oral lore, although the original questionnaires doubtless show more detail than this account. However she stressed the point that a considerable amount of oral information still exists regarding medicinal use and the knowledge of herbs among (older) women in general. She regards the plaint by a mid-nineteenth century author of a herbal book as an exaggeration, that only a few women are familiar with most of the medicinal herbs. He, Rees Price, added that they were, even then, looked upon as relics of a primitive age and only consulted in extremis as the wizard or *dyn hysbys* formally had been. In a paper presented to the American Philosophical Society around the same time, James Mooney described similar beliefs in home-cures and *charms* by local healers he had talked with on the west coast of Ireland. That many were by old women whose stock-in-trade 'was of a few herbs and simple concoctions with a number of prayers and secret formulas to be recited when applying their remedies' seems to confirm Price's views. The second generation Irish American added that every housekeeper there was well acquainted with the virtues of the common herbs and it was only when she had exhausted her resources or was convinced that the sickness be of a supernatural origin that she applied to the *cailleach luibe*, the herb hag or knowing woman, for help.[49]

A recent publication on the new science of ethno-botany in Britain and Ireland includes plant examples from folk medicine in Wales. Apart from some veterinary application, most are from Anne Williams' research and add to her observations above about the common plants such as centuary, plantain, wormwood, yarrow, agrimony and wall pepper. The majority of the thirty-three examples quoted were for kidney troubles, rheumatism, stomach upsets, colds and back ache, which confirms what the herbalist David Hoffmann (who began his practice in Cardigan before moving to the USA) pointed out that illness in the past generally stemmed from external environmental factors, whereas today in Wales disease usually centres on the internal physical body mainly from the overuse of synthetic diets, artificial food additives and atmospheric pollutants. Their main purpose in collecting so much evidence from these islands was to show the wide reach of the folk medical tradition with its botanical spread and in the range of ailments treated. Many of the plants do not appear in the printed herbals which lends support to the idea that the rural tradition may have been self-sufficient through the centuries. But as I have suggested above and emphasize here, the common flora was just part of a series of healing options available to the rural populations, living away from and without the doubtful benefits of pre-modern doctors and their medicines. Until recent interest in oral history, the lack of documentation on the subject meant that earlier historians generally ignored this 'country' tradition and even among sympathetic researchers, interested in old stories, music or the *craic* as it is known in Ireland, few had enough plant knowledge or knew the local botany in the manner of the people there, to be able to access the value of what was being repeated; so that much of the recorded information with the help of a translator, even when conducted in common English, was accepted gratefully without question or further exploration. This is clear from the three thousand individual sources and the records quoted from its very extensive bibliography of printed works. The evidence contained in this volume makes for a fascinating exploration with the index of folk uses and of scientific

163

plant names, that are clearly related to the main text divided into separate chapters devoted to the flowering plants, as one would expect from a work of native ethno-botany.[50]

The non-specific nature of many remedies and lack of precision in describing the plants themselves; as well as their general countrywide spread and usage, is recognized by the authors. However in tracing 'herbs without the herbals', little attention seems to have been paid to the actual movement of peoples throughout Britain. There is no lack of evidence from historical times onwards in relation to the regular shifting of vast armies on foot and the displacement of people as a result of warfare, famine, epidemics and the search for employment. And in terms of friendlier exchange in Tudor times the 'strawberry girls' in London could earn five pounds for a season's work and also bring home their acquired plant lore to Ceredigion. The recorded use of a particular plant is accepted in relation to its source-place as an example of a *folk-herb*, yet seemingly based on the questionable notion of the flora as being totally indigenous to a locality. The authors do state that the distribution patterns that have emerged from the actual data do not coincide with the natural (wild) ranges of the species concerned. However what does emerge is the widespread attraction of particular plants to different cures such as herb-robert for skin troubles in Britain whereas in Ireland it is used for coughs; and there, the germander speedwell is good for jaundice; while in Britain it was widespread as an eye lotion. In Wales the presence of wormwood, feverfew and bogbean to their applications is different from those elsewhere, with the bogbean used for rheumatism while beyond in the western fringe, it was a digestive tonic. Also in Wales is a certain preference for introduced species at the expense of native ones. Early intrusive examples in Britain are quoted such as the greater celendine by the Romans; the presence of elecampane at Celtic church sites on the western coasts (and the Teutonic tradition as described in the Anglo-Saxon Leech-books) on the assumption that these and other exotics became part of a well-rooted body of herbal knowledge. However they do not make clear when or how

164

this occurred. Gerard's Herbal of 1597, in English, with its directives to where many of the scarcer herbs could be found, is seen as a bridge between the later scientific study of botany and a much earlier oral tradition. However their concept of this 'oral' tradition needs some elaboration as Gerard rearranged an unacknowledged translation from the Dutch by a Dr. Priest for John Norton the Queen's publisher who borrowed the woodcuts from abroad with only sixteen original illustrations. One of these was of the new potato plant in his hand on the title page portrait.[51]

PART 3: RURAL PRIMITIVE PHYSIC .

Chapter 7. Herbs, Charms and Old Welsh Medicine

The homestead was the pivot of rural life. Apart from the landed estates, farms were of modest acreage. But whatever the physical extent of the surrounding small fields, barns, paddocks or tenant cottages, the house was the centre, the magnet for a farm's social existence. Drawn to it like bees to a honey pot were the journeymen, drovers, itinerant workers, charmers, wizards, entertainers, beggars, gypsy fortune-tellers and their musical menfolk. All were dependent on the house in an interlocking web of mutual support in a similar manner that the rural population in turn were dependent on and supported the minister, market fairs and the houses and estates of the gentry.

The farmhouse was the place for bible readings and family gatherings. During the long cold months women would card wool and weave while men made wooden utensils and love spoons. It was a place of gossip, storytelling, song and music. Visitors were especially welcome with news of politics for the men and new fashions for the women. What we now call folklore was then the life blood by which their work, social activities and time itself was regulated. Birth, marriage and death had their age-old customs. Each had a pertinent store of stories in conjunction with the appropriate ritual ceremonies, to determine if the likely outcome would end in a good or bad result. Medicine too had its defining anecdotes in relation to any illness. The favoured remedies and well-tried recipes using common herbs were the mainstay of the mistress of the house. However for more long-lasting complaints the local *charmers* and home-healers who mainly dealt with skin maladies such as shingles or warts would be on call. Bone setters usually healed the cattle although they could and probably did help human complaints if called upon for relief.

Work on the land was subject to slow but constant change. In the early eighteenth century many of the larger farm owners had begun to exploit the mineral resources on their estates. Yet they and their workers still lived close to the soil especially during the planting and the harvesting seasons. With the increased demand for wool and meat, extensive sheep rearing and more intensive farming methods were gradually introduced. Since much of the marginal land of Welsh Wales was on high ground exposed to wind and rain, life was hard and unpredictable with all the vagaries of the weather to contend with. Too much or too little rain at the wrong time of year might mean a rotten harvest and two in a row usually created such a break in the delicate cycle of peoples dependence for sustenance, that outside support was called upon like the weather-prophet or the diviner. But if the bad conditions prevailed, it might mean that an unwelcome supernatural agency was at work; deviously maintaining the adverse weather, the stillbirths, the ailing cattle and the poor health of the children. So a wise woman or a wizard might be sent for. In recent years the activities of the old-witch healer have been extensively recorded, but the role of the Welsh wizard, the *dyn hysbys,* is more obscure and was less talked about. Perhaps their adherence to the black arts created a general aversion even to mentioning them let alone having much to do with them socially unless it were absolutely necessary.

Dressed in dark magisterial frock coats — fashionable in a previous era — replete with colourful insignia and loud signs of the zodiac sewn on; the wide deep pockets were useful for all sorts of bits and bobs of conjuring paraphernalia. The wizard, with an impressive hat made from animal fur perched on top of his head, invariably drew a magic circle on the ground around him with a staff or wand before starting any act of conjuration. Such acts were usually performed at night, on the dark moon, and often with fire and smoke to heighten the sense of awe among their audience who outwardly enjoyed the show as a rural entertainment in the manner of the dare-do of young people out at night for laughs. Yet on a deeper psyshic level it would be a continuation of much older rituals in which the dark side of life was a palpable force. The fear of spells and curses manifesting around young children, cattle or in the form of lingering diseases was common in peoples' recitations of their past beliefs and superstitions.

The *dyn hysbys* generally tended towards the dark side of healing. Fear and the unholy charged atmosphere around their outdoor night exorcisms and dubious rituals played a crucial part in creating an attraction that drew people to them at a time when chapel-going and conventional religion was becoming an established part of daily life. Yet it is clear that ordinary people respected and often utilized these colourful characters whose activities not only verged on but apparently used magic rites. Dr. John Harries was said to have had a large magic book with metal locks which he consulted publicly once a year. He would announce the occasion and with a fellow magician cloaked and hooded like himself, retire to a remote place in the woods or at a stone cromlech, drawing a magic circle around them in which they stood in order to consult the famous book. Outsiders were probably unwelcome but since these events were common knowledge, those who wished could stand outside the circle and watch. Local people were always aware of such activities for lightning and thunder was usually said to rock the valleys when the conjurers were at work.[1]

An account collected by John Rhys, in the Brecon Beacons, shows how dangerous it was thought to be involved with them. The wizard was a *dyn ttaw-harn,* a man with an iron hand. Hearing that there was a great treasure hidden in the Mynyd y Drum, he declared it would be secured it if there was but one plunky fellow willing to spend a night with him there. A young man called John Gethin was game and agreed to join him. The wizard traced two circles in the turf touching each other like a figure of eight. He stood in one and placed Gethin in the other telling him on no account to step outside the circle. He then proceeded to busy himself with his special book and soon a monstrous bull appeared. It bellowed dreadfully but the young man stood his ground and it disappeared. Then a *flying wheel of fire* came straight at him which caused him to swerve out of the circle. It then assumed the form of a devil and began to haul Gethin away. The wizard pleaded to let him keep the lad while the candle in his hand lasted. When the devil consented, he blew out the candle and so they both escaped. Yet however much Gethin tried to preserve the candle wax, it began to waste away although it was never lit. He took to his bed and as the candle wasted so did he, until both came to an end simultaneously and Gethin vanished. The mourners put a lump of clay in his coffin to keep up appearances![2]

A question is how far back in time can one place such beliefs — even as folk narratives — in the practices of organized wizardry within the ultra-conservative confines of Welsh rural society. A rare and early account by Gerald of Wales describes the behaviour of a certain group of possessed men, whom he termed the *awennddyon*; literally meaning spirit *awen* and rapture of poetry *wenydd*. When they were consulted about any doubtful event, the *awennaddyon* would roar and shout and become possessed as by an internal spirit. If asked, they never answered a question directly or in a coherent manner. An assistant was on hand who could decipher their incoherent mumblings and supply an appropriate answer to a supplicant's query. When they emerged from the trance state, they usually had no knowledge of what had happened and if consulted again on the same point would reply differently.

We may infer from Gerald's account that he had some personal experience of such an oracle for as a well-travelled churchman he stated that you can find them in Wales but nowhere else. However the description is similar to that of Siberian shamans and to the recorded behaviour of the State Oracle of old Tibet who with great ceremony would pronounce in such manner every year or at times of crisis. Gerald continued his account. Since Merlin and Ambrosous were prophets who foretold the destruction of their nation, he emphasized that they did not become frantic or possessed while doing so whereas others prophesied by dreams, visions and enigmatical sayings, by words and actions. Among the ancient Greeks and Hebrews such forms were common, but in his day it was thought that such gifts were conferred upon people in dreams, as some seem to have sweet milk or honey pouring from their lips (while) others fancy they do it with the help of frantic or ignorant spirits. Even if a written schedule (a charm) is applied to their mouths (in sleep); on awakening they publicly declare that they have received such a gift. Gerald seems to have grouped together the biblical use of prophecy and the divinations from ancient history; with charm magic and the trance 'mouthings' of the twelfth century *awennddyon* he observed.[3]

Welsh wizards

Hugh Llwyd of Gynfal in Merionith was an astrologer and healer. Cadwaladr Davies of Llanycil, a schoolmaster, practiced medical astrology. His *Piser Sioned* is still preserved in the College library of Bangor. Compiled between 1733 and 1745 the manuscript is a mixed collection of medical remedies from other herbals with outlandish magical cures based on the relation between physical illness and the sufferer's astrological birth sign. Wil Awst of Llanymddyfri had a widespread local reputation as a weather prophet and published a work in English under the name of William Augustus on weather signs and natural portents useful to the farmer. James Morgan and his twin Ifan Prys Morgan of Llanggnwyd were popular charmers and wizards around Glamorgan. In the manner that sons or direct relatives continued the lines of the hereditary physicians, so the conjurers also had their offspring who carried on the magical traditions often in the same locality. William Savage a farmer and gunsmith of Llangurig was a famed healer as was his brother-in-law John Morgan. Both their grandsons were recorded in Montgomeryshire as healers carrying on the family business. In south Wales at Llangatwg the Griffith family of charmers were much esteemed locally for their cure of the jaundice. Costumes worn by these characters were usually a grotesque replica of the formal magisterial frock coat. A description of one such wizard in Llanrhaiadr-yn-Mochnant gives a fair idea of their general get-up in a decorated coat of deep broad hems covered with unusual patterns and talisman shapes. On his head was a cap of sheepskin topped by a high plume of pigeon feathers. In his hand he held a rod or whip with a bone handle and thongs of snake skin. He used this to draw a large magic circle on the ground around him and in which he performed his particular loud-mouthed rites. The combination of such a colourful public performance — involving conjuring, bravado and knavery — in the entertainment of a gullible rural crowd goes some way to explain the sustained popularity of the *dyn hysbys*.[4]

Perhaps the most infamous family of magical dabblers were the Harries of Cwrt y Cadno in Carmarthenshire. Harri Shôn Harri later known as Harry Jones was a small-farmer with a reputation as a healer; but it was his son John Harries and his grandson Henry who died in 1862 that were the more influential in drawing the crowds to Cwrt y Cadno and turning their farm into something of a lesser Lourdes. Henry was known as Dr. Harries and both he and his father received some formal education collecting a small medical library of the period. However according to Dr. G. P. Jones who went through their papers in the National Library, they were hardly more than many other unlettered charlatans with pages filled with cabalistic incantations and symbols. They also seemed to have been fascinated by the pseudo-medical ideas of galvanism and electricity and the popularity of James Graham (an impresario of pleasure) who set up his Temple of Health in Edinburgh before moving it to fashionable London town; a far cry from those country people seeking a consultation with the Harries. The ritual they had to undergo was a fairly standard one for the magical fraternity. With the pomp of a high court judge the *dyn hysbys* brought out his *book* to the centre of the table and informed the client that its contents were sacred, and that it had been in the family for generations. No medical advice would be offered until the appropriate section was consulted and only after the person gave a solemn promise not to divulge such information to a living soul. Harries set great store by his *Magic Book*. He tied it with a padlocked chain and kept it locked

171

away. He himself regarded it with the upmost awe so it was no wonder that people were afraid of even touching such a talisman. Unlike ordinary mortals the wizard was not likely to pass on from this life without drama. During a severe gale the cottage thatch caught fire in the middle of the night. Henry Harries was burnt to death with his *book* and other effects lost in the flames.[5]

A strong literary association with local Welsh wizards and wizardry was well established. In popular traditions the devil was more often presented as being outwitted by well known scholarly clerics or by locally famed characters such as Dick of Aberdaron in Anglesey who knew fourteen languages but never bothered to get a degree. Dafydd Ddu Hiraddug (c.1400) archdeacon of Diserth in Flintshire, author or joint author of a treatise in Welsh on the poetic arts was known as a wizard during his lifetime. Centuries later Dr. John Davies the rector of Mallwyd in Merionith wrote about him and his works, and then the tradition of wizardry became associated with this famous scholar. After he died in 1644 a series of rural tales about him and his man-servant outwitting the devil were popular. Such encounters were usually comically anecdotal as when they were trying to cross a river in flood, the parson spotted a horse standing by the bank and told his servant to fetch it. However in midstream with the two of them on its back, his man began to have doubts about the true nature of the beast but only got as far as saying out loud, "Master, God knows" when the horse disappeared from beneath them. However they both managed to reach the far bank wet but undaunted and ready for the next devilish encounter. Another pair of comic characters from the same period in north Wales was the Rev. Edmwnd Prys and Huw Llwyd, a poet who was reputed to have been a solder and a doctor of medicine. Their practical jokes gave rise to a reputation for wizardry. Whilst Huw was drinking in a tavern he saw his friend passing and sticking his head out of the small window invited him in for a drink. Prys who was archdeacon of Merionith would have none of this and cast a spell on him so that a pair of large ox ears sprouted from his head. He was stuck there as an object of mirth until the cleric relented.

However that night Prys had his comeuppance as he passed under a wooden conduit near his home, for Llwyd had a pair of demons drench him from the millstream overhead.

Ellis Wynne rector of Llanfair near Harlech was a miserable skinflint who was said to have been a wizard haunted by the ghost of his dead wife. He became unhappier still after he remarried for he had nine children. It was his early 18th century prose work *Gweledigaethau y Bardd Cwsg* or Visions of the Sleeping Bard which seems to have popularized and conflated the traditions of wizardry surrounding him. In the *Vision of the World* he was *taken away* by the fairies to the hill Y Moelfre near his house and which he described as a fairy rout in blue petticoats and red caps. He hesitated to approach them for he was afraid they were a pack of hungry gypsies who would devour him *saltless*. However looking more closely he saw that the group 'had a fairer complexion than that lying tawny crew.' Wynne's uncomplimentary remarks about gypsies are the most quoted of such references in Welsh literature and no doubt reflected contemporary attitudes to the groups of travellers who provoked the same reaction of fear and fascination as did the local *dyn hysbys*.

In the *Vision of Hell*, shown by his guardian angel, the author is even more contemptuous for he likens them to some 'Scotchmen with packs across their shoulders.' However when the twenty demons were cast down before the throne of Lucifer he saw they were gypsies. The devil shouted. Ho there! How it is that ye who knew the fortunes of others so well did not know where your own fortune was leading? They were so amazed at seeing beings uglier than themselves that they could give no answer. The verdict of the devil himself was to 'throw the tanfaced looms to the witches who would quieten their barbarous chatter.' Due to their dark colouring, the outdoor life they lived, the language and closed world of the Romani, their ability to foretell the future and the manner in which they could disappear from an area as mysteriously and silently as their arrived, all helped to add to the often baleful reactions they probably provoked among the settled Welsh communities.[6]

Romani Remedies

It is uncertain when the 'descendants of the Egyptians' first arrived in Wales but references to them are found from the late sixteenth century onwards. One of the earliest literary anecdotes about gypsies concerns a group who came to Wrexham with their sick chief seeking a physician. A cheekie rhymester known as Hityn the Cobbler pretended to be a doctor saying he could help their lord, whereupon they gave him a gold coin. The englyn he then recited referred contemptuously to such a fine nation so far from the lands of the Jews that not one of them knew what ailed their lord. Such an instance of the *Gaje* deceiving the *Sipsiwn* is rare. Most later references to the 'tawny vagabonds' depicted them as lying cheats by telling people what they wanted most to hear of their future fortunes and extracting an easy living since they were never around for the gullible people to do much about it afterwards.[7]

The Romani mode of travelling during the good months of the year and camping in one place under large tents during the winter; changed over time to pitching their tents inside a barn whilst working on farms; to eventually living inside their houses but still travelling during the summer months. The women told fortunes in return for food and goods and the men would entertain local people with harp and fiddle as they moved around the country. With the spread of Methodism and the chapel male choirs, party music making was frowned upon. However during the Victorian period Romani musicians such as those of the Roberts' family were welcomed in the houses of the gentry. A form of integration with the rural Welsh seems to have begun when the families began to settle in houses most of the year round. Yet even then the 'Children of Abram Wood' as they called themselves in north Wales, still travelled about from one house to another; from Caernarfon to Machynlleth to Bala to Newtown and usually back again on the same circuit. From what has been recorded by such scholars as J. Glyn Davies, Francis Hides Groome who wrote about the harpist John Roberts of Newtown, and Dr. John Simpson librarian of

Liverpool University — a Romani and a close friend of the artist Augustus John — the remedies, omens, sayings and stories of the Welsh gypsies formed the essential basis of their oral tradition. Due to the small numbers of family groups; their Romani language; and the taboos against outside marriage, it may have had a restricted 'narrative' range. Yet in many ways this unique ethnic tradition which was reinforced through personal instruction and family entertainment was not far removed from how the rural Welsh themselves probably perceived and maintained their own unwritten ways up to the industrial era.

Romani names for trees such as clog tree (alder), tree of the fiddle (beech), basket tree (osler) and tree of the harp (sycamore) as well as the more obvious Holy tree of God (holly), witches' tree (mountain ash) and the dead tree (yew) had more to do with their occupations and beliefs than any apparent medicinal use. Associations with their secret names for counties, towns, houses and inns mostly referred to hospitality in relation to food and material goods as were the signs chalked outside houses noting lack of hospitality. Womens' charms were mainly of the love kind, useful for young girls, such as a sprig of rowan in a man's sock to make him love them. The modern practice is often encountered in cities with young women travellers holding a baby in a shawl and silently waving a sprig of heather at the passing crowd.

The remedies used by the Romani appear to have been simples and infusions of single plants. Wormwood for purging, pith of elder for clearing the skin, leek for the gall stone, nettle leaves for goitre, root of lily of the valley for heart trouble and willow bark for rheumatic fevers. Perhaps this last may have come from the correspondence between the willow being in damp places and therefore good for fevers or like the shaking poplar which was useful for the ague or 'shivering complaints.' Since salicin, an extract of willow bark, is now used in the treatment of rheumatic fever the harmony between the Romani and the outdoor life they lived then, is yet another example of that mysterious instinct those peoples had for the natural sources of physical healing. Such knowledge tends to be labelled conveniently under the Doctrine of Signatures but Paracelsus who popularized the term, said that he learned as much from barbers, bar-keepers, women and the magicians who pursued the art of healing as from doctors of medicine. Over a century later a Flemish physician — Jan Baptista von Helmont — writing in the same vein asserted that the barbarians, wild country people and Indians have observed their own simples (medicinal plants) more diligently than the Europeans. In whatever fashion the gypsy groups learned such cures, once the associations between certain illnesses and particular plants became part of their ethnic culture it was passed on orally down the generations. The elder tree was known as the devil's eye and they used its leaves as a cure for eczema and also stewing them into a pulp to ease internal cancers. The elder has been universally associated with witchcraft but according to the authors of *The Welsh Gypsies* the medicinal properties of the 'sinister tree' were useful for a variety of common complaints such as sore throats, skin rashes, warts, rabies and even for snake bite, rheumatics and epileptic fits. They also rubbed wild honey on skin wounds and used the puffball mushroom as well as the ovoid spider's web to staunch blood. The latter was said to have been used by the Welsh soldiers during the Hundred Years War who carried a spider in a small tin box as part of their own medical kit. Its web eased and stopped minor bleeding. The fungus also seems to have been a universal styptic, found to have been used as far back as the fourth millennium BC.

Old Charm Cures

Perhaps one of the earliest collections of such material in Caernarvonshire was from the *ragged manuscript* of Myrddin Fardd. It gives a prayer to the moon as a form of love divination or to bow three times to the new moon to make a wish. It also recounts 'the blessing of the magic rod.' This was done by passing through the aperture of a forked birch, a tree connected with love, healing and as a protection against demons. The ritual of the *split wittan* was

176

subsequently recorded in many parts of Wales to be performed with children who appeared to be retarded or were thought to have been bewitched. A young rowan or mountain ash, which was often grown from seed, was split in two at midnight. The child would then be passed through it nine times back and forth, between the mother and the healer in total silence. In some places she would intone a priestly parody like, "what the land giveth and the more the land receiveth" etc. The tree was then bound up tightly with wool thread. As the tree itself sealed the rupture and grew strong so the child in like manner was thought to become healed.

An extremely long essay on Welsh folklore won the Reverend Owen the first prize at the National Eisteddfod held in London in 1887. The work was published soon afterwards. Elias Owen was diocesan Inspector of Schools for northeast Wales and for seventeen years he visited every parish in the diocese of St. Asaphs in Clwyd. His work became his hobby. He collected stories from young people in the schools and he would ask the local clergymen with whom he stayed, to take him to visit the elderly of the parish and listen to their accounts of the past. An old woman of Llanrhaeadr describing a charm for shingles told Owen that she used to cut a cat's ear to get the blood to rub on a woman's breast in order to stop the progress of a rash. She maintained a cat's blood was always successful in curing swyno. Another charmer said she breathed deeply on the inflamed skin and then spat on it a few times. It helped if the sufferer were fasting beforehand. Another maintained that his healing gift had been transmitted down through the family from one of his ancestors within the 'ninth degree' who had eaten the flesh of an eagle. He would also spit on the rash and rub any inflammation with his fingers breathing nine times whilst chanting the following Male incantation.

> Male Eagle Female Eagle
>
> Blowing I send You over Nine Seas
>
> And over Nine mountains

And over Nine acres of wasted Land

Where no Dog shall Bark and no Cow shall Low

And where no eagle shall rise higher

Burning the shed skin of an adder seemed to have been an extremely common aspect of charming. In fact the burnt skin was guaranteed to grant all kinds of magical attributes. A pinch of the ashes under the tongue could make that person win a wrestling match; if rubbed on the back it would make him invulnerable; if put under the foot everyone would then agree with him. If a maid wanted to succeed in love she merely had to wash her hands in the snake's ashes. In order to be rid of an unwanted neighbour, ashes thrown into the house would do the trick. However, conversely, in order to offset the power of the ashes, rosemary wood was placed under the door. Rosemary was considered such a powerful antidote that if dried in the sun and made into a salve or powder it would heal wounds and sickness. Also spoons made from this wood gave food a delicious taste while the leaves helped prevent beer from scouring. Even sniffing the burnt bark was reputed to get a man out of jail, though it was not made clear to the Reverend Owen how this might be accomplished.

Digging up a human skull from a graveyard and then grinding it into powder was used as a medicine against epileptic fits. Another protection was to make a ring out of a silver offertory-shilling from a church collection. This too seemed to have been quite a regular practice throughout Wales. The procedure involved an intermediary asking the vicar's wife beforehand to procure a shilling that was offered at Holy Communion on the following Sunday. Later the coin had to be given over by the vicar *unasked* and received *without thanks*. That person — most probably a smith — would then make a silver ring for the sufferer. Owen recounted the tale of a young vicar stricken with love sickness. His landlady kindly suggested that he ask a respectable farmer who was also a Wesleyian preacher to charm away the *clefyd y galon*. The farmer first of all asked him if he believed in charms. When the vicar replied that he did not, he

178

was asked to remove his coat and tuck his shirt up above the elbow. The healer with a piece of old yarn-thread measured it from his elbow to the tip of the middle finger. The vicar was then told to hold the thread in his hand and using his elbow to stretch it. Measuring it again the healer showed him that it had become lengthened which indicated that he did indeed have the love sickness. The yarn was then tied around his upper arm above the elbow and was not to be removed until the next visit. When the farmer again measured the yarn against his arm, the vicar was declared to be cured. If it had shortened it was usually a bad sign. He was told if it did not reach the middle joint of the finger, there would have been little hope of a recovery. Each healer had a different way of proceeding with the charm after the yarn had been measured against a sick person's arm. Sometimes it was a prayer to the Trinity or tying the yarn around the neck for three nights or burying it in ashes for three days. When he was a curate of Llanwnog in Montgomaryshire, Owen recounted his own experience with one of the parishioners who eventually died of the sickness. She was a young married woman who had come to live in the parish and was ailing from what he himself thought was consumption. However on one of his visits to the house she seemed very elated. She had had a visit from a charmer and since the thread used had lengthened it was clear she was suffering from *clwyf yr ede wlan* or the woollen-thread disease. Meanwhile the healer prescribed a daily dose of a brew he made from stale beer with an ounce of meadow saffron tied in a muslin bag and into which heated steel had been dipped. Although she said that the yarn had still lengthened each time he saw her, the girl died soon afterwards. In Elias Owen's words, "the charm had failed."[8]

T.G. Jones recorded at least five separate uses of the yarn cure in different Welsh counties. One informant in Cardiganshire who had helped his mother so many times with her cures said he could tell quickly enough if it were going to be successful. He described how his mother would take a ball of yarn and measure it three times from her own elbow to the tip of her middle finger while he held the end of the wool for her. She then measured the yarn a second time in the same way. If the person were suffering from the disease the length of yarn would be shorter. The amount of contraction would indicate the degree of the person's complaint. Having ascertained in this manner that the person was so afflicted, his mother would then measure the yarn again whilst repeating some ancient words to herself. It was by this "measuring", according to her own expression, that she would be "breaking the disease", until finally the yarn would stretch back to its original length. He added that she accepted no payment for her services and even though he tried to imitate her on his own, the yarn would not contract or lengthen unless she took some part in the healing rite. Woollen thread was also useful for people with bad headaches; migraine and what was known as the *little fever*. A woman who had the cure would measure the person's head in three different directions to find out how much the skull *had opened up.* First under the chin and over the top of the head, then from under the nose and over the head and finally it was drawn around the temples. The patient was then told how much the sutures had opened and she would then proceed to kneed them back together again.[9]

A cure for ringworm was to hold an axe over an open fire until it began to perspire and its sweat used to anoint the afflicted area. Another was to spit on the ground outside the house first thing in the morning and mix the spittle with the earth. The salve would then be put on the ringworm. To remove a stye the healer would use an ordinary knitting needle and pass it back and forth across the eye without touching. She would count one stye, two styes up to nine styes and back again to one stye chanting it in one breath; though three attempts were often allowed in order to be able do it in one breath. The stye would disappear the next day. For whooping cough a fresh penny bread roll was wrapped in calico and buried in the earth. It was to be given on the following day to the sufferer who had to eat every crumb of it.

Charms for cattle were often written out on paper, with a mixture of the familiar opening words of a prayer as 'In the name of the Father, Son and Holy Ghost', with arcane magical symbols or the term ABRACADABRA written out in a triangular form. The cover photograph of *The Medicine Tree* is from such a charm found among the family papers of the Welsh-born artist, Mary Lloyd Jones. Her great-grandfather received it from a 'conjer' to protect his cattle. It hung in the byre for many years. As a magic object the document was inscribed with sixteen close handwritten lines; and beneath were five lines of arcane symbols bordered by a magical abracadabra triangle and a double ring with four crossed lines. In her paintings the artist has used many words, marks, signs and texts but she had to ask permission to transpose the 'Swyn Ar Babur' onto canvas. (*First Language,* Gomer Press, 2006).

When Foot and Mouth disease first broke out in Wales many charms were hung on the horns of the sick cattle. However if some of the herd began to die, one of the sick cows was slaughtered and bled. The blood was then boiled and taken to the barn at midnight to be sprinkled over the other cattle. Such rituals taking place on the witching hour were clearly bound up with the black arts but it was also done secretly when people were asleep and only the farmer or the mother as in the split ash ritual would know exactly what had occurred and so be highly unlikely to talk about it afterwards. Charm cures associated with trees and animals retained the veneer of pagan magic but with an overlay of Christian prayers. They were especially prevalent in England during the pre-Norman era and from the written literature appear to have been an important part of Anglo-Saxon medicine. However it is hard to know if this were the case in Wales especially if a distinction is made between medicine and healing. The sheer numbers of plant remedies used and the many different kinds of charm cures would incline one to believe that prior to the wide availability of doctors, they both constituted the general medicine for people who accepted it as their most viable form of healing. It was in many respects a shamanistic approach that blurred distinctions between objective and subjective expectations; and in terms of any possible results. For instance if you wished for second sight, the recipe was to mix the gall of a cat and the fat of a hen. Then praying, rub the grease on your eyelids. If a person was subject to epileptic fits the cure was to whisper a prayer three times in his or her ear. Then administer the gall of a dog and hang its bladder for three days by an open window of the sick room. Meanwhile the flesh was boiled in ale and the soup taken during the quiet intervals between seizures. For the ague it was sufficient to write a long Latin prayer, hang it around the neck or place it on the stomach of the sufferer. In the late 19th century after the Rev. Owen had spent many years noting the beliefs and the folk anecdotes of the people of north Wales — many of whom relayed to him similar charms and for the same diseases — he found it hard as a churchman to accept that so many people professing to be good Christians, should at the same time cling tenaciously to these ancient pagan cures. And not only the very poor, for whom he had an obvious sympathy, but the educated people who he thought should know better than to buy such recipes for themselves, their families and animals.

The question as to what heals or how herb healing might work is paramount to this study. It surfaces time and again in every region of Wales. With so many different plant remedies claiming to cure similar ills or that completely dissimilar complaints could be healed by the same charm, a questioning attitude emerges when confronted with the confusion of oral and recorded material. Is it the chemical, or as formally the elemental, properties associated with particular parts of a plant; or more likely the personal touch of a healer providing comfort and relief by her or his presence! Even perhaps it is our too human susceptibility when in pain, to be relieved by close physical attention; what we might now call the placebo effect. Moreover there are no pointers to actual cures in old medicinal recipes. Few results were recorded in manuscripts or in folk literature, apart from an instantaneous removal of warts and the early 20th century extraction of skin cancers by 'magic' oil. The 'home healing' was commonly done by ordinary people without diploma or graduation ceremony. Those who had the 'gift' and ability to cure people, or animals; the quack-vets, as they were called in West Wales, knew they could deal with specific and known complaints. Active faith beforehand was not always necessary for the sufferer in relation to a positive outcome. The rural healers usually did not extend such ability beyond their locality or the single cure they were known for. Sufficient for them was the knowledge that they had that particular ability, in the way they *always did it*. It was interesting in relation to the *stretched cotton cure* in Ceredigion that the son of the healer, who often helped his mother, could do it when she was present but failed if she were not nearby. Many such cures seemed to have been carried out almost as a social responsibility within the community without expectation of any payment! Gifts were accepted as a form of barter, for coinage then was a rarity with ordinary people, to be prized rather than exchanged. I remember talking to one old man in Montgomeryshire who said that when he married he was given a sovereign by his father; not to spend but to keep, for most of the necessary food and goods could be had on credit against their farm produce. It was the beginning of WW2 that for him altered many of the old customs. In cities and in populated areas of rural Wales now it is largely the resident 'alternative' practitioners who will charge for their services often using a combination of older and newer techniques. However in many country parts of Ireland, the 'quacks' (as they are still called) are held in esteem for their almost respectable ability to heal complaints that are generally long lasting, despite the popular reliance on modern pharmaceutical applications.[10]

Similar questionable issues could be raised in relation to the efficiency of holy wells, early Christian miracle workings, even priestly prayer or spiritual exorcism for illness from what was considered to be demonic physical possession. The various charms used from the Roman period onwards have been recorded but whether they were successful or not is rarely indicated. Epileptic seizures, once called the falling sickness, are now considered to be symptoms of a condition that can be alleviated by chemical drugs. Yet a complete or instant cure still tends to remain outside the domain of medicine. Ancient explanations by the Anglo-Saxon leech in terms of elfin contagion; and in the Middle Ages the work of the devil to be thwarted by prayer; would seem no better or worse than the old Welsh method of digging up a skull from the graveyard to be ground into powder and then given as a medicine or wrapped up into a parchment talisman to be worn by the patient. The mistletoe plant — so beloved of druidic and mid-19th century writers — was generally accepted as a prime herbal cure for epilepsy since the time of Hippocrates and was probably reinforced for early Christians from the biblical account of David being told by an angel that a ring made from the plant and worn on the right hand would prevent the sickness. So it was commonly hung around the necks of small children as a protective charm. The cure by John of Gaddesden, compiler of the *Rose of Medicine* and physician to Edward II, could be helped by reciting the gospel over the patient draped with peony and chrysanthemum amulets or better still the hair of a white dog! In such early written accounts we have to go beyond the received text and view medical recipes as a guide to the inclinations and especially the religious expectations of the period. In relation to ancient professional healers such as the Anglo-Saxon leech, the *leigh* in old Ireland, the hereditary physicians in Wales, the Highlands and Western Islands, as well as the English cunning man prior to the 16th century, a question that could be posed was: could he (and they were nearly always men) be classed as a kind of medium by using spiritual powers other than the priestly kind associated with God and the church. Or did the sufferer somehow precipitate a healing from within and was he perhaps helped by his sympathetic ministrations as in the Greek sense of restoring the balance of the humoral body! On the other hand rural or home healers practising charm-curing may have used some forms of shamanism in their healing rites. Certainly many were recognised as drawing on the devilish side, but perhaps it was more akin to the later druidic or white magic associated with nature and transmitted directly through such soothsayers. Many healers were seemingly able to cope with major trauma and mild complaints but although the techniques used may appear primitive and recipes often stomach churning, such forms of medicine were inseparable from the rough and ready rural farm scene. It was an old traditional family context that included the blackish arts of wizards, weather prophets, wart charmers, 'hag' or herb healers and the *meddygon esgyrn* or bone setter of horses and cattle. Beyond the network of local healers, such well known wizards as the Harries of Cwrt y Cadno in deep Carmarthenshire were popularly held in wide esteem. According to Dr. G. P. Jones writing on the folk medicine of the period this family had been famous for many years as dabblers in sorcery and clairvoyance and that during the 18th and early 19th centuries their small farmhouse became a medical and magical Mecca.

Chapter 8. Healers, Malpractice and the Law of the Land.

In 1827 a fifteen year old girl in Carmarthenshire went missing. Becoming concerned at her sudden disappearance without apparent cause or reason, her people went to Dr. John Harries the renowned wizard to ask for his help in finding her. Harries was a clairvoyant or what was then termed a conjurer, in the sense of being able to *see* both past and future events. The wizard of Cwrt-y-Cadno had a reputation for finding missing people, valuables and possessions. He also seems to have known the local girl. Harries went into a kind of trance and began to speak in a strange way. The people there heard him say that Mari had been murdered by her lover and lay buried at the edge of a marsh. As it was not far away everyone in the house trooped off to find the body and Harries himself brought along a spade. They arrived at the spot he indicated and dug into the soft earth. They soon found the body which had become partly decomposed. It was removed from the marsh and later when the doctor himself carried out an autopsy, he announced that the girl had been pregnant. By this time everyone knew that her young man was involved. He eventually confessed, was tried, found guilty and hanged.

However, solving the mystery of the dead girl's whereabouts without much difficulty led to local gossip. There was talk about his associations with the black arts and possibly even with the girl herself. Eventually Harries was brought before the magistrate who decided that he had a case to answer for, and committed him to stand trial at the next assizes in Llandovery. On the first morning of the trial a large crowd had gathered both inside and outside the courtroom. The judge was a local person as were the members of the jury. So the people present were aware of the background to the case as well as the reputation of the defendant and they were more than curious about the outcome. The magistrate opened the case for the Crown by asking John Harries if he had murdered the girl or was involved in any way or cause with her death. The court waited for the doctor to reply. In a loud voice he addressed the judge. If you tell me my Lord, the day the month and year, you and all the jury members likewise entered this world; then I will tell you the date and time when you all shall leave it. The two magistrates being sensible men replied that there was no case to answer and Harries was discharged.[11]

There was no mistaking the reputation of the wizard among high and low in the society of the county with what seems to be the general consensus that he was more than likely to conjure un-wholesome spirits or scry his magic glass to see what possible futures lay in store for them. His theatrical response showed he had no patience with the usual conduct of the law court. So his discharge was probably inevitable. Had Harries actual medical proficiency in performing an autopsy been called into question, or his foreknowledge of where the dead girl had been found, it might have turned into an interesting case but in this small town it was his wizardry that won the day. However like the case against Dr. William Price a few decades later for digging up his father's body, it shows that the practice of conducting an autopsy by a defendant was one that fellow doctors were not inclined to be associated with in a court of law. Later when Price was charged with malpractice after a patient of his died, he too performed the post-mortem. He was acquitted after stating that the cause of death had nothing to do with his surgery. Both reports show the high regard the medical profession enjoyed even of those who were known to dabble in the black arts or in regard to Dr. Price who had carried out the public cremation of his children dressed in a wizard's outfit with a large hat made of the skin and head of an animal. In fact it was often difficult to know if such wizards used the court hearings to further their reputations. In March 1856, Dr. Price was called as a witness on behalf of a testator who was his patient and before he had died had made a new will in the presence of his doctor. As soon as Price went into the witness box, he was asked to hand the pistol he was wearing to the police. The opposing Counsel in the case began to question him on his own medical history and his previous court hearings, especially after he dug up the body of his dead father to perform an autopsy, but failed to get any straightforward answers. Eventually the judge grew tired of his comic antics and when asked if it were true that he had been promised five hundred pounds if they won the case. Price replied that such a sum meant nothing to him but it meant that their case was finished and the jury quickly agreed.[12]

Yet the more common breed of magician was treated in law differently. Daniel Jones was prosecuted at the Brecon Assizes in 1789 and John Jones from the Vale of Neath was imprisoned in Cardiff for his beliefs in the occult. Later he publicly recanted and was released from jail. William Jones who was aged seventy was brought before the Glamorgan magistrates in 1807 and was goaled for a year. Towards the end of the century William Jenkin was taken several times to the court in Llandaff. A cunning man or 'conjuror', John Mills of Trefechan in Aberystwyth, claimed to be a disciple of Cornelius Agrippa whose treatise on magic had been translated and published during the Tudor period. Mills was brought before Cardigan Assizes in 1840 on four charges of obtaining sums of money under the pretence of charming away diseases. One victim was persuaded that he would be introduced to the woman who had bewitched him. To this end the *dyn hysbys* had prescribed a hideous mixture of the victim's hair, nail-clippings and salt to be spread around the house for protection. A portion of weeds boiled in vinegar had made the poor man ill. Mills was sentenced to three months imprisonment.[13]

If Gwenfrewi's famous well shrine at Holywell represents all that was comforting and beneficial for those prepared to make the long journey to north-east Wales then Ffynnon Elian on the western side could have been described as its dark opposite. The well is situated on the rocky coast, quite some distance from the church of Llanelian, with the old foundations of a chapel forming one side of the natural enclosure where the water gathered in a hollow from a fissure in the rock. It was originally so famed for its healing powers that a number of farms were purchased in the area with donations from it. The rent from them helped the upkeep of a 14th century church which had a Norman tower. Inside the small chapel is an oak chest that is studded with iron and known as *Cyff Eilian.* In this chest a donation was placed after the ritual drinking of the well water on the eve of the saint's festival was completed by the supplicant. Otherwise any blessings for cattle or human sufferings like the healing of the ague, epilepsy or scrofula, would not occur. The chest has a date of 1667 carved on it. Such offerings from grateful pilgrims were sufficient to keep the church in repair for centuries with enough left over for the relief of the poor. That is until the practice of well cursing began. A 16th century bard Gwilym Garyn recounts that when the saint arrived in Anglesey, king Cadwallon had offered him as much land as his tame doe could run in a day. However when it was killed by a greyhound at the old well Elain cursed the people and condemned them to poverty. The cursing well was in regular use until the 19th century. It was considered to be the most potent of its kind in Wales and also the most profitable for the woman in the nearby farm; it is thought that she collected three hundred pounds a year as the guardian of the well. By dropping a bent pin in the well, crying out the name of the man or woman to be cursed, she could also be paid to reclaim the original pin known as 'the offered' for the curse to be lifted. The cursing well may have been as much a part of an older tradition (as was common during the Roman period) yet it seems to have become popular at a time when what has been described as 'frolicing' at Holywell and other Catholic sites were observed with Methodist disapproval in the late 18th century. The common dedicatory metal pins were used but often bent, before throwing them into the water, in order to upset or harass people. A small rectangular piece of slate with initials scratched on it and a wax figure pinned through a hole in the middle has been found there, indicating dark magic for illness on others rather than good intentions. Another cursing practice at Ffynnon Eilian involved impaling a blown-up frog on a skewer with a cork at both ends in order for it to float on the surface. As long as the animal lived it was believed the victim would suffer badly; an active reverse psychology associated with healing charms whereby disease was projected onto a small living creature in order that it should weaken and die thereby achieving the proscribed cure for the patient.[14]

The Ffynnon Elain in Denbighshire became equally infamous for such woeful activities perhaps through an association with the name of the saint. Previously, it too had been famed for healing people and their cattle, from the prayers of the saint. It was still a healing spring when Edward Lhuyd wrote about it in 1695. Yet by the end of the 18th century its reputation for ill was quite firmly established at a time when local magistrates made every effort to stop such practices but to no avail. John Edwards was goaled for a year for defrauding a man out of fifteen shillings after claiming that he would then "pull him out of the well". John Evans was jailed for a year in 1823 for the same offence. Jac Ffynnon Elian, as he became known, was again in jail a year later and as soon as he was released he was back at his lucrative practice. He was again on trial in 1831 for asking a fee of nineteen shillings from a woman to lift the curse on her ailing husband. His offer in court to put a curse for free on the person responsible was declined by the magistrates who committed him to prison for six months. Before he died Jac recounted the rituals he performed in a contribution to a publication about the cursing well. The victims name was written in a book and the initials scratched on slate or a piece of parchment then tied to a lead weight. Pins, corks, wax effigies were also used while the applicant would drink some well water from a cup and throw the remainder over the shoulder. It was repeated trice while passages were read from the bible. To have the curse lifted from the well, the victim or a proxy representative entered the nearby cottage and read out or listened to a reading of a Psalm or a passage from the bible. The curse was then lifted literally by the keeper, who first emptied the pool and removed the slate with the initials on it. He then handed it over while muttering in Latin often using the name of the saint. Jac died a devout Christian but the cursing practices at Ffynnon Elain still continued throughout the remainder of the century for as soon as one wellhead was shut off, yet another

190

seemed to open up again mysteriously. The area was finally dug up and covered over but the old cobbled pathway was still visible during the early years of the last century.[15]

A Robin Hood of the Valleys

Dr. William Price was no stranger to litigation or tangling with the law of his day. On the occasion of being taken to court after his dead son had been ritually burned on Llantrisant Common in Glamorgan, his advocacy of it and subsequent publicity helped make cremation a legal method for disposing of the dead in Britain. Some years after the death and burial of his father, he exhumed the body and then conducted an autopsy to find out if his father who had been declared insane at the age of thirty, had been compos mentis. Local preachers denounced the doctor for desecrating the dead and the dispute was taken to court after a minor assault on him.

Price was a surgeon of some skill, successfully grafting the bone from a leg of a calf onto a miner's crushed limb. He was also considered to be a modern Robin Hood for it was said he would charge the rich large fees but never turn away a patient too poor to pay. He even suggested the extremely radical notion that doctors themselves should pay patients if they failed to cure them, rather than the patient paying regardless of outcome. As a vegetarian for forty years he espoused the natural living he himself practiced. Price's views on the eating of red meat have a modern ring. The flesh of a dead animal corpse was an unnatural food for human beings, and those who ate it descended to the level of the beast. Bodily impurities whether through eating flesh meat or inebriate living were for him the prime cause of most disease and the dispersal of impurities the only cure. Another of his passionate concerns was how medicine then (as now) dwelt upon symptoms rather than causes. Physicians sought to cure by pills and potions that merely provoked an ailment, in order to alleviate its outer symptoms; misleading the public into the false belief that poisonous drugs give health and that what he called the 'medical art of superstition' was, rather than the art of science, so deep-rooted that

191

those like himself who advocated rational methods did so at the risk of losing their practice and reputation.

The fifth child of a large family, at fourteen years old he became an apprentice to Mr. Evan Edwards, a surgeon in Caerphilly. The fee of thirty-five pounds was paid by the Corporation of the Sons of the Clergy. He was so bound for five years and not permitted to haunt the tavern, inns or alehouse; play at cards, dice or other unlawful pursuits. When he had finished, his uncle wanted him to become an assistant master at a local school for a wage of twenty pounds a year, even threatening to discontinue the occasional half-a-crown he gave his nephew. However William Price was determined to continue in medicine and had learnt English and Latin so he left Caerphilly in 1820 at the age of twenty to study at the Royal College of Surgeons in London. There he shared rooms with the brother of Mr. Edwards who was also at the College and passed the examinations of both the College and the Hall while attending regular lectures at Bartholomew's on anatomy, surgery and medicine. He became a qualified M.D. within a year, and soon after became an assistant to a Doctor Armstrong who lectured on the *Materia Medica.* It was probably then that William Price acquired some of the unorthodox medical ideas which he would in later life become popularly associated with — such as vegetarianism, natural foods and his stand against the general use of smallpox vaccinations. He returned to Wales and set up in practice as a doctor at Nantgarw. Seven years later Price moved to Pontypridd where he had been elected to be the miners' medical officer by the majority of the employees of the Ynysnghared Works colliery. Many of the other issues that made him infamous have obscured the fact that for thirty years he was a colliery miners' doctor. Like other pit doctors with large practices of poor people in South Wales at this time, he was a forerunner of the modern G.P. It was a common practice at that time for the miners to pay a small weekly amount into a *club fund* so that they and their families could have free treatment from the medical officer whenever they needed it. A doctor like William Price would have received a set sum of money per year, with extra for an assistant if his patients exceeded a certain number of several thousand.[16]

He was strongly opposed to the idea of vaccination. Voracious in his public denunciations that parents should be forced into allowing their children to be injected by putrid pus scrapings from the bodies of dead calves, he came into conflict with the law on this issue on at least one occasion. The discussion on the use of vaccination using animal pox to counteract the disfiguring disease of smallpox in people had been simmering in medical writings since variolation was first carried out in England by Edward Jenner in the late 18th century. However it was Lady Mary Montagu the wife of the British ambassador to Turkey who first witnessed the procedure there and had it performed on her own son. She introduced the engrafting of the disease from what she described as "the best sort of smallpox" to England in 1717. Five years later Dr. Perrot Williams read a paper to the Royal Society pointing out the ancient Welsh method of inoculating those at risk with fluid from the blisters or pustules of an actual sufferer. He said it went under the name of *buying the disease* which was common in the country of Pembrokeshire. To cure the distemper they either rubbed the pustules on several parts of the skin or pricked the arms with pins that had been infected with the diseased pus in order to contract a mild form of pox. And although never bothering with purging and the like, people generally came off well enough and he had not heard of anyone afterwards having suffered it a second time. A surgeon in Haverfordwest collaborated this with evidence from one of his patients who had died of old age but remembered having it being done during his childhood. Another writer who witnessed the ritual near Newport said that it had been practiced there since time immemorial. They call the method, *buying the smallpox* as it is the custom to purchase the matter of those affected, like children do with warts off each other. Such accounts were published soon after an outbreak of smallpox killed over seventy people in Carmarthen in 1723. By the end of the century, vaccination by engrafting the skin with infected animal matter was being used as a more effective preventative measure against the disease. Yet the haphazardous application of blistering and venesection to contagious diseases by doctors and many lay healers continued and William Price, like some surgeons and doctors in London, was an articulate critic of such doubtful practices.[17]

In 1873 he was committed for trial on a charge of manslaughter. One of his patients, also named Price, had originally come to him about a swelling on the knee. Dr. Price carried out an operation at Bridgend but the patient died soon afterwards. A suit of malpractice was brought against him and in court he denied the allegation. He then demanded that the body of the man should be exhumed for a post-mortem examination. As he had earlier discovered in relation to his father, the public and chapel reaction was extreme. Judge Bruce (later Lord Aberdare) deliberated long before agreeing to Price's request. There were either few competent doctors available or many did not wish to flaunt ancient Welsh taboos by cutting up the dead, so he himself carried out the examination. The results of the autopsy, according to Doctor Price, showed that the man had not died from the operation. Price conducted his own defence. He submitted that as the patient had not carried out his post-operative instructions to go straight home to bed but had continued on with his trade as a street hawker, therefore he had not mistreated his patient. Other doctors called to the witness stand differed in their opinions on the probable cause of death. Price was found not guilty and discharged. The fact that as the defendant in such a serious trial, he was permitted to perform the autopsy and thereby exonerate himself from any blame for the patient's death indicates the social demarcations of the period. It also shows the special renown in which surgery was held whereby the word of a doctor, who was generally considered to be unorthodox in both his practice and in public life, could determine the outcome of such a court case. Medical cases of malpractice and quackery were, then as now, front page news. Doctor Price with his many court appearances no doubt contributed to that element of general public entertainment. However it was towards the end of his life that his most notable activities of burning the bodies of his dead children, made him a household name.[18]

William Price had been a lifelong vegetarian and advocate of fresh air and exercise. He would not prescribe toxic medicines and refused to use surgery on people except as a last resort. During his long career in South Wales he was an active proselytizer, publicity embroiled in many issues from public health to pox vaccination. He had studied the *materia medica*; was interested in eastern languages and religion; and in later life, Celtic druidism. Price was among the 'weird and the wonderful, the bizarre and the eccentric' who had gathered in Llangollen in September 1858 when the National Gorsedd of British Bards was accompanied by a Grand Eisteddfod. According to one observer, Dr. Price was dressed in a green trouser suit over which he wore a scarlet mantle, and a headdress made of fox skin. Gweniolen (sic) who was named as his daughter 'the Countess of Morganwg' was in fact his housekeeper. She was mounted on a horse, similarly attired and wrapped in a scarlet mantle. He usually performed open-air rituals in his characteristic high fox fur hat, with a long staff; the traditional garb of the magician. It was at such a ceremony when he placed his dead daughter's casket on a pyre that led to his court appearance on the issue of public cremation.[19]

The first child by his housekeeper Gwenllian Llewellyn was born when the doctor was eighty-three. He was named Iesu Grist Prys Mab Deu, or Jesus Christ Price, the son of God. A daughter Penelope was born the following year but died after five months. In 1884 dressed as a druid, Price prepared her funeral pyre on Llantrisant Common. The local people objected and the police were called. When they arrived a police officer kicked over the burning casket. A small bundle rolled out and the flames were extinguished. It was then that the crowd grew threatening, shouting, "lets burn the old druid". The doctor spent a night in custody for his own safety. The press and the pulpit created an even greater furore than after the exhumation of his father's body nearly forty years previously. However when he repeated the burning ritual after the death of his

195

son Iesu four years later, he was committed for trial. Price was eventually acquitted and his case established a legal precedent in Britain for the use of public cremation after death.

In accordance with his own wishes, when he died at the age of ninety-three, his body was burned in a bizarre druidic ceremony on Llantrisant Common. Black&white photographs, now on display in St. Fagan's Folk museum in Cardiff, show his fox fur hat dangling from the magician's staff over the flaming pyre. William Price is historically courted as one of the town's more famous sons. A massive purplish coloured statue of him with arms outstretched and holding some strange objects stands at the junction of the narrow street entrance to the town. It was erected on the centenary of his birth. In front of it is a small memorial herb garden that was created on the hundredth anniversary of his death.

Sleeping Women

It was Thomas Pennant in 1770 who first described the incredible condition of Mary Thomas who was to become known as the Fasting Woman of Tyddyn Bach. She was thirty-seven then and had been bed-ridden for many years in her cottage near Dolgelley. At seven she had had measles and later became so sorely affected that she could not bear the least touch of any material on her body, save for a sheepskin. Each springtime and autumn she had the same swellings and eruptions and was confined to her bed. She told Pennant that she once made a journey to the shrine at Holywell in hopes of a cure. A decade previously another attack of the same complaint had put her in a coma for over two years. From what she said, it seemed to her as if she had only been asleep for a night. When she awoke she was hungry and asked for food but could not eat any of it just barely wetting her lips with some whey. For the following seven years she remained in the same condition in her bed scarcely able to touch much food.

Pennant had published the first volume of *A Tour in Wales* and the second two-part volume some years later in 1782. The vogue for this picturesque topographical description laced with tit-bits of history; houses and stories of the gentry; oddities, curious people and bizarre local events had produced a lot of dull writing and Pennant who was not the worst of the bunch of journeymen to fill the pages of popular almanacs, came to the genre late in life when he was past fifty. He had already acquired a distinguished scientific reputation before he embarked on his Scottish tour and the later journeys around north Wales. At his next visit in 1786 he found Mary Thomas in much the same state; thin but not too emaciated. Her mind was clear. She said she sometimes ate a small amount of bread and water but often abstained from eating for days on end. She spoke quietly to him and was uninterested in the affairs of the outside world. Another visitor who came to see her in the year prior to her death in 1818 described her appearance as frightful. Ears, eyebrows and mouth were prominent. The skin of her face was pallid and leathery. Her head appeared to have grown very large in relation to the rest of her body. Her mind was still alert. She spoke well repeating the story of her life much as she had told it to Pennant forty-seven years previously.[20]

A similar case of long fasting by a woman called Anne Moore of Tetbury was published in the August issue of the Gentleman's Magazine in 1811. Her original condition of living without food had been brought about through illness but when it was found that this state was deliberately carried on by imposture — after she claimed that all the lower parts of her body were useless and that she could not move — the fifty year old woman was declared to be a fraud. Many other instances were reported of so-called invalids living on a modicum of food for years on end or sleeping for long periods without eating. The saddest story was that of Sarah Jacob who became known as the Welsh Sleeping Girl. Ten year old Sarah lay in a coma for two years and news of her condition had become widespread. It was during a childhood illness when the third daughter of Evan and Hannah Jacob went into a coma and remained unconscious for a month. She recovered but refused all offers of food except for warm milk. By the tenth of October 1867 she became comatose again and would remain so for the following one-hundred and thirteen weeks in a small back-bedroom of the farmhouse of Llethneuadd Isaf in Carmarthenshire, until she died.

The public and medical interest in the girl's condition appears to have stemmed initially from a letter to the Welshman by the vicar of Pencader stating would it not be worth their while for medical men to make an investigation into the nature of this strange case? In a further letter to the paper, he was convinced that her condition was due to a miracle. As news reports and stories about Sarah's condition increased, the small bedroom of the Jacob cottage was turned into a shrine. At the Pencadar railway junction, a mile or so away, there were signs with 'To the Fasting Girl' and even guides to Llethneuadd for sale. People brought gifts of flowers, special foods and money; they put silver shillings and sixpences, florins, half crowns and even gold sovereigns in the box, placed for the purpose on the chest of the girl. She appeared to be fairly healthy, not at all pale and was dressed as a bride.[21]

There have been similar cases widely reported. Most recently in Boston USA when after a prolonged state of coma a young girl eventually became a cult figure. She was described as a pure being and stories about mysterious healing especially in the proximity of her sleeping body began to circulate in the media. As a result bigger crowds arrived to see and even touch the sleeping girl as more people became curious about such an unnatural phenomenon although in the Far East such occurrences are more common. There is also the less publicized effect on the parents and immediate family relatives in such circumstances. In the beginning the Welsh parents would have been worried and so concerned about their child that they were grateful for any help and advice. Gradually the strain of protecting the sleeper from the intrusion of so many strangers from far away and at the same time maintaining her in such a manner that their social betters would be impressed after making the long journey to visit the fasting girl certainly seemed to have affected the father Evan Jacob. After nearly two years, when it was suggested that she could be (forcibly) fed, he maintained that he had promised his child that he would not insist she eat until after she herself asked for food. His seemingly rigid stance in the matter troubled many people. A doctor from Llandovery even took the matter into his own hands. Having broken into the house in the evening to examine the body of the child, he was charged with assault on her person but was later acquitted. Discussions ranged from the vicar's assertain that the Great Father had possession of her to the Lancet highlighting the possible medical conditions and effects causing the comatose state, along with the suspicions that it was being deliberately maintained. Evan Jacob decided that a committee of 'watchers' were needed at night to show that there was nothing underhanded taking place. The first lot of relatives and locals were inconsistent in their vigils and the results were inconclusive. A second group that included doctors and nurses from Guy's hospital was formed in December 1869 to sit and record the movements of the girl and her family throughout the night. Their vigils revealed some disquieting aspects in relation to how they apparently cleaned her bed and that the child seemed to have a bottle of perfume in her armpit. Much of the recorded notes seem innocuous enough except for the fact that since the parents had claimed she had not eaten for so long, yet during these nightly vigils her physical condition grew extremely worse and she became noticeably thinner, becoming comatose towards her eventual death before the end of the month. An inquest was held soon afterwards and it was from the evidence of the doctors and the written notes of the professional observers that the father was found to be responsible for not feeding Sarah Jacob who was his twelve year old child.

In the Methodist climate of rural Wales at this period, rumours began to circulate after her death. There were suggestions that the mother and father had deliberately withheld the gifts of food from their daughter and for their personal gain had kept her in that sleeping state thereby causing her death. It aroused a lot of controversy in the popular press and in other journals. Its Christmas message *Starved to Death* was headlined in The Lancet. The trial was held at the Summer Assizes in Carmarthen during the following year with seemingly well argued cases both for and against the defendants. The judge summed up and the jury found both parents guilty of causing her death. Each was given terms of imprisonment with hard labour. Such a harsh legal judgement brings up many disquieting aspects of Welsh life at this time. The extreme mood-swings from the initial expression of public concern to suspicion and then blame, with the harsh punishment of her parents, appeared to be set in train by well-meaning outsiders contributing to the media. That there were clear social differences in how the law treated members of the medical profession, such as William Price and the poor parents is nothing new, then and now. The family may have taken advantage of the material gain to their lives in coping with the young girl's unaccountable illness. However the lack of any coherent medical explanation or even proper diagnosis when confronted with such long term fasting or a comatose sleeping state, produced many different opinions and conflicting professional statements. The unfortunate cases of Mary Thomas and Sarah Jacob were made into objects of passing interest by pompous writers and professional medical men. Medical science was becoming more generally accepted, but outside London and the official teaching establishments it was largely fragmented, faddish and pursued with enthusiasm by individual doctors confined to universal case studies in papers like The Lancet. It was unlikely that any (home-grown) psychological implications in relation to the sleeping women would have been taken seriously then although pre-Freudian explanations of female 'hysteria' and 'nerves' that had become fashionable in high society, were beginning to be aired. Hysteria, from the Greek word for the womb or uterus 'wandering' or moving around the body that explained the cause of womens' erratic (and erotic) behaviour, was beginning to be seen as a symptom, among many other sensations, that seemingly occurred in the absence of any apparent inner cause. Hovever, many medical commonplace explanations (as apposed to psychiatric ones) such as escaping from recurring unpleasant situations, attention-seeking, or even malingering were not thought to have been deliberately brought on, for such hysterical symptoms were then believed to be beyond the individual's control. It is interesting that in the conclusion of his book on Sarah Jacob, Dr. John Cule, who spent many years in psychiatric medicine, seems to infer that it was the girl herself who maintained her role as the centre of attention, by forcing the parents to act as they did in colluding with her self-regarding condition; and that her death was probably brought about through starvation during the period while the medical 'watchers' were in the room throughout the night.[22]

The case highlights the enormous gulf that still existed then between the home where women of all social classes were 'kept in their place' and the public arena of male Welsh society that was deemed to be beyond female interest and intelligence. It was an accepted means of gender suppression over the ages and often it is only by inference in some old texts or letters that the male attitude to women as a lesser breed can be glimpsed. In a poem by Guto'r Glyn of the mid-15th century, a pious noblewoman is praised for her qualities of good housekeeping — a warm fire, excellent food and wine. The poet had been troubled by his rheumatic knee but her hospitality so alleviated the ailment that in return the *crwydd* he composed praising her worth, was in fact a gift to her husband. His patron's generosity was a capital virtue to be eulogised in verse. The role of the healer in his poem was not the well-bred woman who might be expected to know about home remedies but it was Daffyd ab Lean, the abbot of Valle Crucis Abbey that the poet had turned to after hurting a rib. It was the same abbey where Guto'r Glyn retired as a crippled old man suffering from blindness and rheumatism.[23]

In contrast to the witch hunts carried out in particular areas of England and Scotland it is noteworthy that only a few court cases involving witchcraft have been recorded in Wales. Perhaps the socially accepted function of the *dyn hysbys* or male wizard, in counteracting the beguiling power of the female was deemed as a sufficient deterrent here as in the mainly apocryphal accounts when John Dee exorcised a hag called Gwen Goch, Red Gwen, who had spread pestilence in one area of the Clwyd valley Two cases were brought before the Assizes in Flintshire. In 1656 Dorothy Griffith was accused of witchcraft by her husband but in the evidence presented it was clear that it was he who should have been on trial. The woman was rightfully acquitted. In the following year Anne Ellis was also discharged, even though in the meanwhile she had escaped from goal and had been recaptured. Some evidence was found against her but she was considered not to be a destructive person and had not used her powers to make a living. The presider in both cases was John Bradshaw the Regicide — one of those who had signed the death warrant of king Charles I — and who had already dealt firmly with three women in Chester, who were executed two years previously. A case in Cardiganshire in the final decade of that century with charges of witchcraft laid by a man and her neighbours against a Katherine Rees of Nancwnlle was also dropped. Extracting a few facts from the evidence as 'a farrago of nonsense', Gerald Morgan in his recent history of the country, describes the woman as with a wall eye — whatever that might mean — a sharp tongue and uncompromising manner. Perhaps there is some justification in the view that even though female sorcery appeared to have been practiced, it was not considered to be a social threat to the prominent male society. In later Welsh folklore mention is often casually made of witches but not in the revered manner that specific wizards were regarded.[24]

There are many examples of the abject state of women in early-modern Wales but none so lowly as married women being led to market by a rope around their neck in order to be 'divorced'. The husband had to lead them to the town by a halter, and the woman was tied to a wood post all day like any other animal for sale while the town crier made the public announcements to get other men interested in the bidding. It appears to have been a quite accepted method and a way whereby poor hill farmers could avoid the expense of a legal divorce. Once a deal was struck between the two men, the woman got her bill of sale as evidence that she was not a prostitute or had not been thrown out of her house but was in fact a proper married woman. A court case occurred in Newtown in mid-

Wales due to a new 'husband' claiming *amobr* (a dowry) from the woman's family. When they refused to pay he took them to law; but the judge decided that with the woman's rightful bill of sale, it was clear she had been previously married along with her dowry, so any 'new' husband could not claim her bride-price a second time round.[25]

Prior to the final decades of the 19th century women in Wales had few of the social rights we normally take for granted now in relation to public life. They were forced to endure a long established form of repression from both fathers and husbands in what was in effect a generally accepted method of confining them to the house. The total exclusion of women from pre-modern medicine, as from the other learned professions, denied them much choice of an outward social role in public life. It was one of the issues raised by a suffragette group demonstrating in Cardiff in 1907. This situation in relation to women in general is of interest in the wider study of orthodox medicine for a number of important reasons. Firstly the women of the house once had a range of common herbal remedies that could be applied when necessary to many of the family complaints. Not only did they maintain the good health of the farm but they also organized seasonal food from the fields by picking, storing and preserving fruits, berries, nuts as well as drying herbs and flowers. They usually passed this basic *materia medica* on to other women of the extended household, especially the eldest daughters who would eventually take on the mother's role. Secondly women bore, nourished and took care of the children as best they knew how and were therefore more compassionate to others as a result of their frequent birthing experiences. They often acted as midwifes to younger women in childbirth. As they grew old some became known for their herbal wisdom as local healers; nonetheless they were often seen as unwelcome competition by physicians as they did not charge for such services. The famous English surgeon of the 14th century John of Arderne disdainfully called them 'ladies bountiful' for the same reason. As medicine became more widespread throughout Wales, the 'wise woman' was rarely held in high esteem by the medical profession. *Cyfareddion Gwrach waeth*

waeth, each wise woman's charm increases the harm, is from a book of proverbs by Henry Vaughan, the metaphysical poet and hermetic doctor. Thirdly the servile condition of women is a useful reminder of their almost total exclusion from the practice of medicine in Wales, as from the other learned professions of the law and poetry. It was maintained through social upheavals of every kind through the early industrial period up to recent times. Yet some doctors' wives in the 18th century were acceptable in the public role of midwife. Lewis Morris referring to the wife of his family doctor wrote that she, Mrs Evans, was the best midwife in North Wales. However this praise, as in the poem by Guto'r Glyn, was in relation to the fact that the doctor had died suddenly leaving her with a number of small children to look after and that there was no other medical man in the locality to treat his mother.[26]

The Dictionary of Welsh Biography up to 1940 has over three thousand double-column pages devoted to eminent men who have shaped the religion, history and society of ancient and modern Wales. Their concise written descriptions come in all shapes and sizes from King Arthur and the early saints to soldiers, scientists, doctors, churchmen and lawmakers. It was an English language work, well-written and with a well-documented biography; it had taken twenty-two years to complete. Housed in the reference library in Cardigan it was my bible in many ways whilst researching this book. Names were listed alphabetically by surname and first name or initial so the more common Welsh surnames took up most of my time while searching for individual medical doctors and physicians or their family backgrounds. As the librarian in the Heath Hospital library in Cardiff informed me on my single visit there, they did not carry old Welsh books but more recent works on British medicine. So searching through the Dictionary for medical material was like a pick and mix detection operation in establishing what I might find interesting. It was only when copying and correlating my copious notes, did I realise how few references to women they contained. There was the entertaining saga of Mary Evans, a cult figure in the 18th century known as 'Mountain Martha', Y Fantell Wen or 'White

Mantle' who was betrothed as a bride of Christ. Elizabeth Davis of Bala had led a chequered life and was a nurse in the Crimea but the probable reason for her entry was the publication of a two-volume autobiography in 1857. Frances Elizabeth Hoggan from Brecon was educated abroad and studied medicine in Zurich University. She moved back to Wales and was the first woman MD to be registered in Cardiff in 1885. Dr. Hoggan was clearly concerned about the plight of Welsh women in terms of their health and physical education as some of the titles of her many publications indicate. I am certainly willing to be corrected on this but she seems to have been the first and only 19th century woman doctor to be so listed. The growing interest in relation to academic research on women and literacy and on the role of women and gender, from the medieval to the modern period, is evident in a number of recent publications.[27]

Cancer Curers of West Wales

By the late 19th century the long established divisions of medicine and surgery had begun to splinter into smaller professional groups. Although still classified as doctor or surgeon, numerous fellowships had formed their own accredited Associations of men with particular teaching methods and medical agendas. The many advances in the scientific application of medicine as well as the availability of medical training schools in Wales was one side of an equation, with more general health care and education on the other, that helped alter public perception of general medicine and its acceptation as *modern* and more reliable than the traditional kind of their forebears. By the turn of the 20th century traditional remedies and charm healing had become marginalized although the home-curer was still often the easiest and cheapest source of relief for the afflicted poor. Yet there was often a renewal of interest in the older methods if a new health fad or a well-publicized miracle cure became news. It was during the period between the First and Second World Wars that David Rees Evans began to get national publicity for his remarkable cure of skin cancers.

Evans, like his father and uncle from whom he inherited the cure, was of low standing but with a zeal to heal people of all classes of what then was such a common and disfiguring disease. He was also attempting to interest the medical establishment. According to his account the treatment was successful and involved no more cost than the straight forward application of his 'magic oil' on the damaged outer skin. He worked tirelessly to have it accepted by a profession closed to those like himself that had no university medical training or surgical expertise. While the medical profession could only hopefully recommend surgery — with or without radium treatment — to the many thousands so afflicted in Britain, it seemed beyond the healer's comprehension, and that of his many influential supporters, that this successful eradication of malignant growth which in the process helped the skin to regenerate, should not at the very least be subjected to proper clinical trials. In fact such trials had been conducted in America and the *Picture Post* magazine ran a strong editorial alongside a words-and-pictures story, asking why the British Health Service was so very reluctant to allow this cure to be available to all those who wished to be healed of skin cancer.

The cure first became known publicly in west Wales during the early years of the 20th century. It was stated in 1907 that Cardigan resembled a cancer settlement rather than a seaside town. It had become such a gloomy place that it was impossible to walk in any direction without seeing men with disfigured faces and ladies covered in thick white veils. Such people had come from all over the country and even from England to be cured, attracted by the fame of the cancer healers. In the event the sight of the sick frightened the usual summer visitors away and the town's death rate — generally low — had become the highest in the land. Many of the inns refused to admit the afflicted, some of whom claimed that even the chapels did not welcome them as they underwent their daily treatment of the magic oil. Daniel and John Evans were born on a farm a few miles from Cardigan. They were ship builders by trade and preached in the local chapel. As the brothers were known to be able to treat sore legs and skin eruptions with herbal remedies, their cures began to get more than local renown. It is not clear when they turned their attention to malignant growths but probably it was part of a growing confidence in their treatments and the success of a mystery ingredient that they never would reveal except to call it a *magic oil*. Perhaps they themselves were unaware of how it actually worked. The oil caused a black encrustation on the growth to form a hard skin, like a scab, that would eventually fall off leaving the skin beneath looking clean and healthy. The elder brother Daniel, a nervous man and a musician, was the more outgoing and it was he who was said to have found a special herb growing by the seashore that made their oil so potent. He became known as Doctor Evans. The method of treatment was simplicity itself. No attempt was made at a diagnosis of the patient's condition or medical history for according to Daniel every growth on the skin was a cancer that had to be slowly drawn out by its roots. The oil was dabbed on daily and the length of time the process took seemed immaterial to the 'doctor' for the person was only declared healed when the hard crust or scab fell away of its own accord. They had these on display in jars in a small shop in the main street of Cardigan which they called their surgery for those too poor to be attended at home. As their fame spread into the national newspapers, a number of medical men came to ascertain for themselves what was going on. One of these, a Doctor Hadwen, had been asked to write about the cures. When he first met the brothers he was shown the trophies in their shop with pride and even acquired one for his own private medical examination. He did suggest in his article that mercury or some such poison might be involved in the process. He also mentioned the increase of deaths in the town and that untold numbers may have died later in their homes. However he concluded that the brothers had not sought out such notoriety but believed they did genuine healing. However by 1912 Cardigan town had returned to its usual sedate pace and nothing more was heard of Daniel and John Evans or of their miracle cures.[28]

Daniel Rees Evans (John's son) had served in a medical corps and after the Great War set himself up as a herbalist in Cardiff in 1919. He even advertised a cure for cancer but business was not very brisk so he moved to Liverpool, and when his wife became involved with a group of Spiritualists he began to make a better living. Gradually through some of the more publicly known members of this movement his claims for cancer curing began to get newspaper coverage. Through the beneficence of Lord Bute and especially his mother, Evans and his wife moved to central London where they were able to live comfortably in a large house that included his surgery. The Picture Post magazine devoted a lot of space to the herbalist and his famous cure, adding to the demands that the government look into the results of a radically new approach to a disease that now afflicted hundreds of thousands of sufferers in Britain alone. Lord Bute's estates had included a large part of central Cardiff and in 1950 an even more famous Welshman Aneurin Bevan — the founder of the National Health Service — agreed to set up a committee that included Alexander Fleming the discoverer of penicillin. However by the following year the Labour Party was out of office and the new Minister of Heath received the committee's report which was never published. The minister did read out a summary of it in the House of Commons, saying in effect that Mr. Evans had been unable to provide convincing evidence of lasting success in any undoubted case of cancer. It was the end of a saga of a David battling against the Goliath of the medical establishment that had run on for almost half-a-century.

Curiously enough it mirrored an almost similar set of circumstances in north Wales with claims of cancer healing during the same period. In 1971 the Department of Health asked the healer Griffith Griffiths to submit details of his cure for clinical testing. He was then the landlord of a pub in Derby but died suddenly during the following year. This put an abrupt end to the pressure on the British Medical Association to recognize his cure as a legitimate one for certain types of skin cancers without the use of surgery or the radium treatment that was still fairly general at this time.[29]

Griffith Griffiths was the last in a line of healers based at Siop Pen-y-craig in Llangwnadle near Pwllheli on the Lleyn peninsula. His grandfather of the same name (1814-1891) had carried on a family business in the corner shop as draper, ironmonger and chemist. He was also known as a healer of warts with a special ointment which his grandson later described as a potion he distilled from locally grown herbs. However its exact composition was a secret that had been in the family for over a hundred years. His grandfather was known as the village medico and had acquired the recipe from a friend after he had cured him of an illness. John Griffiths obtained his apothecary's certificate in 1874 and continued the business of shopkeeper as well as the practice of wart healing until his death in 1921. His brother Owen who was the father of Griffith took over both sides of the business but died suddenly five years later when his son was sixteen. According to an article he wrote in the Liverpool Post and Mercury (1932) the secret recipe of the family remedy was nearly lost due to his father's sudden death for the cure had not been passed on to him in the traditional manner. However with the help of his cousin he was able to resume manufacture of the Wild Wart cure for external skin growths. 'All the Griffiths had been men of rare natural healing gifts' and he was then the sole holder of this method of healing that had been passed on down the family for a century or more. Part of this tradition was to treat the very poor free of charge, if only to prove its never-failing curative powers. He claimed in the article that thousands of people had been cured of these unsightly malignancies by his assertive motto: *the only cure that really cures!*[30]

The county medical officer for Gwynedd declared that a woman they had treated with the special paste had died from heart failure brought on by the incidental infection of a wart. The practice of Griffith Griffiths and his cousin was suspended in 1932. However the County Council at a special meeting supported them and decided to write to the Health Minister for clarification. He, however, said he had no powers in the matter, nor could he guarantee the Griffiths against any consequences arising from their secret cure. The

Council ruled that they could continue to treat people. The healer, who was also the postmaster of Llangwnadle; and his cousin, a fellow practitioner of what they called *dafed wyllt* or the Wild Wart, announced in the local press that they were resuming their successful joint practice. The case was widely reported and the publicity about traditional healing revealed other wart healers throughout Wales, some of whom also used a secret paste. A Llanrwst tradesman named Maddocks said he had cured warts successfully for over thirty years. However he would only attempt to heal the worst of them at the very early stages of a possible malignancy. He revealed that before he started the local people had flocked to Lloyd Williams, a dyer who possessed the paste. When Williams died his brother inherited the cure and had asked Maddocks if he would try it for himself. But he refused until the other man told him what the ingredients were. Unlike the Evans brothers of Cardigan and the paste they claimed was made from herbs and its secret ingredient which they would not divulge, Maddocks wrote that he assumed it to be arsenic. The general availability of such poisons became restricted in 1911 after the Crippen murder trial. It created publicity on both sides of the Atlantic, and when it became known that the murderer did not have a medical degree but was a quack who called himself Dr. as they did, the Evans brothers ceased to heal people publicly. The poison ingredient was confirmed in the paste the Griffiths used by another correspondent. He was a veterinary surgeon of Pwllheli known as Roberts the Farrier and revealed that he had a special arrangement to supply the poison to John Griffiths during the First World War. Arsenic, he said, was the particular ingredient in the cure of Rodent Ulcers. The farrier in his turn then used the paste he received in kind from Griffiths to treat similar skin conditions on animals.

Griffith Griffiths moved to England and no doubt continued his practice. After he became the landlord of the Ram Inn in Derby he informed the British Medical Association in 1967 about his cancer cures. A headline in the local paper: MINISITER CAUTIONS, was the guarded response after the letter had been passed on to the

Ministry of Health. People were reassured that adequate medical and surgical methods existed for treatments of all cancers and if treated early the prospects of success were extremely favourable. However in 1971 the Department of Health consented and asked the healer to submit his cure for clinical trials. A subsequent press announcement written by him stated that Mr. Griffiths had worked from five clinics in north Wales and Liverpool between the two World Wars and (had) successfully treated hundreds of cancer cases. However he had to suspend his practice when new legislation had been introduced that would make him liable for legal claims if anything went wrong. He was confident that the Minister of Health would vindicate his method by proper clinical trials. However the sixty-two year old healer died suddenly in the following year and no more was heard about such trials.

Both cancer curers claimed that the essential healing ingredient in their magic oil or paste came from a plant they found growing by the seashore. Neither would reveal the actual ingredients used even though they were obviously pressured to do so during the long years of battling against a seemingly indifferent medical establishment. Yet there was clearly more than a suspicion that the special addition may well have been a mineral poison. Much of their work was in terms of prevention, and tackling a range of complaints at an early stage. They were also readily available and willing to do so mainly in the home and without the fees doctors would have charged. They had a sense of social responsibility, a commitment to use properly what they termed their 'magic oil' at a time when major surgery and radium treatment appeared to be the only alternative offered by the NHS. As healers they appeared to have had an ability to heal particular forms of skin disfigurement that were common during the early years of the 20th century; in distinction to the general medical doctors who treat major and minor external and internal complaints of people of all ages and backgrounds with the prescribed chemical drugs that usually deal with symptoms rather than causes of illness.[31]

211

It is important to have in mind in relation to the history of medicine, that current cover-all descriptions like disease, illness, cure, medical healing as craft or profession, and the word medicine itself whether as in herbal, syncretic or chemical is prone to a wide divergence of meanings when applied to a distant past. Such terms as relating to insular rural groups or emerging societies of a distant era should be understood within the tangled web of accepted legal ties and restrictions; likewise the binds imposed by their social betters often ignorant of or ignoring out of hand peoples' allegiances within the lower social groups. This was especially true in the pontificating of 'proper health' as with smallpox vaccinations from the 17th century onwards and in the vain struggle of the West Wales healers to gain some official recognition.

Chapter 9. The Secrets of Nature Revealed.

There have been quite a few doctors called John Jones, some of whom have enhanced the obscure story of Welsh medicine. John Jones *phistion* in 1574 issued *A briefe, excellent and profitable discourse, of the beginning of all living things,* and in 1597, *the arte and science of preserving bodie and soule in healthe...* Jones with Thomas Phaer are considered the forerunners of modern paediatrics There was a John Jones surgeon who is named on a tombstone at present fixed to the west end of the Myddfai church in Carmarthenshire; alongside that of his father David Jones who 'died in 1718 aged sixty-one years who was an honest, charitable and skilful surgeon'. John, the eldest son of the said David Jones, 'departed this life the 25th of November 1739 in the 44th year of his Age and also lies interred hereunder'. Both John Jones and his father David are considered to have been the end of the line of the famous hereditary physicians, the Meddygon Myddfai. John Jones, *Myrddin Fardd,* in his 'ragged manuscript' included ancient charms and a chapter on the healing wells of Caernarfon with some of his bardic compositions. John Jones of Conwy published a work on Phrenology and five years later in 1844 John Jones, a member of the Royal College of Surgeons produced *Observations on self-supporting dispensaries...* Professor John T. Jones published a surgical anatomy of the horse in four parts from 1906 to 1914.[32]

Dr. John Jones of Pentrych in Glamorgan was a cleric before becoming a physician. He was educated at Jesus College Oxford where he obtained BA and MA degrees; then in 1677 his DCL Doctor of Civil Law, at the College of Physicians. In the following year he was licensed to practice medicine which he did at Windsor. He published a Latin treatise on fevers. In 1691 he was appointed Chancellor of Llandaff Cathedral in Cardiff. The tomb of John Jones (1645-1709) is near the west door. He is thought to have invented a mechanical clock which moved by air showing time vertically. The necessary observation and affinity to detail in such subtle movements seemingly underscores both his *Practical phonography*: or *the new art of rightly speling and writing words by the sound thereof,* and his most noted work published in 1700: *The Mysteries of Opium Reveal'd*. It is probably one of the earliest accounts of the drug to which, like many later eminent poets, Jones was addicted. Unlike the works of the playwright Thomas Shadwell who was thought to have died of an overdose, the Welshman's extravagantly coloured prose combined his own imaginative reactions to the poppy experience with the shrewd and practical observations of a physician; and one who clearly had observed other addicts during and after the ingestion of opium.

John Jones was certainly well established in the literature of the Romantic Movement. His digressions on the nature of sensation and perception with the metaphoric illustrations he used such as candle-flames and their reflections, bells heard along hollow valleys and the reverberating sound of a pinhead falling into a brass cauldron found their way into Coleridge's notes and De Quincy's *Confessions of an English Opium Eater*. The overtly expressive use of language, especially with the Welshman in full tilt, with an almost unlimited self-confidence often culminated in sudden outbursts of praise for his own inventive genius. His medical discoveries could not but benefit mankind he reckoned, for he compared his flights of fancy to William Harvey's account of the circulation of the blood. He described the tactile pleasures of an opium eater in terms of what eventually became the imaginative grounding of the Romantic poets by way of vivid life-like dreams, freedom from anxious pain and worry as well as the avid exploration of delicious states of expanding mental illumination. On the other hand, Doctor Jones detailed many of the less favourable and actively unpleasant affects of the drug; especially the unnerving, awful depressions and the 'cold' physical distress caused by withdrawal from it. Yet like the orthodox medical opinion of his time, Jones believed that the constant use of opium and especially its most popular form as a tincture of laudanum would alleviate the worst pains of common ailments such as gout, catarrh, asthma and dropsy. The cure for that bloating of the body due to fluid retention and heart disease would be the common foxglove — *Digitalis purpurea* — discovered by William Withering much later in the century. Jones considered opium a great boon for fevers, amputations, measles and colic as well as dysentery, although the restrictive pain of constipation or the hard green stool that Coleridge alluded to in his letters, was an unpleasant side-effect for the addictive user. Jones had even suggested that his opiate cure-all would prevent plague and cholera but he was probably confusing some ancient medical prescriptions. Like a confirmed addict, Jones listed the different preparations in fashionable demand at the turn of the 18th century such as Venice treacle, Sydenham laudanum, London laudanum or Dr. Bates' pacific pill.[33] *The Mysteries of Opium Reveal'd,* according to Alethea Hayter, was an insidious misleading work but non-the-less engaging for being slightly mad. Yet it was a mouth-waterer for many of the fancies and errors about opiate use that would fill the pages of later and better literature by writers such as De Quincy, Baudelaire, Wilkie Collins and the poets Coleridge, John Keats and Francis Thompson. At this period people from all walks of life, rich and poor alike, used the drug in pill, powder and more generally as tincture or in liquid form. De Quincy kept his supply in a decanter in the parlour where unwary visitors thinking it was port often helped themselves with humorous results. Almost all the writers and many with literary aspirations had their first taste of it as children sipping elixirs and syrups that were sold under popular brand names like Godfery's Cordial, Dalby's Carminative, McMunn's Elixir, Bately's Sedative and Mother Bailey's Quieting Syrup. Collis Brown and other laced syrups were still popular for keeping children quiet during the early years of the 20th century.

The Gorsedd of the Bards

His fellow countryman Edward Williams — an avid reader of books and old Welsh manuscripts — may have been familiar with

Jones' work. He first admitted to taking laudanum in 1773 when he was twenty-six in an attempt to rid himself of a cough he had had since his childhood asthma. Twenty years on, Williams was so convinced that opium had saved his life that he dedicated his first published poems to the drug he named as his faithful friend in all his grief 'and, in thy soft arms I find relief'. Many of the effects that John Jones had elaborated upon a century before have been observed as dire manifestations in the life and work of Iolo Morganwg. He was to have a fifty-year addiction to laudanum. In his old age people would point him out in the street as mad Neddy or poor old Iolo whereas at the beginning of his literary career he began his letters with the proud flourish of 'I Iolo Morganwg'. Yet the gradual inability to perceive that his makeshift drafts and endless preliminary essays to projected masterpieces were part of its intoxicating daydreams while his wife, pleading for him to come home, called it building castles in the air. Perhaps it was a remembered line in an early poem written under his pen name of 'Iorwerth Gwilym' that he eventually published in *Poems, Lyric and Pastoral*. 'The poet in some garret high / thro shatter'd window views the sky / to number there / his realms of castles built in air'. It was a foretaste of Williams' refusal to leave London until he gained the proper recognition due to him as a Welsh journeyman poet. Unlike the fame that came to Robert Burns in Scotland, or the incarceration of the poet John Clare, it resulted in him having to endure endless depression, terrible dreams, illness, poverty and the thoughts of suicide that plagued him in the squalor of the city.[34]

David Samwell as the secretary of the Gwyneddigion Society and a known poet probably helped him more than was generally realized with introductions to his wide circle of friends and also probably supplying him with laudanum. Because of his experiences and travels as a ship's surgeon Samwell probably did not have the parochial outlook and disdain shown by the other north Walians towards Iolo who claimed that Glamorgan was the epicentre of ancient Welsh poetry. Williams had attended some of the early meetings in London and was given access to the Society's library manuscripts and eventually admitted as a corresponding member. He was later to claim to be one of its founders, perhaps from a genuine belief in his own importance and a desire to build bridges between the northern and his Welsh bardic faction. The list of subscribers to his English *Poems Lyric and Pastoral* published in 1794 is certainly impressive so during those four years in London Iolo Morganwg was no slouch in presenting himself as the 'Bard' to the rich and famous. Not only did it include the Prince of Wales to whom it is dedicated but George Washington, Hugh Walpole and known radicals like Tom Payne and William Wilberforce. Iolo was also in contact with Robert Southey, Samuel Taylor Coleridge and the Romantic addicts of radical tendencies. Laudanum reveries certainly helped the common Romantic attachment to notions of creative madness and the grandiose delusions of exploration and discovery by way of the active imagination. Samwell, by virtue of his own sea-going travels thought it was quite plausible that America could have been visited in the period long before Columbus and he may have fired Iolo to a Rousseaun back-to-nature regime in order to prepare himself for the rigorous journey across the Atlantic in search of the Welsh descendants of a prince Madog and his crew whom he believed had sailed there in 1167.[35]

The venture added fuel to his accumulative reconstruction of an imaginary history of ancient Wales which would eventually find expression in his later rewritings of its druidic past. Some of Edward Williams' brothers actually had slave plantations in Jamaica which he only mentioned in a few letters many years later, so visiting them may also have been an important factor in his decision. He went sleeping out in the open woods; bathing naked in rivers; living on grass and drinking his own decoctions of elder flower, peppermint and wormwood. He had always been frugal in his habits, never eating red meat or rarely drinking alcohol and as he said in a letter home, living on gallons of marshmallow and chamomile tea. However as a result of this outdoor activity in his late forties he developed rheumatism and was forced to drop out of the scheme. John Evans of Waunfawr in north Wales who had been convinced by Iolo to be his companion on the journey, did actually travel on his own to America and got as far as the Missouri river. He found no traces of Welsh-speaking red men. Humphrey Lhwyd in the 16th century had been the first to give form to this story of the discovery of the Americas by a Welshman Madoc ap Owain, long before the time of Columbus. It was a tale much appreciated by those Elizabethans who faced the challenge and enterprise of the New World. Lhwyd referred to a Francis Loues who asserted that Christians had lived there prior to the Spanish. John Dee made a marginal note of this in the manuscript of Lhwyd's *Cronica Walliae* that was in his possession and he passed the information to Hakluyt who included it in his *Voyages*.[36]

The first of the learned societies founded by prominent Welshmen in London was the Honorary Society of Cymmrodorion that had been established under the patronage of Richard Morris in 1751 but its role in the spread of native learning and promulgating the literary interests of those living outside Wales was gradually taken over by the Gwyneddigion Society, founded twenty years later. Its library contained the extensive manuscript collections made by the Morris brothers, from which Iolo rewrote his own versions of Dafydd ap Gwilym's poetry that were published as such in the 1789 volume *Barddoniaeth* of the 14th century poet by Owain Myfyr. Both he and Robert Hughes were founder members of the Society and David Samwell became secretary in 1788. As a son of William Samuel the vicar of Nantglyn in Denbighshire and grandson of the poet Edward Samual, he had published poetry and was known in Welsh as 'Black David the Doctor'. After qualifying at the Royal College of Surgeons he became a medical officer in the navy. With his experiences and travels as a ship's surgeon serving in seven different man-of-wars, even going to Greenland, he did not spend much time in England. Samwell's claim to fame was sailing with Captain Cook on his third expedition to the South Seas. Cook was killed on a beach in Hawaii after a skirmish with the natives in 1779 and Samwell as First Mate on the Discovery, witnessed the incident. He included it in the journal he kept of the voyage and an account of it was subsequently published seven years later as *A Narrative of the Death of Captain Cook*. It became an important source book for both the exploration and anthropology of the South Seas due to his candid accounts of the sexual commerce during this time. He casually stated in the journal that his supply of nails and hatchets had become depleted in exchange for sexual favours with the women of the islands. He also wrote a pamphlet called 'Observations respecting the Introduction of the Venereal Diseases into the Sandwich Islands' by the English sailors during Cook's three voyages.[37]

William Stukeley's drawings of Stonehenge were published earlier in the 18th century and after his 1740 publication of *A Temple Restor'd to the British Druids* the general consensus of opinion among the closely knit echelons of antiquarian societies was that the monument was the greatest of the druidic stones although the confused debate still continues as to who, when or even where the original builders came from. John Toland had formed the Ancient Druid Order in 1717 and in 1781 the Grand Lodge of the Order of Druids was created by a party of friends who met at the Kings Arms tavern in Poland Street 'to promote good fellowship, hilarity and brotherly love'. Subsidiary lodges were established throughout the country and members set down their druidic accounts and literature in occasional publications. London at this period was a hotbed of esoteric groupings, many having members in common as well as being prominent in the Royal Astronomical Society, the Freemasons and the radical stirrings of British Socialism. James Mac Pherson's Ossian or translations of heroic tales from the Scots Gaelic (1778) had reached unprecedented popularity even in Europe, to the extent of being quoted by Werther — Goethe's romantic hero. If Iolo's inner search among the uncharted regions of his creative imagin-ation found strange byways among the London Welsh speaking community, they had been well trodden by numerous other writers and radical journeymen.

There is no doubt that he did actually achieve a dream in making later generations of Welsh druidists and scholars aware of their own literary heritage. It began, innocuously enough, after he had persuaded six gentlemen of the Gwyneddigion Society, as they were called in his 1791 proclamation: 'all being licensed in the privilege of the Bards of the Isle of Britain, along with himself being a Bard by Privilege and Custom, to repair to Primrose Hill near London, in a year and a day, where there will not be a naked weapon against them'. At his first ceremony Iolo laid out a circle of twelve stones with one in the centre to represent *Maen Llog* on which was placed a sword. He read aloud his poem *Ode on the Mythology of the Ancient British Bards,* significantly in English rather than Welsh. He initiated David Samwell, William Owen Pughe and the others as founder members of the Gorsedd of Great Britain and it was clearly no accident that Iolo had chosen the same hill on which John Toland had formed his Ancient Druid Order nearly seventy-five years previously. Other traditional hill sites of 'free speech' in London were the Llandin at Parliament Hill Fields between Highgate and Hampstead; Gospel Oak where Edward the Confessor renewed the Charter of Rights for the citizens of London Town; Tower Hill at Kennington; Whitfield's Mound at Greenwich and Tyburn before it was moved inside Hyde Park at Speaker's Corner. Iolo's second meeting was mentioned in the columns of the Gentlemen's Magazine, probably written by David Samwell: 'This being the day on which the autumn equinox occurred, some Welsh bards resident in London, assembled in congress on Primrose Hill according to ancient usage'. We have no idea to what ancient usage the writer referred although probably to Morganwg's own forging of so-called ancient Welsh lore as there is a plan of a *Gorsedd* in the collection of his papers in the NLW in which the sun was likened to a harpist playing to a circle of seven stringed symbols at the ritual points of the year. He symbolically related the high quarters of the year with the word *alban* and so named each of them. *Alban Eilir* was the vernal equinox associated with the clover plant; the blessed oak of *Alban Heflin* at the summer solstice; *Alban Eifed* the autumn equinox with the ears of corn; and the mistletoe with *Alban Arthan* at the winter solstice. He then subsequently convened Gorsedd

220

ceremonies in south Wales on some of the quarter days from 1795 onwards after he had left London.

It might seem that once his ambition to publish a volume of his poetry had been achieved that he returned home to the safe haven of Cowbridge where he then set up as a shopkeeper with a license to sell tea, coffee and sugar. However the political situation in the capital for people like him had become quite dangerous. The authorities had begun to stamp down on the radicals and Rational Dissenters and for many thinkers the excesses of the French Revolution had soured their former ideals of freedom which was such a feature at the beginning of the last decade of the 18th century. Iolo may have become a figurehead for local Unitarianism but it was a far cry from the former radical outpourings of the Bard of Liberty, although much of this evidence is only available now in his archive, from copies of the letters and the mountain of (discarded) written material he accumulated during his lifetime. According to Ann-Marie Constantine, who is heading a group of academics currently researching his extant work as a figurehead in a what they grandly call the Romantic movement in Wales, Iolo appears to have stored away all of his letters and written working drafts. She describes his existing archive as 'copious, omnivorous, repetitive, contradictory'; and with all this material, 'there is an added twist that he might be making it all up'. Since he never had a university grounding in literature his passionate piecemeal accumulation of poetry and especially what he was ferreting of the ancient bardic tradition of south Wales was continuously being 'reformed' by him and in that William Blake sense of vision being revealed in the actual writing, he was making it all up as he wrote it down. His versions of the poetry of Dafydd ap Gwilym had already been included with the authentic poems in the 1789 edition by Owen Jones (Owain Myfyr), without anyone being aware that they were close imitations of the 14th century poet. Having left London behind him, Iolo began to work closely with Jones and William Owen Pughe in collecting the early Welsh texts that were brought together and published as *The Myvyrian Archaiology* (1807). The third part devoted to the *triads*, is 'peppered with (his) forgeries'. A poetic genre which few at the time knew much about but to many people Iolo's incandatory forms and his secret alphabets, the *Coelbren y Beirdd*, in which he successfully embodied his bardic and druidic teachings became extremely popular in the latter half of the century after his death in 1826.[38]

Small groups of his friends had gathered spasmodically throughout Glamorganshire over the next twenty years or so particularly at the celebrated Rocking Stone or the Y Maen Chwff at Pontypridd; until the Gorsedd of the Bards was fused into the wider component of the Eisteddfod convened in 1819 by the Cambrian Literary Society at the Ivy Bush hotel in Carmarthen. Iolo set out on the front lawn, a circle with stones 'in the face of the sun and the eye of light'. At the ceremony convened by Bishop Burgess of St. David's, Iolo took centre stage as the officiating bard to give an address in Welsh and English. His visionary idealisation that the Gorsedd of Bards should become important in Welsh public life is certainly evident at present day national gatherings when the colourful ceremony of the bards in Welsh is presented as its central core during the annual international presentations of national poetry and song.

Wesley's Electric Hair Straightener

When he was a young man, John Wesley spent almost three years in America and was impressed by the rude health of the Native Americans of Georgia whom he described as users of real *primitive physick*. If anything happened to them such as falling ill or being bitten by a poisonous snake, the tribal elders knew what herb to apply so they recovered very quickly. He was also a great believer in cold fresh water as a heal-all combined with eating moderately, plenty of exercise and the use of simples, the single plants that people had always taken to cure specific complaints; for instance, garlic for coughs, betony for headaches, valerian for the nerves, turnips and oranges for scurvy. Both, as we know now, contain vitamin C. Scurvy grass was a well-tried cure of foul ulcerous effects inside the mouth since Roman times and was advised as the most immediate remedy available from almost every large river bank by the Elizabethan John Gerard. The preacher's recommendation of the juice of fresh fruit anticipated the exhaustive treatise by James Lind (1716-1794) on that disease and it was made over a half-century before the Admiralty decided to give the order for a ration of lemon juice to every sailor aboard a man of war.

One of the most popular of John Wesley's books in Wales during the latter half of the 18th century was *yr Prif Fessyginiaeth.* John Evans of Bala — its translator and publisher — began the Bala Methodist Society in 1745 and five years later he donated the land to build the first of the Methodist chapels in north Wales. During his long industrious life Evans had been a weaver, lead miner, road builder and a tallow chandler. He officially became exhorter at the Adwy chapel in 1765, six years after he had published the Welsh edition of *Primitive Physic*. At that time many of the dependant poor along with their tenant farmers were being evicted, because of their public adherence to the new faith. It had attracted the women, for as their men had to abstain from drunkenness and visiting the public house which was such a feature of male evening entertainment, the close network of family life gave the early Methodists moral strength and a sense of exclusion from both the people around them and the officially-professed Anglican creed.

Primitive Physic was not a spiritually uplifting work except in the deepest sense of how the Welsh underclass had put their trust in home remedies from familiar plants. It was written in the language of the rural country person who usually relied on old healing recipes and cures passed on by their grandparents. The value of such local lore, as to where and when to find specific plants, was certainly being undermined, if not lost, in the large scale population shifts to the shanty towns that mushroomed around the coal mines of the Valleys and the lead and slate quarries of north and mid Wales. Not only were the untold thousands of labouring men, women and children far from their ancient rural environments but the ability to

223

heal themselves from nature's own pharmacy, in the old manner, was on the wane. It was a problem the Methodist preacher tried to confront with his compilation of home cures. Wesley and other ministers collected simple remedies from ordinary people on their missions around Britain. Since the book cost a few pennies, it was probably easy to sell enormous quantities at the chapels and outdoor Methodist revival meetings. For the displaced Welsh it was part of a growing sense of communal awareness, with its medical cures from far and wide, written out by people they identified with and in which they could both add to and take from this common pot of home relief. Essentially it was a small domestic handbook of cures and remedies set out in alphabetical order beginning with abortion (and how to prevent it) and ending with wounds. Being a collection of individual cures from all parts of Britain it did not exhibit the marked anti-physician bias that was expressed in John Wesley's own introduction. It is hard to gauge how much such a clearly influential work became identified with and part of the Welsh oral tradition. During the late 19th century the collecting and printing verbatim of folkloric accounts, regardless of where they had come from originally, was the prerequisite of the interested clergyman. It must have been very difficult during the following century for the dedicated folklore researcher or collector of plant lore to disentangle expressed oral healing traditions from the printed versions; and from the overlaying of equally expressive religious concerns.[39]

Initially printed in 1747, *Primitive Physic* was very much a product of the spirit of the time and the religion they preached with its mixture of wild hope and self-help; dissenting against the authority of the established church as much as the orthodoxy of the medical profession with its rigid application of *starving, purging and bleeding* as both a preliminary and final antidote for almost every illness. The credo that Wesley nailed to the church door was the book's subtitle: *An easy and Natural Method of Curing most Diseases.* It may sound rather a mild exhortation now when so many health food stores and alternative living magazines hype such panaceas with the same unproven hope and total conviction as did the Methodist preacher. Thus Culpeper, a century before him, had the subtitle of his *English Physician* stating very clearly that it was a *Compleat Method of Physick* 'whereby a man may preserve his body in health, or cure himself being sick... with such things only as grow in England, they being most fit for English bodies'.

The Welsh translation, from the fifth edition in 1759, found its place alongside the five-shilling family Bible; the Book of Common Prayer; and the yearly almanacs in the hovels of the poorer classes. As the author succinctly put it, 'whoever owned a copy had a physician always in the house and one that attends without fee or reward'. This would have been especially welcome to the mass of the working population. Not only was the town doctor beyond their horizon but if afflicted with serious illness they often could not afford to buy the patient medicines that were always guaranteed to cure all and every disease known to humanity. However more to the point were his comments on the contents: "I have ventured to recommend to men in plain unbiased reason such remedies as air, water, milk, honey, treacle, vinegar and common English herbs with a few foreign medics equally cheap, safe and common". The Welsh book went into many editions during the following half-century indicating its popularity during the height of the Methodist revival.

John Wesley (1703-1793) had been educated and ordained at Oxford. After a spiritual conversion at the age of thirty-five, he felt destined to preach and devote his life's work to those outside the established church. He made two successful tours of Wales and in 1749 married Grace Murray in Builith Wells whilst on his way to preach in Ireland. He was a complex man of his time and with so many beliefs in relation to the healing capacity of 'medicines' that were as wacky and as unpredictable as those of the many so-called health fanatics since. Fashionable and new cures were equally attractive, for he maintained that before they went out of fashion the latest medicines must be given quickly "whilst they are still curing". And rather prophetically added, that "might not electricity then, whatever wonders it can now perform expect soon to share the same fate". He advocated the use of his electric chair for almost

225

everything. He had four made of metal but modelled on the large-backed wooden chair; they were then electrified and placed in chapels at Southwark, Moorfields in Seven Dials at Covent Garden and in the City Road chapel (now a museum) where he set up a dispensary for the poor. He recommended a daily charge of electricity for those suffering from gout, headaches, shingles, disordered feet and blindness, amongst other complaints. The chair was highly regarded as a cure for men's baldness. After rubbing the scalp vigorously with a mixture of honey and onion, the electric charge would make the remaining hair stand up straight. Along with free bars of tar soap and bible readings, such remedies were freely dispensed along with Wesley's dictum that, to be electrified twice daily was a cure for many diseases.[40]

A few Welsh Methodist preachers dabbled in medicinal remedies. Griffith Jones, a preacher from Llanddowror, dispensed them freely to the poor. He may have followed the example of George Winter a farmer who included medicine in his *Compendious System of Husbandry,* noting that he practiced physic on his servants and the poor of the neighbourhood. William Pantycelyn also compounded remedies by consulting *Domestic Medicine* one of the most popular of the anti-physician books of the previous century. William Buchan wrote in his familiar caustic manner that he thought the administration of any medicine was always doubtful and very often dangerous. He would rather teach men how to avoid the necessity of using such poisons. He stressed the importance of diet, hygiene and cleanliness. With its simple remedies, every cottage in Scotland was reputed to have had a copy of Buchan's work, alongside the family Bible.

Stinking Spas and Acrid Waters.

For the Rev. Theophilus Evans staring at the surface of Llanwrtyd well, it was an extremely healthy looking frog that prompted him to throw caution to the winds and quaff the stiff smelling waters. Within a few weeks of regular imbibing he was cured of his scurvy.

Such a recovery might have had miraculous overtones in a previous religious age but in 1732 Evans decided that it was due to the mineral content of the sulphur pools and iron from the chalybeate springs. As the wells became more known and acquired a reputation for their medicinal qualities, it was not long before a bath-house was built; followed by large guest house nearby as well as other popular amenities of the day. From the beginning of the eighteenth century the custom of taking the waters was established in London and at English spas attracting money and rich custom. The growth of Llanwrtyd Wells in Powys was therefore not an isolated event but part of the emerging social pattern which could best be observed at Llandrindod Wells and to a lesser extent at the other spa towns of Llangammarch, Builth, Llandudno, Trefriw and Trelleck. In fact Edward Lhuyd in his 1695 *Additions to Camden's Britannia* noted that the healing wells at Trelleck were 'much frequented and reckoned to cure scurvy, colic and other distempers'. Traditionally there had been nine wells fed by four separate springs and each deemed useful for different complaints. A visitor in 1706 wrote that the Virtuous Wells had been found to be very medicinal — as in the nature of the Tunbridge Wells in Kent — flowing from iron-ore mineral beds. It had a paved open pool with cups for drinking and stone seats that are almost hidden now by the raised floor slabs.

The smallest of the spa towns — Llangammarch Wells — had waters that contained barium chloride which was believed to be helpful for heart and rheumatic ills. The popular story of the well's health-giving capacity was attributed to a sick pig that had jumped into the waters and was completely healed. This is reminiscent of the tale recounted by Geoffrey of Monmouth about the discovery of the healing springs at Bath by diseased swine wallowing in the hot mud. When their minder, the leper son of a legendary king of Britain waded in after, in an attempt to drag them out, he realized that both he and the pigs were cured of leprous sores. The waters at Bath flow from deep within the earth and are said to contain over forty minerals and a high iron content. The Romans lined the pool with large sheets of lead and it was enclosed by a high vaulted roof.

227

They had *saunas* in small heated rooms and a cold plunge pool. The present structure was built in the early Victorian era and the spa provided much the same mixture of physical healing, relaxation, bathing, entertainment and social gossip as it did for the Romans. The three black sulphureous springs at Llanbister parish in Radnorshire were reputed to cure skin disease. Lewis Morris in 1748 wrote that Builth Wells tastes of sulphur and smells like gunpowder. Nevertheless, he maintained, that it was good for distempers and to be drunk for asthma and diseases of the lungs. The Welsh names of Ffynnon Ddrewllyd, Ffynnon Ddrewi and Ffynnon Chwerw refer to the stink and acrid smell of the medicinal wells. When Lewis visited a chalybeate purgative spring in Cardigionshire, he recommended that its mineral water should be drunk "with judgement" implying that some people might imbibe more than was good for them regardless of taste or smell. The 18th century seems to have been a time when people were willing to try anything from laudanum to electricity for an instant cure, however disagreeable the physical consequences. It was also a time of intense competition for the favour of the middle classes. The smaller Welsh spa towns had to compete with the better amenities built at Llandrindod Wells. [41]

It was Beau Nash, the very personable Master of Ceremonies, who helped turn the Pump Room at Bath spa into a centre of high fashion at the beginning of the 18th century. His father was a Swansea tradesman but his mother was related to the Poyer family which helped her son's social aspirations. Such maternal influence seems to have been an important factor in many young Welshmen at this time, like Iolo Morganwg subsequently achieving fame if not fortune. Nash left Jesus College Oxford due to an affair of the heart and joined the army, but as military discipline was not to his liking he began to study law. He then enjoyably filled up his time at the Middle Temple between the occasional legal brief with a series of amorous dalliances. However when invited to become the Master of Ceremonies, after Queen Anne's visit in 1703, he brought Bath spa into social prominence. It was he who persuaded the company to build the Assembly Rooms, a new square and the Pump Room in which he officiated in a tall white hat. Visitors could attend the evening balls for a subscription. Ladies were not permitted to wear their aprons nor gentlemen to carry their swords. The entertainment commenced each evening at seven o clock and ended promptly on the stroke of eleven. A full sized statue of Beau Nash was erected in the Pump Room between the stone heads of Isaac Newton and Alexander Pope. It was said that "wisdom and wit were little seen but folly at full length", borne out after the considerable fortune he had amassed at the tables disappeared when gaming there began to be suppressed in the middle of the century.

The socially established resorts were in London and Bath with the ultra fashionable ones like the Temple of Health in Edinburgh. When James Graham moved to London he opened a Temple with decor that included drapes, mirrors, lights and milk-baths with beautiful girls revealed as goddesses of youth and health. Graham was an impresario of pleasure. The double sized 'Celestial Bed' was said to have cost him more than ten thousand pounds. It had pillars of brilliant glass and if titled to slope backwards was guaranteed to bring on a pregnancy at fifty pounds a time. An ornate magnificent throne which he described as his masterpiece was said to administer mild electric shocks or 'frictions' to the scantily clad clients seated on it. The medical use of electricity was then the latest fad. When popularized by the Temple of Heath it was extensively copied in London. The poet Edward Williams sought relief of his uncontrollable nervous twitching from an "operator in electricity" in Old Compton Street, Soho. In his journal Iolo described how Mr. Long electrified him; drawing sparks from his hands, arms, breast, knees and the rest of his body. He failed to observe if the treatment relieved or accentuated his nervous condition.[42]

The connections between muscular movement and static elctricity were fashionably commonplace through the findings of Volta, a professor at Pavia in Italy. He showed that muscles could be thrown into continuous contraction by successive stimulation which helped create a novel idea of the elixir of life. William Henry (1774-1836) a

Welsh chemist who formulated what was known as Henry's Law, published important literature in medical chemistry on salts, gases, acids and on the theories of the *Excitment of Galvanic Electricity*. In Mary Shelley's novel *Doctor Frankenstein* written in 1818, electricity became the invisible force in living matter that would bring about the regeneration of life as in the creation of the hapless monster.

At the same time the need and fascination with scientific rationalism became focused on the spas and on the nature of healing. Chemists and doctors were employed to analyse the waters of medicinal wells in order to show to what degree each possessed certain chemical properties. After the Rev. Evans, at the Stinking Well Y Ffynnon Ddrawllyd in Llangamarch was cured of scurvy "and very near leprosy till my blood and juices were all tained," its waters were duly examined by one doctor Blenkensop of Abergavenny. Beneath the surface stones there was a stratum of black turf; then one of dark clay mixed with marl; then a bed of gravel from beneath which the waters bubbled up. The whole excavation was only stopped for fear of spoiling the spring and the doctor pronounced its properties to be useful for the scurvy and nephritic or kidney: "for the waters sit easy on the stomach and pass quietly through the patient's kidneys." A prospectus was issued in 1825 concerning the Llanarthney wells in Carmarthenshire after the waters were analytically verified by the Doctors Saunders and Babington under the direction of Sir William Paxton, owner of the estate. Similarly a Doctor Wynn Williams published an account of Ffynnon Cegin in north Wales where he sent his patients to take advantage of the healing waters.

After the hamlet of Llandrindod had built its first hotel in 1749 it grew in size and prosperity in order to accommodate the sixty thousand visitors each year at its peak of popularity. Dr. Dietric Wessel Linder wrote a treatise on the wells setting out the background and the chemical properties of the spa waters. Seven years later in 1758 he published another tract entitled, *An Experiment and Practical Enquiry into the waters of Ffynnon*

Llangybi in Caernofonshire. Its legendary character and register of miracle cures were included as a kind of preface so that the once famed healing well of St. Gybi on the Llyen peninsula was thus proved to possess the proper mineral properties; and after, its owner had a pool and a new stone house built around it. In 1760 Lewis Morris whose interest in medicinal wells is clear from the letters he wrote to the secretary of the Cymmrodorion Society dismissed this pompous book by Dr. Linden probably as it had included some of Morris's own favourable remarks asserting that its Rock Water "was drunk time out of mind to cure ague." Morris described some of the social niceties of the Llandrindod spa. Any kind of fasting was not required as part of the cure; and the custom there allowed people to breakfast, dine and sup as usual on all manner of meat, fowl and fish. The bread — wheat, rye and oat bread — was excellent with milk and butter. It was near to the church and not far away from a public-house fit to entertain the best of company. Not only was there a ballroom, bowling green and billiard tables available but the surrounding countryside was fine for fishing and shooting. The country people spoke English although, as he says, Welsh was more natural to them. When Morris had arrived at the spa he suffered from a cough and asthma; profuse sweats day and night; besides old age and grossness of body which is not surprising given his interest in food. At the end of the six day cure he reported that he felt much better, that he could put on his own shoes and stockings which he had been unable to do for six months and mount his horse without using a horse block which he not been able to do for the previous two years.[43]

The close connection between self-interest and financial profit in extolling the waters of Welsh spa towns continued into the 19th century. The quite unpleasant sulphureous waters of the Stinking Well or Ffynnon Ddrewllyd in Glamorgan required the publicity of prominent prize-fighters to extol its strength-giving potency and to attract the general public there. It showed that the medicinal and social attractions of spa towns were on the wane and even the spread of cheap rail travel that had encouraged visits from the lower middle classes did not help once the fashion for seaside holidays and splashing in naturally clean tidal waters became a cheaper outing for the whole family.

Medicine in Transition

To the medical historian the association between the name of the Myddfai hamlet in Carmarthenshire and the 'birth' of Welsh medicine, may seem as unlikely as the notion that local health care for the poor began with Aneurin Bevan's National Health Act in 1948. Yet both can be viewed as book-ending the period under review. The legend of the Meddygon Mydffai (related in the Introduction) was in fact a mid-Victorian foundation story of native healing. The National Health Act came into being as a consequence of many important social and political changes that had occurred during the previous century; such as the spread of teaching hospitals and medical societies; a more widespread acceptance of 'modern' medicine by the rural population, the rise in education and reading standards among the poor and the recognition of Wales, separate from England with Cardiff as its capital city, that was spearheaded by the newly emergent cultural nationalism of prominent individuals. One such was John Williams, an eminent surgeon and collector of Welsh books and rare manuscripts. His acquisitions would become one of the cornerstones of the newly founded National Library of Wales that was inaugurated in 1907, with him honoured as its first president.[44]

As well as the social and financial divisions between the rich minority and the majority of the monoglot poor living in Wales, a basic problem for the latter in trying to understand the general transmission of medicine through the ages, centered on the language used. The lingua franca of medicine up to the 18th century was Latin. Very gradually English had begun to be used once the Civil Wars ended, and in 1660 the monarchy was reinstated. The Welsh rural society was certainly marginalized and from the Tudor period onwards may have been cut off from the gradual advances made in orthodox medicine by the barrier of the native language they conversed in. The movement of workers to the coal mines and slate quarries during the industrial period and up to the late 19th century displaced countless thousands of families from their once familiar rural environments. The botanical knowledge of cure-alls that had been passed on through generations of rural households was of little use in the vast overcrowded shanty towns that sprawled among the slag heaps of the south Wales valleys. Deprived of the seasonal plants and the known herbs that women had always relied upon for health and family care, expensive and often useless patent medicines were their only recourse as few could afford to visit a doctor. The cholera epidemics and rise of tuberculosis throughout this region is in part a result of what had been lost in home-healing by people having to cope with long hours of hard unremitting work, malnutrition, lack of sanitation and often rudimentary medical care.

During the 16th Century there were spasmodic but frequent outbreaks of the first two of what would become known as the 'big four killer diseases'. In Wales they were smallpox, typhus fever, cholera and tuberculosis. Morris Lewis in a letter to his brother Richard in March 1763 about an outbreak of smallpox in Cardiganshire, wrote that we have a terrible fever here. It kills in four or five days and in my opinion (it is) as fatal as the plague was in London in 1660. There had been an earlier outbreak there in 1759 and during 1723 seventy-one people died of it in Carmarthen. The end of a five year epidemic in 1741 had killed hundreds in many parts of the country. Lewis wrote of a further outbreak in Cardiganshire in 1747 — which presumably was rife elsewhere — that it had caused untold deaths with general destitution among the poor, leaving houses empty to fall quickly into ruin.

The second scourge got its name from the Greek typhos for smoke, with the inflammation and darkening of the face. After the initial headaches, high fevers and delirium, gangrene set in to rot the fingers and toes of the victims. It was often called 'camp fever' for it dogged the vast armies that periodically moved across Europe from the time of the Crusades. It was especially rife in the 16th century killing fourteen thousand French soldiers in a month to end the siege of Naples. In the Balkans during the war against the Turks, the emperor Maximilian was forced into an armistice because many tens of thousands from both armies had died by 1566. It was endemic again during the Thirty Years War. In the following century, typhoid wiped out Napoleon's armies and his aspirations in Russia during the winter of 1812. Other names for the disease were 'ship fever', 'jail fever' and even 'Irish fever'. During the famine years of 1845 to 1848 typhus — rather than hunger — and along with relapsing fever, scurvy and dysentery are now considered to have killed over a million people after the potato crop, a basic food source rotted in the ground. The potato also blighted throughout Britain but it was the poor in rural Wales and in the Scottish Highlands that mostly suffered as a result though nothing on the scale of the devastation in Ireland where it has been estimated that half of the population of eight million died or emigrated to America as a result of the famine.[45]

The 'Cholera Revivals' of 1832 and 1849 in south Wales were stimulated by horrific outbreaks of the disease, especially among the shanty towns that had quickly mushroomed around the coal mines and iron works in the Valleys. The death toll in Merthyr during the second epidemic was seventeen-hundred. In Cardiff it was four-hundred with numbers in between for the dead in many other towns along the industrial heartlands where half the population of Wales lived at this time. Living conditions were appalling. Drinking water — the main carrier of the cholera — was totally polluted. The Noncomformist preachers held massed open air religious revival meetings that played on peoples fears of what to them was an incurable disease. They also held prayer meetings at the mine pit heads before the workers went underground. The fear of sudden death below was as much part of the grim statistics as the cholera above. The Rev Thomas Rees, on his way to a meeting in Beaufort, passed many funerals and saw scores of coffins carried through the streets of Merthyr Tydfil and other towns on his route. The text of his sermon to the fifteen-hundred people standing in a field in front of him was the awful sentence from the Matthew gospel: "How can you escape the damnation of Hell?" Similar open air meetings were held near the lead mines of mid-Wales and by the slate quarries of Blaenau Festiniog, where it has been reckoned that one third of the people of Merionith worked.[46]

The death rate for the country as a whole in the mid-19th century was estimated as 22 per 1000 people but this average figure had many anomalies especially during the cholera outbreaks. The last was in 1866 when two thousand died. In Merthyr the mortality of live births was put at 184 per 1000 of those recorded, but the numbers of stillbirths at this period are unknown. Diptheria, measles and scarlet fever were endemic among the young but it was tuberculosis, with its feverish night sweats and coughing-up of blood that raged in the poverty stricken and over-crowded shanties. It is thought that three thousand young people a year were dying of consumption at this time. Even after the first of the Public Health Acts had been passed few local Councils did much to alleviate the terrible sanitary conditions that had prevailed in the Valleys of South Wales from the earliest industrial mining of coal. In the frontier towns like Methyr there had been a series of colliery disasters, almost every few years, since the 1850's, that killed hundreds of men and boys working underground. The families of the working poor in these shanty towns — and apparently those in rural areas — suffered the cyclic effects of ill health, dismal working conditions, bad housing and almost no sanitation. Susceptibility to ever-recurring epidemics and diseases such as tuberculosis particularly affected children and young adults.

The Public Health legislation of the 1840's and 1850's had been made obligatory on all local authorities. Often it was the very visible suffering from the cholera that brought about some necessary changes. The nausea, vomiting and diarrhoea, internal cramps and a desperate craving for water were symptoms that preceded 'the puckered blue lips in a cadaverous face,' indicating death was near. In a spate of epidemics between 1832 and 1866 thousands had died throughout Wales. The mayor of Caernarfon noted that the disease

235

proved an efficient ally in obtaining a good water supply and effective drainage in the town. Twenty years later in 1886, the local paper smugly declared that the fear of cholera on the Continent had brought many holiday visitors and that its appearance in Italy would induce a few more to come to north Wales. This in fact had been the fifth major pandemic in the 19th century of a disease that had infected all the cities and most of the towns of Western Europe since it first spread from the Indian subcontinent in 1819.[47]

Early in the 18th century, on a stormy day with a weather-eye on the lookout for contraband, a man saw a raft drifting into the cove below Bay Porth yr Hwch, near Carmel Head on Anglesey. He scrambled down the cliff slope and found two small children lying on it. They were taken to a farm called Maes by the church of Llanfair. Neither spoke any English. The girl died soon after but the boy recovered. He was adopted by the childless couple called Thomas. He showed remarkable skill in setting the bones of animals and as a young man he began to treat local people. His son went further afield when his reputation as a healer grew, and his sons followed in a family lineage of bone setters, known in Welsh as *meddygon esgyrn*. They eventually become bone surgeons through to the boy's great-great grandson Sir Robert Jones who opened the first hospital in Britain solely devoted to orthopaedic surgery in the late 19th century.

The unknown Spanish boy was the sole survivor of a ship that went aground and he took the name of the family that had looked after and adopted him. It was his son Evan Thomas (1733-1804) who eventually became known through north Wales for his ability as a bone specialist. His son Richard ap Evan (1771-1851) who was then called Richard Evans had a successful practice as a bone setter but was not so widely known as his own son Evan Thomas (1804-1884) who had an extensive practice in Liverpool in the treatment of bones and joint diseases. His method with chronic disability was long periods of rest thereby reducing the common amputation of limbs and using slow traction or an overhead pulley to reduce dislocations. Evan married Jane Owen of Anglesey, a sister of Dr. Owen Roberts of St. Asaph who would later train all five of his nephews as apprentices prior to entering medical colleges.

Hugh Owen Thomas (1834-1891) the eldest son went to College in London. He qualified as a Member of the Royal College of Surgeons and moved to Paris to study surgery in French hospitals. When he returned to Liverpool he joined his father in practice for a year before setting up on his own. In 1866, H. O. Thomas enlarged one house so that it had two waiting rooms, four consulting rooms, a surgery and a workshop. He converted a second house to a private hospital of eight beds with a trained nurse in charge. He also employed a blacksmith and a leather worker making splints and appliances to his own designs. The clinic with its 'cottage' hospital was unique in Britain and in later years became famous worldwide for its approach to bone surgery and healing of broken limbs. The surgeon himself prided his family background as meddygon esgyrn. The manner in which he devised splints and appliances for injured bones — with his watchwords of rest and alignment — and the meticulous aftercare for his patients meant that he was treating more bone fractures successfully than other specialists. This was prior to the discovery of X-rays. He refused to divulge his methods at scientific meetings so his books did not receive the recognition they deserved. A hard working and private person he was probably closer to his family roots as a folk-healer than to the Victorian society that his university training and original surgical applications seemingly dictated.[48]

It was his nephew Sir Robert Jones (1857-1933) who finally succeeded in bringing those methods to the attention of the surgical profession. The Thomas callipers used to measure the inside and outside diameter of limbs, saved many thousands of lives when it became part of standard medical practice during the Great War. In the family tradition, Robert Jones, after being educated at Sydenham

College in London, trained with his uncle in Liverpool and later he became a Fellow of the Royal College of Surgeons. As Thomas's assistant he received a unique training in orthopaedic surgery. As an established surgeon he held many important posts in the North of England and in 1904 transformed a convalescent home in Salop into a large country orthopaedic hospital, with outlying clinics, the first of its kind in Britain. He became a lecturer at the University of Liverpool and applied his radical teaching methods at a number of hospitals. Knighted in public recognition of his work for the sick and injured, his greatest honour was to be elected as first president of the International Society of Orthopaedic Surgery.

The above manner of individual teaching from one generation to the next was the most characteristic form of Welsh medicine, prior to the introduction of the first general teaching hospitals in the late 19th century. It can be traced back as far as the medieval physicians who taught their sons or nephews the rudiments of the craft of healing in much the same manner that the later pre-modern doctor often began as an apprentice in a local established practice, prior to formal study in the medical schools of London, Dublin or Edinburgh. After qualifying they usually returned home to become partners in the surgery before possibly setting up on their own and they often continued the cycle of family teaching by having some of their younger boy relatives as apprentices. Medicine with all its accepted applications was, and still is, initially an applied craft to be experientially learned by the student and then to be gradually assimilated in terms of professional practice. In this respect the university trained physicians with their necessary cramming of textbook knowledge demanded by the teaching authorities, were in many ways no different from the generally more empirically minded approach of the hereditary healers of the Celtic hinterlands. Many of the Beaton family of doctors from the islands of the Inner Hebrides of Scotland — who are often presented as a model for the medieval physicians of Myddfai — studied in Europe and were employed by the Kings of Scotland. It also was a matter of degree in terms of the expectations by their patients. For both it was an applied art that reflected the higher idealism of their societies. Medicine, often in the form of bleeding, purging and herbs provided a rationale of meanings and explanations in the face of the unexpected intrusion of illness. When disease intervened either in terms of an individual complaint or by affecting large numbers of the dominant social group, the assorted medicines of the time proposed to remedy such disruptions. This can be seen clearly from the death-bed treatments of kings and nobles surrounded by their many physicians. However often in the face of traumatic outbreaks — like the periodic epidemics of the 'big four killer diseases' in many parts of Wales — orthodox medicine proposed remedies but with little cure. This seemed to have been an acceptable solution in a hierarchical class and church-ridden society for in essence each chose for itself a particular approach to healing that was acceptable to both the doctors or physicians and the social group who valued their services and medical ministrations.

Describing himself as a practitioner in physic in his will, Thomas Wynne (1627-1692) is an interesting example of the deviation of the common (father to son or nephew) male hereditary line of the Welsh physicians. Wynne, with other Quaker families in Wales, had a patent for 5000 acres of land in Pennsylvania and sailed with William Penn to America in 1682. Little is known of his early life here except he was born near Caerwys in Flintshire and that he spent six years in a Denbigh prison for his religious beliefs. In one of his pamphlets he wrote that he became apprenticed to a Richard Moore who took him to dissections in Salop that were carried out by the anatomists Dr. Needham and Dr. Hollins. Needham (1631-1691) was the author of *De Formata Foeta*, published in 1667. When he was released from jail Wynnne, "betook himself wholly to the practice of Chyrurgery".[49]

Wynne's eldest daughter Mary married a Dr. Edward Jones from Bala and with sixteen other families they were among the first group of Quakers from the same area who sailed in 1681 to found a new settlement to be called 'Merion' in Pennsylvania. Hugh Roberts, also from Bala, was a member of the deputation who went to

London to discuss with William Penn the formation of the Welsh settlement and the purchase of parcels of land. He led the second group in 1683 that included Thomas Wynne. His grand-daughter Martha, who had been born in Wales, eventually married John Codwalader in 1699 and it was their son Thomas (1708-1779) who became a physician. Their fifth child Evan after an apprenticeship with his father also became a physician. His son John Jones (1729-1791) was to become the famous surgeon and personal friend and physician to both George Washington and Benjamin Franklin. An interesting facet about this interrelated American medical family is that it was first established through the marriage of the eldest daughters, rather than the sons as was usually the case in Wales. This may have been partly due to their Quaker beliefs as much as the hard frontier life such independent women endured in raising and caring for large families.

The mother of John Williams was equally exceptional in bringing up a large family after his father died of typhoid fever when he was two. She managed the farm and helped to educate her eldest daughter and four sons. John, the youngest, was born at Blaenllynant in Carmarthenshire and went to a local school. After attending one in Swansea, John Williams entered Glasgow University in 1857. When returning to Swansea two years later, he became a doctor's apprentice and at twenty-one, began his formal medical studies at the University Hospital in London. A decade later Williams became a Fellow of the Royal College of Physicians; eventually to become a professor of obstetric medicine. It was during his long professional life in London that he acquired a large collection of rare manuscripts and books in Welsh. His long held dream of a National Library for Wales in Wales became a reality when the NLW at Aberystwyth was granted its charter in 1907. Two years later he donated his magnificent collection of books, prints and drawings which included the Rev. Moses Williams complete collection of nearly all the Welsh printed books up to the 18th century. Sir John Williams as he was titled then also donated a complete collection of the Peniarth manuscripts he had acquired after the death of Owen Wynne. The unique set of coloured illustrations from a Welsh law book known as *Peniarth 28*, with the Latin text of the law of Hywel shows the king on his throne holding a sceptre. The other illustrations depict some of the twenty-four court officials and various aspects of medieval life that related to the various sections of the laws. Williams was the first President of the National Library and continued his generous support until he died, helping to make the library the repository of Welsh literature and printed culture that it has become a century after its charter.[50]

ACKNOWLEDGEMENTS

The work here has evolved through different aspects and changes over many years so I am grateful to the editors and readers whose comments and opinions helped me through its numerous re-workings. Writing in English of orthodox and popular Welsh medicine on a canvas of dark social history; the work of Dr. J. H. Cule MBE, biographer and medical historian, has been a constant inspiration. His numerous writings and especially the two books *Wales and Medicine* gave me courage to persist with this study. I am especially indebted to Derek Bryce of Llanerch Press for the time and attention he has spent in helping to bring it to fruition. I add a special thank you to Mary Lloyd Jones for use of her painting 'Swyn' on the cover; to Sarah Sharp who turned an untidy manuscript into a coherent form and to Gareth Evans of the National Botanic Garden of Wales for his reflections on plant botany.

Some different versions of texts were originally published in *Pembrokeshire Life* and in *Country Quest* magazines; acknowledgements to both editors; and for permissions from Macmillan & Co. and Abner Stein Literary Agents for the poem by Rainer Maria Rilke; from Francis Boutle Publishers of *The Turn of the Ermine* for the words of Iannik Kokard, by J. Gibson & G. Griffith; from Profile Books Ltd, in association with the Welcome Library, for *Alchemical notes by John Dee* in *Cures & Curiosities* edited by Tony Gould; from Heart of Albion Press for Maelgwn's Death' in *Taliesin's Travels* by Michael Dames; from the University of Wales Press for a poem by Ceri Davies in his *Welsh Literature and the Classical Tradition*; from Melinda Gray of the North American Journal of Welsh Studies for Welsh and English versions of the cunning man of Cwrt y Cadno by R.C. Allen in *Wizards or Charlatens - Doctors or Herbalists;* from *Alchemy* edited by R. Grossinger, Richmond, USA for the work of Edward Kelly and Thomas Vaughan; and from Derek Bryce for the inclusion of the original Latin and Welsh plant list in the 1861 edition of The Physicans of Myddfai.

BIBLIOGRAPHY AND NOTES.

Select Bibliography. (The notes include additional references).

Bannerman, J. *The Beatons,* Edinburgh, 1986.

Beith, M. *Healing Threads, Traditional Medicines of the Highlands,* Edinburgh, 1995.

Cule, J.H. *Wales & Medicine,* Aberystwyth 1980.

Cule, J.H. *Wales & Medicine,* Llandyssul, 1975.

Davies, L.T. & Edwards, A. *Welsh Life in 18th century Wales,* London, 1939.

Fleetwood, J. *A History of Medicine in Ireland*, Dublin, 1953.

Griggs, B. *Green Pharmacy*, London 1981.

Gould, T. *Cures & Curiosities (inside the Welcome Library),* London 2007.

Hoffmann, D. *Welsh Herbal Medicine*, Abercastle. 1998.

Jarman, A.O.H. & Jarman, E. *The Welsh Gypsies*, Cardiff. 1991.

Jenkins, G.H. *A Rattleskull Genius, (lolo Morganwg)* Cardiff, 2005

Jones, Dewi. *The Botanists & Guides of Snowdonia*, Llanrwst, 1996.

Jones,T.L. & Jones, D.W. *Cancer Curers - or Quacks*, Llandyssul, 1993.

Lynch, F. *The Holy Wells of Wales,* Cardiff, 1954.

Pavord, A. *The Naming of Names, Order in a World of Plants*, London, 2005.

Porter, R. *The Greatest Benefit to Mankind, A Medical History of Humanity,* London. 1995.

Rawcliffe, C. *Medicine & Society in Later Medieval England,* Stroud, 1995.

Singer, C. *From Magic to Science*, (Dover paperback) NY. 1958.

Williams, J. *The Physicians of Myddfai*, (reprint of *Meddygon Myddfai*) Lampeter, circa 1990.

Ziegler, P. The Black Death (paperback) Stroud, 1997.

243

NOTES

The Medicine Tree

1. The discovery of the 'Red Lady of Paviland' and the subsequent revaluation of the findings in Goat's Hole Cave on the Gower peninsula, with the growing acceptance and popularity of the natural sciences of geology and early archaeology through the late 19th century are set out in: A. Schnapp, *The Discovery of Archaeology,* London, 1993; W. Hughes, *Prehistoric Sites of the Gower & West Glamorgan,* Little Logaston, 1999; S. Aldhouse-Green, *Palaeolithic & Mesolithic Wales,* in F. Lynch(ed*) Prehistoric Wales*, Stroud, 2000; J. Sharkey, *The Meeting of the Tracks, Rock Art in Ancient Wales,* Llanrwst, 2004.
The National Museum of Wales in Cardiff has recently opened a new exhibition called *Origins of Welsh Culture* which has a red skeleton in a glass case on show with their collection of art and archaeological artifacts.

2. J.H. Wilks, *Trees of the British Isles in History and Legend,* London 1972.
W. Linnard, *Welsh Woods and Forests.* A History, Llandyssul, 2000.

3. G. Dimbleby, *Plants and Archaeology,* London 1978.
D. Yalden, *The History of British Mammals,* London.1999.

4. I.M. Stead, J.B. Bourne, & D. Brothwell, *Lindow Man. The Body in the Bog,* London. 1986.

5. R. Rudgely, *Lost Civilizations of the Stone Age,* London 1996.

6. Rev. J.Williams (ed), *The Physicians of Myddfai,* Llandovery. 1861.

244

7. Sir J. Rhys, *Celtic Folklore,* Oxford 1901.

Some interesting versions of the Lake Legend were collected by John Rhys during the late 19th century. However he failed to verify the story when he visited Myddfai in 1880.

Last summer I went to the village to see if I could pick up any variants of the legend, but I was hardly successful; for though several of the farmers I questioned could repeat bits of the legend, including the Lake Lady's call to her cattle as she went away, I got nothing new except that one of the them said that the youth, when he first saw her at a distance, thought she was a goose — he did not even rise to the conception of a swan — but that by degrees he approached her, and discovered she was a lady in white, and that in due time they were married, and so on.

A version that Rhys failed to include in his book, had been collected earlier by Richard Fenton, the Pembrokeshire historian: 'I heard from an old woman about the origins of the Meddygon Myddfai, that when the first of that family was fishing in the lake he heard a voice from the deep desiring him to bait his hook with bread. When he did so he hooked a girl who came out of the water with six cows and was married to the physician; and that after the three careless blows she left him to return to the waters'.

From the *Notebooks of R. Fenton (1727-1821)* edited by John Fisher in M.E. Owen, *Addendum to Studia Celtica, Meddygon Myddfai.* 1981/82.

A story by Wirt Sikes printed in the Cambro-Briton, vol 2, 1881, was included in D. Parry-Jones' *Welsh Legends & Fairy Lore,* 1992.

'The young man is said to have bought some lambs in a neighbouring fair and taken them to graze near Llyn y Fan Fach, out from which, whenever he visited the lambs, three beautiful maidens appeared to him. He tried to catch them but they always reached the lake before him. From the security of which they taunted him: *Cras dy Fara, Anhawdd ein dala.* Your bread is dry (or hard baked). It is not easy to catch us. After he had eaten some moist bread which they had sent ashore, he chased them again and managed to catch one to his great delight. Their subsequent talk moved at a rapid pace and before he knew it was over, he had proposed and she had accepted, if on the following day he could distinguish her from her sisters'. The account followed the well known version, except that the three light blows were given on one and same occasion, and were sufficient to break the marriage contract. She returned to the lake with her cattle, seven cows, two oxen and one bull.

Two accounts sent to Rhys by A.G. Edwards Warden of the Welsh College and Llymarch Reynolds of Merthyr Tydfil were included in his Celtic Folklore. 'An eighty year old woman from Myddfai remembers thousands and thousands of people visiting the Lake of the Little Van on the first Sunday or Monday in August and (that) when she was young she often heard old men declare that at the time a commotion took place in the lake; and that its waters boiled which she took to herald the approach of the Lake Lady and her oxen'. This was corroborated by a Mr. Joseph of Brecon who said (that) 'on the first Sunday of August, Llyn y Fan Fach is supposed to be boiling (berwi). I have seen scores of people going to see it on that day. I don't remember if any of them expected to see the Lady of the Lake. As to the boiling of the water I have nothing to say, and am not sure if there is anything in the statement of an old fisher-woman from Llandovery that the best time for eels is in August when the north east wind blows on the lake and makes huge waves on it. The eels can be seen floating on the water.' 'I have just heard a sequel to the Myddfai story, got from a rustic on Mynyd y Branwen, to the effect that after the disappearance of the frown (the damsel) into the lake, the disconsolate husband and his friends set to work to drain it in order to get her back if possible. They made a great cutting into the bank when suddenly a large hairy monster of hideous aspect emerged from the water and stormed at them for disturbing it and wound up with this threat — *Os na cha'I lonyd yn ym tle, Fifoda dre' Bryhondu.* I shall destroy the town of Brecon if I get no quiet in this place'.

8. In the *News from the Net* in *Archaeology Ireland,* Spring 2006 was a report from the BBC of a Bronze Age burial on the Black Mountain in Carmarthenshire in which archaeologists found evidence for the use of flowers in funeral ceremonies. The remains of a child aged about twelve were found in a cist together with the burnt bones of two pigs and perhaps a dog. Pollen tests from the site showed that the burial was accompanied by floral tributes of meadow sweet. The excavation on Fan Foel, above Llyn y Fan Fach, the lake site of the above legends, was carried out by the Llandeilo-based Cambria Archaeology.

Their findings, according to Adam Gwilt of the National Museum of Wales, 'give tenderness to otherwise remote and impersonal burial rites'.

B. Griggs, *Green Pharmacy, A History of Herbal Medicine,* London 1981. In her opening sentence she states that grains of flower pollens were found thickly scattered in the soil around the bones of a Neanderthal in a cave in Iraq. Family and friends of the dead man had surrounded his body with clusters of flowers. Analysed some 60,000 years later, the pollens were identified as from eight different genera of flowering plants, all of which flourish in the woods and fields of Shanidar to this day.

Part One. The Dark Ages and Beyond.

A great pestilence broke out, known as Y Fad Felin,
                              'The Yellow Plague.'
In this instance, History reared its head, 'either as a basilisk,
                              or under the form of a fair woman'.
She was a 'strange creature' from Morfa Rhianedd.
Fearing for his life, Maelgwn fled to St. Mary's church at
                              Llanrhos, a mile from Deganwy.
In the last resort, it was the mother of Christ to whom he
                              turned for help.
She could not touch him. However curiosity led him to peer
                              out through the keyhole of the church door,
Whereupon he was fatally contaminated.

Maelgwn's death by Michael Dames.

Chapter 1. Popular Roman Medicine

1. C. Singer, *From Magic to Science, Essays on the Scientific Twilight.* N.Y. 1968. Generally considered the greatest medical historian of the 20th century; his seven scholarly papers range from *Science under the Roman Empire* to *The Visions of Hildegard of Bingen.*

2. Sconocchia (ed), *Scribonius Largus, Compositiones,* Leipsig. 1983.
B. Jackson, *From Papyri to Phamocopocia,* in F.N.L. Poynter, (ed) *The Evolution of Pharmacy in Britain. London.* 1990.
Scribonius was probably a Greek freed-man and military doctor. His work is thought to have been produced as a handbook of medicine for the military expedition to Britain. It included a large number of prescriptions based on herbal remedies, with several ingredients such as opium poppy and ginger root which would not have been available in Britain. The book gives detailed instances of

248

the storage of such drugs and specifies the various containers designed to preserve their effectiveness. He divided the 250 receipts of his *Compositiones* into symptom and therapy. The formulae for remedies were grouped according to disease and ailments for which they were to be used, many of which the author had tested on himself so the virtues of them had been vouched for by his personal findings. The simples preparations are described first, then the more complex ones. The ingredients he used were largely of herbal origin such as leaves, roots, gums, oils and resins; though minerals like alum and copper salts were included, in addition to animal substances like fat, honey, wax and blood. His theriacs and antibodies were formidable. Theriac primi was for bites of serpents, for ictus afflatus etc. An antidote of Mithriadac was composed of thirty ingredients. Fern roots and santonicas were to be used against infestations of worms; plaisters and ointments contained sulphar salts for wound infections. Galen, a century later, made use of some of the formulae of Scribonius.

J.S. Hamilton, *Scribonius Largus on the Medical Profession,* Bull. Hist. Med. 60, 1986.

The *Seplasiarii* became established in Britain after the legions left. Drug sellers and unguent makers, as on the general stamps of the ocularii, used their own named preparations. The stamp of Caius Sylvius, Tetrious a lotion for inflammation of the eyes, was found in the excavations of the City of London.

3. K.V. Smith, *The Illustrated Earth Garden Herbal, A Herbal Companion,* London, 1979.

The oldest illustrated example of the Dioscorides herbal known as the *Codex Vindobonesis* was written in the 6th century. It was seen by a Sicilian traveller in Constantinople twenty years after the city fell to the Turks and nearly a hundred years later it was offered to a Flemish scholar at the court of Sultan Suleiman the Magnificent, for 100 ducats. In 1570 it was in the Imperial Library of Vienna. Some of the leading libraries of Europe, Australia and America have later illustrated versions of the Dioscorides. The 10th century one in the

249

Pierpont Morgan Library in New York is thought to be, in part, a copy of the *Codex* or even from the same source. Many translations of the herbal still exist, including an Arabic one and an English hand-written version with a parallel Greek text done by John Goodyer in the mid-16th century. It remained at Magdalen College, Oxford until it was edited and published by John Gunther who included in it some black & white versions of the original Codex illustrations.

4. J.D. Comrie, *History of Scottish Medicine,* London 1932.

In relation to the influence of Scottish medicine in medieval Europe especially that of the wizard and astrologer Michael Scot who was personal physician to Frederick II, he quotes one of his *experimenta*: Take opium thebacci (?), mandragora bark and henbane root...pound them together and mix with cold water... (a recipe) if you wish to sew or cut a man, dip a cloth in this and put it on his forehead and nostrils, and he will swiftly sleep so deeply that you may do what you wish (with the patient). Frederick too, had a *curiositas* on the subject of surgery. The Emperor cut off a notary's thumb because he did not spell his name how he wished as 'Fridericus' rather than 'Fredericus'. On another occasion, he fed two men most excellently at dinner. One he sent to sleep and the other to hunt. The next evening he had them disembowelled in his presence as he wished to know which of the two had digested the meal better. It was judged by Scot, his physician, that he who slept had enjoyed the best digestion! He also tried a similar outlandish joke on Scot himself who after computing the distance between the top of the palace and the heavens found a discrepancy in a similar calculation he made months earlier. Frederick who had had the building lowered in his absence, was delighted, and called him a 'true astrologer'. In 1217 he had been a translator in the Arabic tongue at Toledo, a centre of study his contemporaries associated with dubious activities; and especially after Frederick had been excommunicated by the Pope; many stories of Scot's devilish activities became current after his death, such as after the magic contest with Roger Bacon he flew to Rome with snow on his hat, to prove the point. In the sphere of 'philosophy' he was usually styled as Master Michael Scot.

5. C. Barker, *More Mysterious Wales*, London. 1987.
The stone of Melus is illustrated on page 94; Bedd Porius on page 99; the Carusius Stone on page 111; Llanrhidian Church (leper) Stone on page 109.
V.E. Nash-Williams, *The Early Christian Monuments of Wales*, Cardiff, 1950.

6. J. Sharkey, *Celtic High Crosses of Wales*, Llanrwst, 1998.
M. Dames, *Taliesin's Travels*, Loughborough, 2006. In this mythic poet's travelogue, Gildas is described vilifying Maelgwn as, 'the first in mischief, exceeding many in power and also in malice; licentious in sinning (and) drenched in the wine of Sodom'.

7. J.H. Cule, *Pestis Flavia*, in Cule, J.H. (ed*)* *Wales and Medicine*, Llandyssul, 1983.

8. J. Knight, *Penmachno Revisited: the Consular Inscription and its context.* CMCS Aberystwyth. In May 1915, Mr. Pritchard of the R.C.A.H.W. had recorded three early Christian inscribed stones in the church. He noticed a fourth built into the garden wall of the Eagles Hotel at Penmachno and made a preliminary note of it. A longer account by Sir John Rhys was printed in Archaeologia Cambrensis which was to be his final contribution to early Welsh epigraphy, for he died later that same year. The slatey stone had split down the centre leaving a vertical text of FILI AVITORI, and probably preceeded by 'here lies'. Beneath it was an incomplete three line horizontal inscription that he suggested as: 'in the time of Justinus the Consul'. This reading was confirmed by Nash-Williams, a later authority of Welsh stone inscriptions, and since Justinius was western Consul in 540, declared that the stone was carved in the same year. Ignoring Rhys's reservations on the issue, this stone became the dated benchmark for all early Christian carvings in

Wales as being the only one with reference to a Roman ruler. Knight points out that the text 'in the time of' makes little sense as it stands; meaningless except as a form of a casual griffito. Equally important for him were the inscription's Gallic parallels on other stones which show the trading connections between the Continent and the western area of Britain, especially the early Chi Rho monogram of the Carausius stone, now in Penmachno church.

D. Keys, *Catastrophe,* London, 1999. The evidence from natural causes, plague and famine early in the 6th century is presented as the 'catastrophe' which was a major factor in finally bringing the old world to a close and helping to lay the geo-political foundations of the modern one. In the years 435/436 John of Ephesus described the sun growing darker at Constantinople and continued so for eighteen months. 'Every day it shone for about four hours as a feeble shadow'. A decade later he described the devastating effects of the plague when hundreds of thousands of people died and massed graves were dug into a high hill outside the city. From recorded evidence here the Justinian epidemic may have been carried into western Britain in vessels from the eastern Mediterranean, plying wine and fine table ware. The main entry points at this period, as modern excavations have revealed, were at Tintagel on the north Cornish coast, at Cadbury Congresbury on the River Yeo two miles from the Bristol Channel, at Dinas Powys on the south Wales coast and at Port Madoc. Ten miles to the north was the royal citadel of Dinas Emrys where fragments of a wine amphora and a plate decorated with a Chi Rho symbol were found. Deganwy, the fortified centre associated with Maelgwn on the coast of north Wales, as with the other named sites appeared to have became totally depopulated later in the same century.

9. M. Braillie, *Exodus to Arthur: Catastrophic Encounters with Comets,* London 1999.

The Professor of palaeoecology at Queen's Universty in Belfast had already suggested the same scenario as the dimming of the sun; the Justinian plague; famine and death in the Annals of Wales and

Ireland; earthquakes and inundations of the sea; not only as the beginnings of the Dark Ages but their probable cause. He cites the evidence of tree rings and ice cores to show the effects of climatic change then. Beginning with the dates for the death of Arthur around 540, the myth of the sky sun god and the idea of the 'wasteland'; he suggests a resemblance to the events at the biblical Exodus. He lists the possible causes of such catastrophic change such as earthquakes and geological occurances but suggests that it was due to fragments from a comet passing close to earth. 'A cometary bombardment, not a full-blown comet because we would- n't be here if we'd had that'.

10. P.J. Casey & B. Hoffmann, *Roman Temple Excavations*, Lydney Park, Glos. The Antiquaries Journal, 1981.

Mortimer Wheeler excavated the Temple of Nodens and the associated buildings; a Bath House he called an abation and a courtyard building he identified as a Guest House in 1928/29. The ramparts of an Iron Age hill fort in which the Temple was set were established. There was also a lead mining operation beneath it and a settlement of a group of huts that preceded the conversion of the site to religious use. Based on the re-examination of the published data and the numismatic evidence, their dating was earlier than Wheeler's, suggesting that the religious buildings were from the second half of the 3rd century, with some refurbishment in the following one. The owner of the Lydney Park estate had carried out large scale explorations beginning in 1805 and discovered a series of mosaics and a significant number of coins. The site was tidied up with new surfaces laid and made presentable for visitors. His son then continued the ad hoc excavations and added to the material from the Temple site that was preserved on the estate.

11. T. Wright, & H. Johnson, *Excavations at Wroxeter*, Arch Camb 1859. A stamp of a Roman physician of Uniconium named Tiberius Claudius marked his eye salve or dialibanum, for all complaints of the eyes, to be beaten with the yolk of egg before use. It was found

at Wroxeter in 1808 and a very inaccurate copy was made at the time for the *Gentleman's Magazine*. It then disappeared but according to the authors of this note, it was found to be in the possession of a farmer from whom it was purchased and then presented to the Wroxeter Museum. The sheet gold eyes, 6cm across, found in the excavations of this Romano-British site, are also in the museum.

12. M.W.C. Hassall, & R.S.O. Tomlon, *Roman Chester*, Britannia Vol. VIII 1977. The die was discovered below the Weights and Measures office car-port in Gross Street, Chester in 1973. The report in the journal specifically states that it was found in a *post-Roman context.* (This would certainly help to bring the dates of Martinus of Chester and the father of Melus, closer together.) The stamp was made of green mudstone and the four faces measure roughly thirty nine by nine millimetres thick. The texts were cut retrograde.

Q -IVLMARTI / NISTACTVM, Q (uinti) Iul (ii) Martini stactum Q- IVLMARTIN / DIAPSO[RICVM], Q(uinti) Iul(ii) Martin(i) Diapsoricum.
Q- IVLMARTI / NIPENICILLI, Q(uinti) Iul(ii) Marti(ni) penicilli.
Q- IVLMARTIN / CROCADASPRI,Q(uinti) Iul(ii) Martin(i) croc(odes) adaspri(tudinem).

The patent medicines, prepared and presumably available in a small container ready to be stamped with the correct facet of the die, were *stractum* an unguent or ointment; *diapsoricum* an anti-irritant; *penicilli* referred to ointments; and *crododes ad aspiritudinem* a saffron salve for soreness (of the eyes).

13. C.Singer, *From Magic to Science* (ibid*)*.
Bede, *A History of the English Church and People,* London. 1955.
The Venerable Bede of Wearmouth monastery in Northumbria completed his best known work around 731. The title indicates its

focus and scope. Angles, Jutes and Saxons had moved into England from the end of the Roman period. By his time they had established themselves throughout the whole of eastern Britain from the Isle of Wight to the Firth of Forth with the Mercians in the Midlands. After the arrival of Augustus in 579, the Christian faith gradually replaced Teutonic paganism to become the established religion under royal patronage. It was almost as if Bede were setting out a literary framework in which the beliefs of the former Germanic heathens would be restated in Christian terms in a new land they had recently claimed as their own! He makes little note of their pagan past, or indeed their racial affinities; nor of the Anglo-Saxon destruction wrought upon the Celtic indigenous tribes during the period when they re-populated the whole of eastern England; a gradual incursion over centuries that probably began with the Romans bringing them in as Fedaerati; an intrusion that was generally completed by the 8th century; Bede (673-735) asserts that four different peoples inhabit the Isles of Britain — Irish, Picts, British and the English.

The English church with its stone buildings, illuminated books, Latin liturgy and European outlook had helped to weld these various peoples together to become known to history as the Anglo-Saxons with a common language and identity. It is interesting to note that at the Council of Whitby, held in the presence of Edwin, the Anglo-Saxon king, the religious debate about the dating of Easter — with its underlining agenda of the century old Irish missionary incursion from Iona into England — was conducted in English rather than Latin, the lingua franca of Christian Europe. It enabled Bishop Wilfred to converse in his native tongue, referring to the Irish Church with its antiquated customs as in 'one remote corner of the most remote island'; while the discourse of the Irish abbot Colman of Lindesfarne was translated by the Anglo-Saxon Bishop Cedda.

14 H. Williams, *The Lorica of Gildas*, Y Cymmrodor (Record Series No 111). Known as the *Book of Cerne*, this 8th century version is the earliest of six manuscript texts. The slightly later BL Harley ms 2965A is in Charles Singer's *From Magic to Science*. A late 10th

century version in BL Harley ms 585, by O. Cockayne, was set in the midst of an Anglo-Saxon receipt book known as the *Lacnunga*.

Most texts associate the introduction of the charm-prayer of Gillus or Gildas into Ireland with Laidcend, the son of Beath the Victorius. In a 14th century manuscript *Leathar Breac* or the Speckled Book, he was handed the *Lorica prayer* by Gildas who had brought it over to Ireland and placed it (as a gift) on the altar of Patrick the Bishop, probably at Armagh where his principal church was located. The opening lines of the *Lorica* states that Gildas composed it to expel demons that beset him, 'so that the plague of this year may take me not with it.' This may be a reference to the bubonic epidemic or the yellow plague (of the native scribes) in which hundreds of the saints of Ireland and Wales died. However if the date of Laidcend's death in the Irish Annals for the year 661 is correct it could be the later epidemic that occurred there around this time.

15. O. Cockayne, *Leechdoms, Wortcunning and Starcraft of Early England,* (3 vols) London 1864.

There were a number of different English translations of the Lorica that became incorporated into the general framework of Anglo-Saxon medicine. Its demotic linguistic form, favoured by Irish and British monks, was based on the writings of Isidore archbishop of Seville (c.560-636). A Hisperic Latin text was bound into the *Lacnunga* manuscript and is dated to the 11th century. According to Singer, who researched the genesis of the manuscript, a number of Roman remedies from the *Herbal* of Pseudo-Apuleius were written down much earlier by a leech (physician) who grouped them in a common plan from the head down to the rest of the body; but it was incomplete. A second leech added the *Lay of the Nine Twigs of Woden,* relating how diseases arose in the world. At a later date the collection came into the hands of a third compiler, probably in a Northumbrian monastery, who added the *Lorica of Gildas*. However confusion set in when the manuscript was rebound though the major contributions remained in recognizable sets. This was later copied by a scribe early in the 11th century who added yet more material and the manuscript recorded by the Rev. Cockayne is now in the British Library collection (Harley ms 585).

16. Whether the English material contained in his three volumes, reflect their contemporary medical practices or were a compendium of old Teutonic magic and beliefs overlaid with a Christian gloss, is now impossible to establish. Yet much of the written material is exotic, colourful and magically evocative as in the charm: 'twig runes do ken/if thou a leech will be/ and ken to see'. Medical scholars such as Charles Singer, William Bonsor, John Payne and other specialists in early English medicine, have attempted to abridge it within their own particular perspectives. Singer for instance in *From Magic to Science* focused on its historical roots and described their healing practices under three broad headings. The first was their use of charm magic, incantations and auguries. Secondly herb healing based on a limited understanding of ancient Greek texts that were written into Latin. Healing was usually carried out in conjunction with folk charms or Christian prayers such as the *Lorica of Gildas*. And thirdly, their collection of magical remedies and Teutonic lore to ward off malign spirits and the poisonous elf-shot. This could, in turn, affect other parts of the body by way of contagious venum. A good example of this was the *Lay of the Nine Herbs*, describing how diseases arose in this world. Its inclusion of the many coloured venum, winds and breath as part of the healing process is mirrored in North American shamanism. R. Grossinger, *Planet Medicine, From Stone Age Shamansm to Post-Industrial healing*, N.Y. 1980. For their ritual connection between the ground and the heavens: R.A. Williamson, *Living the Sky, the Cosmos of the American Indian*, USA. 1989.

17. The contents of the charms were arranged by *J. Payne, English Medicine in Anglo-Saxon Times, Oxford 1914,* under the following headings to give some indication of their origins and derivations. It is interesting in relation to the variety of medical charms in Wales,

recorded or written much later: (1) The prayers, invocations or other verbal formulae addressed to the plants. The special observances used when gathering herbs or other natural remedies. (2) Prayers and mystical words chanted over the patient. These were written down sometimes in an unknown language and often applied to some part of the body as an amulet. (3) Direct conjurations or exorcisms addressed to disease as if it were a living entity. (4) Narrative charms as anecdotes relating to sacred and legendary people who had similarly suffered or did something analogous to what the patient might be suffering from. (5) Material magic. The attribution of magical powers to certain objects that were then fixed to some part of the body as an amulet or periapt hung around the neck. (6) The transference of disorder by a verbal formula or a ceremony to some animal or natural object or in some fashion to the outside world, as shown in the cover painting 'Swyn' by Mary Lloyd Jones.

The charm cures in Welsh folk medicine were often used by way of transference to trees, snails and as written amulets to be hung on cattle to counteract disease. Such methods of healing seem to have been a common rural practice throughout Britain until fairly recently. It may also indicate a continuity of the universal transference of human illness onto the natural world, from prehistoric times. Perhaps it may have been suggested by the anthropomorphic likeness of *faces* in tree trunks and *heads* in natural rock formations. Or even from the suggestive female figurations of earth goddesses in curved hills and mountains of Scotland. O. Swire, *Highland Tales, 1966.*

A common word in western Scotland for such a rounded hill was *mam*, as in Welsh, which was also generally used for mother, breast and by association any kind of round lump on the human body. A healing procedure for removing such a swelling was carried out in the 19th century in Glenelg. The swelling was divided into three imaginary sections. A basin of spring water was set close by for a needle and axe to be dipped into it. The needle was first pricked (without breaking the skin) against each of the three parts. Then the axe was brought down as if to drive the needle into the body with great force but at the last moment was diverted into a piece of wood. Whilst striking the blow, an old woman recited an appropriate hymn that named three rounded hills on the old road to Glenelg. "Be this strike upon the Mam of Pomhaillear in the name of the Father of the Son and the Holy Ghost." The people in the room replied. "Amen. Thy pain be in the ground. Thy pain be in the earth. Amen." This refrain was repeated with the second strike on the Mam of Gleann Eilg and the third strike of the axe on the Mam of Ratagon.

Chapter 2. Riders of the Apocapalypse

18. C. Rawcliffe, *Medicine & Society in later Medieval England.* London, 1999.

19. J. H. Cule, *Pestis flava: y fad felen*, in J. H. Cule (ed) *Wales & Medicine*, (ibid)

20. K. Nicholls, *Gaelic and Gaelicised Ireland in the Middle Ages,* Dublin, 1972.

21. C. Creighton, *A History of Epidemics*, London, 1891.

22. M. Richter, *William ap Rhys, Wiliam de Braose and the Lordship of Gower,* Studia Celtica XXX11. 1988.

This account of the events leading to the canonization of Thomas Cantilupe, formally Archbishop of Hereford was translated from a Latin text. It concerned the execution of a Welsh nobleman who had died on the gallows but was brought back to life by the intersession of the saint. Both the wife of the lord and the victim had prayed to the saint and Rhys was subsequently allowed to live when she interceded with de Braose on his behalf. Rhys was the leader of an assault on the Lord of Gower, and de Broase in 1289 insisted that he be hanged by his own relatives and friends who were surrounded by mounted warriors. The Papal Commission of 1307 questioned nine people concerning the case and specified the language used by

259

each of them in Latin, French, English and Welsh. This strange account, which could be the central scenario of a historical novel, was part of the evidence of miracles brought about by Thomas Cantilupe, collected by the commission for a possible canonization which was duly done soon afterwards.

23. Recent publications with their graphic titles include:

S. Scott, & C. Duncan, Return of the Black Death: *The World's Greatest Serial Killer*, Chichester, 2004. O. Benedictow, *The Black Death 1346-1353: The Complete History*, Woodbridge, 2004. J. Kelly, *The Great Mortality: An Intimate History of the Black Death*, London, 2005. W. Naphy & A Spicer, *The Black Death 1334-1730*, Stroud, 2000. W. Rosen, *Justinian's Flea: Plague, Empire and the Birth of Europe*, London 2007. The 'flea' was first studied using handmade microscopes by van Leuenhoek in the 1660s. His discovery of *animancules* or micro-organisms was a scientific turning point in modern medicine.

24. P. Zeigler, *The Black Death*, Stroud. 1997.

25. R.A. Griffiths, *The Interaction of war and plague in the later Middle Ages*, & G.P. Jones, *The Welsh poet as medical historian*, in J. Cule (ed) *Wales and Medicine*,(ibid).

26. J. Phillimore, *Leprosy*, Archaeologica Cambrensis, 1920.

G.P. Jones, Some Aspects of the Medical History of Denbighshire, Trans. Denbigh Hist.Soc. 1950.

'The prevalence of Leprosy here in the Middle Ages has been exaggerated. It is probable that such places as the *Terra Leprosorum* in Wrexham and the *Werglodh y Kleivion* in the Sorum in Wrexham were not more than a few acres of land endowed by the church for the benefit of the lame, the blind and the feeble. Similarly the *Dunlasau (Ty Lasar)* near Penmachno was a lazer-house for the relief of the *paupers Christi*. The designation *Leprosus* included a variety of diseases. Likewise the synonymous term *clafr* in Welsh was not specific to any disease, 'and that the ritual expulsion of lepers from society hardly ever occurred here in Wales'.

A *domus leprosum* of St. Mary Magdalene was built by the east gate of Cardiff town. It was a house providing beds for 'twenty-four leprous persons, poor and feeble'. Rees, *History of Cardiff*, 1969.

27. *G. Owen, (ed) H. Owen, The Description of Pembrokeshire, 1892.*

In *The Itinerary Through Wales* Gerald refers to the only legitimate prince of a Welsh lord who lost his inheritance because of a facial defect. He was named Iorwert Dryndwn which meant flat nose. As one rotted away by disease rather than broken in a fight, it would seem more in keeping with the ancient taboo against physical defect in a ruler. A similar assumption of leprosy may underlie an inscription on a small stone called *Bedd Porius* near Trawsfynydd in Gwynedd. Dated to the 7th century it was inscribed in Roman capitals to read, *Porius lies here in the mound.* The line below has PLANVS FVIT, he was a plain man. There has been debate in scholarly circles about the first word which may mean flat face or a leper who had lost his nose. The fact that the find-spot is far from a church added to the leprous interpretation. However Edward Lhuyd who made a record of the stone in 1696 wrote PIANUS; but it has been suggested that due to a break in the word Porius, he may have been described as a Christian. The original stone is in the National Museum in Cardiff and a cast now marks its find spot.

28. E.M. Murphy & K. Manchester, *Be Thou Dead to the World: Leprosy in Ireland*, Archaeology Ireland, Vol.12 No 1 Issue No 43, Spring 1998. Idem, — *Evidence for Leprosy in Medieval Ireland, Leprosy past and Present*, Proc. 3rd International Congress on the Evolution and Palaeopidemiology of Infectious diseases. In C.A. Roberts (ed) Bar International Series, Oxford Archaeo-press, 2004. The evidence for leprosy in Ireland, as in Wales, is mainly restricted

to historical accounts and the occurrence of place-names which may have been derived from *lobhar,* an Irish word for leper. In addition, in Ireland, research has indicated that at least fifty leprosaria would have existed during the medieval period, mainly in Munster and Leinster. There were also a few leprosy hospitals in Dublin.

'The rickets are of late rife in Ireland, where few years agoe they were unknown; so on the contrary it hath been almost quite freed from another disease, one of the very worst and miserablest in the world, namely, the leprosie which in former times used to be very common there, especially in the province of Munster; the which therefore was filled with hospitals, expressly built for to receive and keep the leprous persons. But many years since Ireland has been almost freed from this horrible and loathsome disease, and as few leprous persons are found there as in any other countrie in the world, so that the hospitals erected for their use, having stood empty a long time, are quite decayed and come to nothing'. G.Boate, *Ireland's naturall history 1604-1650: Being a true and ample description of its situation.* 1652.

29. M.A. Constantine, *Breton Ballads,* Aberystwyth, 1996. Versions of the 19th century anonymous ballad or 'gwerz' of Iannik Kokard refer to 'earlier events' when leprosy was common in Brittany. J. Gibson & G. Griffith, *The Turn of the Ermine, An Anthology of Breton Literature,* London, 2006. Included is the Breton original version of the ballad with an English translation. (pp236-243).

'When Iannik went for water / He did not know he was sick; /Until he looked at the water, /As he looked into the fountain, /He was rotten with leprosy'. His father and mother ask him 'Iannik Kokard, tell us? What gave you leprosy? 'Drinking wine, a full glass /From a girl I loved; /Drinking wine poisoned /By a cursed leper girl..... The final verse as spoken by Mari Tili: 'I have loved eighteen clerics,/And given leprosy to the eighteen./ Iannik Kokard, the last,/ Has broken my heart!/ One drop of Blood from my little finger,/ Would kill a hundred as easily as one'.

Chapter 3. Healing in the Age of the Saints

30. L. de Poar, *Patrick's World*, Dublin 1994.

31. M. Herbert, *Iona, Kells and Derry*, Oxford 1988.
E. O'Donnell, *Columcille*, Donegal. 1997.
J.R. Walsh & T. Bradley, *A History of the Irish Church , 400-700 AD*, Dublin 1993.

Even in the womb many signs and prognostications of Colm Cille's sainthood and future mission were evident. An angel — in a dream — gave his mother a colourful woven cloak that covered Ireland and Scotland. A sign of his future influence! On the night before he was born a radiant youth appeared to her saying that she would bear the promised son and there was a broad flagstone on a nearby lake. She was told to take the stone to a certain place for the child to be born on it. "How shall I get the stone from under a lake and how will I know it from all others?" "It will be floating on the bosom of the lake". She found the stone on the following day and her people without any trouble took it to the place she indicated. It was under him at his birth and she laid the baby crossways so that it was marked on the stone. The figure of the cross inside the circle, known as the Greek Cross is still evident on the tall stones at Garton his birth place in Co. Donegal.

32. W. Davies, *The Place of Healing in Early Irish Society,
Sagas, Saints and Storytellers (ed)* D.O. Connain, Maynooth 1987. (pp 43-55).
R. Black, *Studies in Honour of James Carney*, CMCS No 23, Cambridge 1992.

33. F. Lynch, *The Holy Wells of Wales*, Cardiff, 1954.
J. Sharkey, *Pilgrim Ways*, Cardigan, 1994.
P. Lord, *Medieval Vision, The Visual Culture of Wales*, Cardiff, 2003.

A pencil drawing by T.H. Thomas, *Saintwell* at Coedaritydyglyn in Glamorgan in 1899, shows some rags on overhanging branches of a nearby tree.
Edward Lhuyd, *Parochial Queries*, 1693.

34. F. Lynch, *The Holy Wells of Wales*, ibid.
R. Suggett, *The Buildings in Context*, D.Miles (ed) *A History of Haverfordwest*. Llandyssul. 1999.

35. S. Baring-Gould, and J. Fisher, *The Lives of the British Saints*. 4vols. London 1907-13.
A.W. Wade-Evans, *Rhigyfarch's Life of David*, London 1923.
T. Johns & N. Rhys, *Pilgrimage. A Welsh Perspective*, Llandyssul. 2002.

36. E.R. Henken, *A Study in Patterned Lives*, Cambridge. 1986
E.R. Henken, *Traditions of the Welsh Saints*, Cambridge 1987.
'The saints of Welsh tradition led patterned lives. Figures of great local importance, they became the subject of legend, the focal point around which stories clustered. The stories took on a traditional shape or pattern which revealed the saint not simply as the protagonist, but as a Christianized folk hero.' The major stages of the saint's life appear to be: 1. Conception and birth; 2, childhood (education); 3, performing a miracle which indicates spiritual maturity; 4, going out into the world — founding churches, making pilgrimages, retiring to the wilderness, journeying as a missionary; 5, conflict with secular powers (kings or beasts); 6, ruling a territory; 7, death.

37. *Autobiography of Gerald of Wales*, Woodbridge, 2005. New translations of his writings in Latin.
Giraldus Cambrensis, *The Itineary Through Wales*, London, 1908. In his second preface to Stephen Langton, Archbishop of Canterbury, the author states: 'I have thought good to commit to writing the devout visitation which Baldwin, archbishop of

Canterbury, made throughout Wales; and to hand down, as it were in a mirror, through you, O illustrious Stephen, to posterity, the difficult places through which we passed, the names of springs and torrents, the witty sayings, the toils and incidents of the journey, the memorable events of ancient and modern times, and the natural history and description of the country; lest my study should perish through idleness, or the praise of these things be lost by silence.'

38. The reference to St. Vitus dance at St. Almeda's church is from C.H. Talbot, *Medicine in Medieval England,* London 1967.

39. M.E. Owen, *The Prose of the Cywydd Period,* O.A.H. Jarmen (ed) *A guide to Early Welsh Literature* (1282-1556) Cardiff. 1997. M.E. Owen & D. Jenkins, *Women in Welsh Law,* Cardiff 1997.

The rape of holy women as a definition of sanctity and as a means by which some attained sainthood — as with Non in order to become the future mother of David, and Gwenfrewi fleeing from Prince Caradoc who hacked off her head as she reached the church door while her family huddled inside — is explicable when seen as a reflection of the social conditions of the period. It was both a devious and obvious metaphor of suppression until fairly recently, and can be traced back in Wales to the time when the saints Lives' were written and the medieval laws were being formally regulated. The king's court was presented as a role model of feudal hierarchy. In relation to the head of the household each member had a specific place and duty. As virgins, young women had a barter value and their bride price depended on the position of the family within the whole kin structure. Once the woman went through the rite of marriage, with her dowry, she then effectively belonged to the husband; a reflection of his social standing; and subject to the man as exemplified by tradition and the law. The role of the noble wife as set out in the king's household was such that a woman in marriage was aware of the penalties to expect if she insulted her husband in public or used the three shameful words. For wishing a blemish on his head (penis?), casting aspersions on his sexual prowess and wishing dirt on his teeth or calling him a pig in some texts, she had to pay a fine to the king and could be beaten by her husband with a stick anywhere except around her face. Her ultimate shame was to consort with another man. The various ways this was proven are explicitly stated. If she were found kissing, having a finger up her vulva; copulating and coming from behind a bush with a man, or seen beneath a blanket with one between her thighs. She could however maintain that it was a rape and the man in question was obliged to pay sarhaad (a fine) to both the wife and husband or bear the consequences of a feud. Crying rape may also have been disturbing for her own people as she could be thrown out of the new home and then they would lose her bride price.

40. The treatment of women in the tales of the Mabinogion as when Rhiannon has to act as a *public mount* by the castle gate for seven years of wedlock or Branwen imprisoned in the servants' quarter of the Irish king lose much of their symbolic imprint. Similarly the account of Gwenfrewi beheaded after she had reached the sanctuary of the church highlights the healing powers of saint Beuno. However it was related without any 'judgement' on the social consequences of such a murderous act. In law the prince could pay *galenes* or *life-price* to her family and thereby be freed of any further retaliation.

41 *Healing Skull of St. Teilo,* Archaeologia Cambrensis, Vol.XV, 5th series 1898. On the drive up to the ruined chapel of Llandeilo, some of the party had a discussion as to how the name Melchior should be pronounced. After this had gone on for quite some time, one gentleman who had not spoken for an hour, ventured, somewhat timidly, that Mr. Melchior himself might be able to say how his name was pronounced. On being asked whether his name would be

as in Greek, in Welsh or in English, he said smiling, no not like that, we call it Melshior.

A few of the leading members of the Association asked about the inscribed stones which were exposed to the weather, and some of the letters on which are already indistinct, if not obliterated. These are known as the *Andagelli* and *Coimagni* stones. The former is now difficult to read accurately, but the inscription on the latter is much more distinct. There is a cross and Ogam inscription on the *Andagelli* stone. The Roman letters are of much the same age and character as those on the Llandysilio stones. The Ogam is said to spell *Andagelli;* but is at present almost unreadable.

N. Edwards, *A Corpus of Early Mediaeval Inscribed Stones and Stone Sculpture in Wales,* Vol II, *South-West Wales,* University of Wales Press, Cardiff, 2007.

42. R. Fenton, *A Historical Tour Through Pembrokeshire,* ibid.

43. Joel, J, *Nanteos,* Cardigan, 1996. A. Wagner, *The Holy Spirit and the Holy Grail.* CD. Media Quest. 1993.

44. E.E. Roberts, *With Harp, Fiddle and Folktale,* Denbigh. 1981. B. Rogers, *The Bank Manager and the Holy Grail,* London. 2000. The Welsh-born speaker and journalist in his *Travels to the Wilder reaches of Wales* adds a more recent version of holding the Nanteos healing cup. The Bank Manager in the title of the book, and also that of the epilogue, refers to a Mr. Jack Jones of Lloyds Bank in Aberystwyth where it was placed for safe keeping. He said, when finally traced by Rogers, that the package was entered in the books as the Nanteos Cup and not as the Holy Grail. He thought it was something to do with racing. It had been removed previous to his time in the bank. The cup had been on exhibition in the National Library of Wales and one man Rogers talked with had held the cup. "For a moment I held it in my hand. And it was very cold. I was, and I must admit, impressed." By using the telephone dictionaries for the whole of Wales, the author came upon its present Guardian "in a

little house in a lane". The cup is in a different bank now and it is taken out whenever people ask to drink from it. Bryon Rogers admits he has some of its holy water in a brown plastic bottle standing on the top shelf of his bookcase. He treats it carefully! He promised not to give the woman's name to anyone. "There is", he adds in a final comment, "just a little house smelling of dogs in a lane where one afternoon I called and am not sure as to what I found".

Part Two. Chirurgia Work of Skilled Hands.

'The blades of grasse, thy Creatures feeding,

The trees, their leafs; the flowers, their seeding;

The dust, of which I am a part,

The Stones much softer than my heart,

The drops of rain, the sighs of wind,

The Stars to which I am stark blind,

The Dew thy herbs drink up by night,

The beams they warm at i'thy light,

All that have signature or life,

I summoned to decide this strife.'

Henry Vaughan Silex Scintillans, 1650.

Chapter 4. Bloodletting, Bleeding and Ancient Pathology.

1. K. Haeger, *The History of Surgery,* London 1989.
Rev. J. Williams,(ed) *The Physicians of Myddfai,* ibid.   A Facsimile
reprint of the Welsh text is now o.o.p. but the English one is still in
print. Llanerch Press, Lampeter, 2005.
J. D. Comrie, *History of Scottish Medicine,* (ibid)

2. C. Moorhead, *Sun Dancing, A Medieval Vision*, London 1997.

3. J. Fleetwood, *A History of Medicine in Ireland*, Dublin.1953.
J. Minahane, *The Christian Druids, on the filid or philosopher-poets of Ireland*, Dublin, 1993.
L. Buckley & B. O'Donnabhain, *Trephination: Early Cranial Surgery in Ireland*, Archaeology Ireland, Vol. 6 No 4 Issue 22, Winter 1992.
The cover has a page from a 14th century French manuscript with six panels that show the stages involved in cranial surgery, with the patient clearly awake as in most modern operations. It was a dangerous procedure to try to remove a portion of the skull without damaging the brain or any of the blood vessels overlaying it. The medieval surgeon in a long gown has one foot pressed on the patient's, no doubt to gain some leverage. The top three panels depict scenes in the *Life of Mary* from the Annunciation to the Birth of Christ which may strengthen the association with women healers and the need for divine help. The above appears to have been standard dress for a surgeon, and another page of six panels from the same work, *Chirurgia of Roger of Salerno*, shows the death of Christ in the top three while a surgeon below, dressed in a long gown and what appears to be a head scarf, examines six male patients with different wounds. It was reproduced as the frontispiece of C. Rawcliffe, *Medicine & Society in Later Medieval England* (ibid) as 'Christ the Physician offers spiritual healing through his sacrifice on the Cross, while a surgeon examines his wounded patients before applying earthly medicine'.

4. M. Wainwright, *A Head of its Time*, a Guardian newspaper report. 6.10.2004.
An Anglo-Saxon skull, found during the excavation of the Wharram Percy deserted medieval village in Yorkshire over a forty year period, was among a hoard of 700 skeletons. Examination of the bones has been going on since 1990 and this was the only example of an operation on a living person who recovered after the

trephination, for the gap in the skull had closed over with scar tissue. The forty year old man had been whacked on the head with a blunt instrument and the unknown surgeon remodelled the healthy bone and also removed broken splinters. Simon Mays, a skeletal biologist with the English Heritage team, suggested that the man was a peasant whose status was identified by nutritional evidence and its burial site; and that such an operation was carried out by a 10th century itinerant healer of unusual skill for it predates any known medieval surgery by a century.

D. Jenkins, *Hywel Dda,* The Law, Llandyssul.1986.

J. Williams, *Introduction, Physicians of Mydfai,* (ibid).

5. C. Singer, *From Magic to Science* (ibid).

The most elaborate of the *Petrosairis Spheres* that were written at Glastonbury Abbey reflects a yearning for elegance of expression by way of perfect spiritual symmetry. This search and its expression is evident in the 'diagram' drawn by Byrhtferth of Ramsey about 1000. Originally it was from written Latin (and then reproduced in English) showing the macrocosm and microcosm as depicted between the internal and external realms of man and nature which was one of the most important theorems of the Middle Ages. A copy of the *Sphere of Apuleius* also from Glastonbury, done towards the end of the 10th century, depicts two figures Life and Death. The figure of the angel depicts LIFE. The day of death could be discovered by the method from the *Sphere of Pythagorus* written at the English monastery of Echternach in the 9th century. In conjunction with the many scientific and medical books they produced, the *Sphere* is a fair indication of how far the intellectual climate of Anglo-Saxon England had moved from its early magical healing charms to a synthesis of classical and abstract systems of thought.

The humours of the body correspond with the four elements of Fire, Earth, Water and Air. Initial letters in Latin of North, West, East and South make up the name ADAM to whom the term *protoplast* is attached. The solstices and the equinoxes on the

271

cardinal points of the year have letters in Latin where they join at the apex of Summer (June 20) to Winter (December 21) and Spring (March 21) to Autumn (September 20) that forms the word ADAM inside the centre circle. It in turn encloses circles of 'microcosmos' translated as the word MAN. Concentric rings hold the elaborate design in place and include the astrological sun signs of Aries, Taurus, Gemini, Cancer, Leo, Virgo, Libra, Scorpio, Sagittterius, Capricorn, Aquarius, Pisces; with the number of days in each. The four seasons of the year are connected with the four ages of man: childhood, youth, manhood, old age. In fact the diagram as a whole makes an extraordinary spiritual calendar showing the groundwork of English medicine and provides a visually philosophic system based on the medieval doctrine of *as above so below.*

A. Roob, *The Hermetic Museum; Alchemy & Mysticism,* London, 2006.

From the original German edition of 1997. An extremely wide ranging visual introduction to 'a rich world of images edged into the consciousness of modern man, despite the fact that it is not available in public collections, but lies hidden in old manuscripts and prints'.

6. C. Rawcliffe, *Medicine & Society in Later Medieval England,* (ibid).

7. M. Chamberlain , *Old Wives Tales, Their History, Remedies and Spells,* London .1981.

8. R. A. Griffiths, *Interaction of War and Plague,* in *Medieval Wales,* J.R. Cule (ed) *Wales and Medicine* (ibid).

Wales & Medicine contains the papers presented at the Ninth British Congress on the History of Medicine, organised by the British Society for the History of Medicine and held at the University College of Swansea and the Welsh National School of Medicine Cardiff in September 1973. The Congress was opened by Baroness Lee who spoke on the contribution of her late husband Aneurin Bevan to the National Health Service. The twenty-three papers presented were chosen for their wide range of interest. The first paper was on David Lloyd George and the National Insurance Act of 1911. Fifteen of the speakers were then working as consultants or teaching in Welsh hospitals Four papers were on industrial diseases common to Wales; two on the Welsh doctor-poets; two on war and plague; two on the Meddygon Myddfai and Bened Feddyg, a lay practicioner in the late medieval period; eight papers on Welsh medical doctors; two on the new hospital buildings in Wales; and one on the early contributions by the family of Jones to American medicine.

9. A. Owen, *The Ancient Laws and Institutes of Wales*, 2 vols, Royal Commission, London 1841.

The most important 19th century study on the Laws of Wales, Owen's method was to divide the Welsh and Latin manuscripts into three groups, being the later variants of the laws as they came to be applied in the three regions of Wales. Of these he made composite texts. The Venedotian Code referring to the northwest (Gwynedd), the Dimetian Code to the southwest (Dyfed) and the Gwentian Code to the south (Deheubarth). Of the ancient manuscript sources some thirty-five were written before the 16th century and an equal number were written during the following three centuries. 'It is now recognised that the ancient legal MSS were essentially composed of individual treatises or tractates on particular aspects of the law gathered together as Lawyers' textbooks. Aneurin Owen's nomenclature has been replaced by the not wholly satisfactory substitution of the names of Iorwerth, Blegywryd and Cynferth; and his composite texts of the Codes simplified' (J.H. Cule).

The law codes appear to have been first written out from the period when native society was under threat by force and guile from the English king Edward I. The first recorded eisteddfod was held in Cardigan Castle in 1076 in the presence of the Lord Rhys. It may have been both a high point — in the sense of the culmination of native culture — and a watershed of the political changes that would bring about its demise. A colophon in the earliest of the Myddfai

273

manuscripts refers to his son Rhys Gryg who inherited Dehaubarth; part of the kingdom that included Carmarthenshire. After his death in the 13th century it was under Norman control, like most of Wales.

10. D. Jenkins, *Laws of Hywel Dda,* (ibid).
J.R. Cule, *The Court Mediciner and Medicine in the Laws of Wales,* Jour. Hist. Med. & Science, 1966.
  Unfortunately there are no illustrations of the mediciner among the many court officials in the Latin MS Peniarth 28, although the drawing showing the act of hair-pulling was wrongly captioned as 'a twelfth century leech at work' in T. Lewis's *A Welsh Leech Book.* The text makes the context clear. This method of fighting among men was sufficiently in vogue to include the following penalties: a penny for every hair pulled out from the head by the root; and a penny for every finger which shall touch the head; and twenty-four for the front hair; as well as the *sarhad* that the attack itself justified.

11. H.E.F Davies, & M.E. Owen, *Meddygon Myddfai,* in J.R. Cule (ed) *Wales & Medicine,* (ibid). H.E. Sigerist, *Materia Medica in the Middle Ages, A Review of various editions of the Dioscorides Herbal.* Bul. Hist. of Med, Baltimore, Vol V11. 1939.
He notes that since the *Materia Medica* was available in Latin, it appears not to have been translated from the Arabic in the 12th century as so many other medical treatises were.
Rev. J. Williams (ed), *Physicians of Myddfai* (ibid).
J. Bannerman, *The Beatons: A medical kindred in the classical Gaelic tradition,* Edinburgh, 1986.
M. Beath, *Healing Threads, Traditional Medicines of the Highlands and Islands,* Edinburgh, 1995.
  In his discussion of medicine and medical men, Bannerman points out that the only real difference between the medical practicioners of Gaelic Scotland and those of the non-Gaelic parts during the medieval period is that the latter, like their counterparts in England and the Continent, continued to practice medicine on the basis of the Latin medical texts. Whereas the Gaelic hereditary physicians of

both Scotland and Ireland, beginning as early as the 14th century, made the startling commitment of translating into Gaelic and/or commenting in Gaelic on these same Latin texts. In Wales at the same period, Latin manuscripts were being translated into Welsh but with the exception of the *Red Book of Hergest,* there is no record of either the compilers or the commissioners of the texts. The Beaton physicians of the Inner Hebrides between 1300 and 1750 are recorded by name and place of residence such as Husabost with nine doctors; Culnaskea with eight; Pennycross on Mull with ten. In the Outer Isles, South Uist had six; North Uist had two and there were six other physicians. In the main *The Beatons* deals with the historical and genealogical concerns of this hereditary family of healers, and only in a minor way with their medical and non-medicinal manuscripts, whilst generally ignoring the content of the medical texts.

12. M.E. Owen, *Meddygon Myddfai, A Preliminary Survey of some medieval medical writing in Welsh,* Studia Celtica, Vol x-x1, 1975.
'Nevertheless although there are references to the physicians of Myddfai in Welsh literature before the time of ab Ithel (John Williams) such as in the work of antiquarians like Edward Lhuyd, Theophilus Evans and Lewis Morris, men who themselves were interested in folklore and marvels, I have failed to find a single reference to the physicians' connections with the lake story, which has so obscured the other parts of the tradition during the last hundred years'. (M.E.Owen)
D. Hoffmann, *Welsh Herbal Medicine,* Abercastle, 1978.
'An introduction to the lore of the old herbalists of Wales, the Physicians of Myddfai, with a guide to modern medical herbalism.'
B. Griggs, *Green Pharmacy,* (ibid). 'Alongside the Druid priest-healers, an independent school of physicians with a rational rather than a priestly approach to their profession had developed at Myddfai by the sixth century A.D.'
A.E Jones, *Folk Medicine in Living memory in Wales,* Folklife 1980.

'The folk remedies that have been passed down to the present day through the medium of the Welsh language derive from both written and oral sources. The earliest extant Welsh medical manuscripts date from the late 14th and early 15th centuries, and most of these were partly based on the works of the Physicians of Myddfai, near Llandovery, and were actually used as manuals'.

13. G.H. Jenkins, *Facts, Fantasy and Fiction, the Historical Vision of Iolo Morganwg,* Aberystwyth, 1997.
G.H. Jenkins, (ed*) A Rattleskull Genius. The Many Faces of Iolo Morganwg*, Cardiff, 2005.
M.E. Owen*, The Medical Books of Medieval Wales and the Physicians of Myddfai,* The Carmarthenshire Antiquity, Vol. XXX1.1995.
M.E. Owen*, The Prose of the Cywydd Period,* in Jarman, O.A.H. (ed*) A Guide to Welsh Literature (1282-1556)* Cardiff, 1997.

The second so-called *Myddfai* text written about 1400 is an extract from the Jesus College MS that originally formed part of the *Llyfr Coch,* the Red Book of Hergest; a compilation of a group of manuscripts written by Hywel Fychan ap Hywel Goch, 'on the instruction and by the command of his master namely Hopcyn, son of Thomas son of Einion'. It was the greatest of his surviving books which contains a broad selection of medieval literature and, according to Owen, the contents include a trilogy of Welsh historical writing; a collection of prophetic texts in translation; a series of medical, scientific and historical texts; a bardic grammar; eleven tales of the Mabinogion; and collections of poems from the Myrddin and Llywarch Hen Cycles. Hopcyn ap Tomos is little known historically although it would appear that he was an important patron of literature, praised by the eulogies of the poets noting his learning and wisdom. He was referred to as Master of the Brut, on account of his familiarity with history and prophecy. Owain Glyndwr consulted him in 1403, as a seer, on his forthcoming campaigns.

14. W.G. Harries, *Bened Feddyg,* in J.R. Cule, *(ed) Wales and Medicine* (ibid).

15. The Prelude was carefully written out in Welsh. Its opening words *In Principio* are familiar from the Carpet Pages in Irish and Northumbrian illuminated Gospels. The prelude or *Proem* was of special devotion from the early days of the Christian Church but by the Middle Ages it had become much abused from the chanting of it by beggars and wandering friars. It was also used as a prayer charm for a cure of epilepsy and to exorcise devils or to drive away bad dreams, as noted by Geraldus Cambrensis. Bened recommended Macer's Herbal as a useful guide to medicinal plants. It was originally an 11th century Latin poem describing the virtues of seventy-seven plants. A British Library version was *turnyd into Ynglis* by a Hereford school-master in 1373. Popular Middle English versions that had remedies for serpent bites and cures for eye troubles may represent a transition from the earlier Anglo-Saxon leech-books to the first printed Latin edition of *Macer Floridus,* published in Paris in 1491, a half-century or more after Bened the Welsh physician recorded the Macer work and which indicates his breath of knowledge and interest in many aspects of medicine of the time.
K.V.Smith, *Earth Garden Herbal,* (ibid).

Chapter 5. Welsh Humanists and the Renaissance

16. P. Lord, *Words with Pictures,* Popular Press 1640-1600, Aberystwyth, 1995.
R. Porter, *The Greatest Benefit to Mankind, A medical history of humanity from antiquity to the present,* London, 1997.
I. Herbert, & G E. Jones, (ed's) *People and Protest,* Cardiff 1988.
P. Lord, *Medieval Vision,* Cardiff, 2003.

The large wooden effigy of Derfel Gadarn (with eyes and arms that could move mechanically) believed to be capable of saving condemned souls from hell, was removed from his shrine of Llandderfel in Merionith to be burnt at the stake in Smithfield market on the orders of Henry VIII. The Welsh had a prophecy that this image should set a whole forest afire, which prophecy took effect, for he set this Friar Forest on fire and consumed him to nothing. This poem was attached to the scaffold.

'David Derfel Gardarn / As sayeth the Welshmen. / Now he is come, with spear and shield, / In harness to burn at Smithfield, / For in Wales he may not dwell. / And Forest the friar / The obstinate liar / That wilfully shall be dead, / In the contumacy / The gospel doth deny, / And the King to be Supreme Head'.

The burning of the wooden image seemed to be a cause of much greater concern among the native Welsh than the actual suppression of the Catholic religion they had venerated for nearly a thousand years. The horse or stag part of the effigy was left behind and is the porch of Llandderfel Church.

17. J H. Cule, *Wales and Medicine,* Aberystywth, 1980.

Based on the dates in this bibliographic source-list for printed books and papers 'showing the history of medicine in relation to Wales and Welshmen'; that from the period which elapsed between the printing of the first prayer book called *Yey Lhyvyr hwan* or *In this Book* by John Prys of Brecon, Lord Chancellor to Henry VIII, it would be forty-two years before Bishop William Morgan's translation of the Bible into Welsh made its appearance and almost a half-century later when the edition of what was known as the *five-shilling family Bible* was printed. This was at a time when many significant upheavals in religion, politics, language and social values had become manifest in Wales. John Cule has estimated that four-hundred thousand copies of medical works were printed in England during this period but few were printed in Welsh. It indicates a lack of interest in the written language by literate readers, perhaps reluctant to buy books, and who were more than likely to be a small minority among the monoglot population.

18. P.J. French, *John Dee,* London 1972; J.O. Halliwell (ed) *The Private diary of D. John Dee etc,* London, 1842; B. W. Wolley, *The Life and Magic of Dr. Dee,* London 2002; H.C. Agrippa, *3 Books of occult Philosophy,* London 1652; K. Thomas, *Religion and the Decline of Magic,* London 1971.

19. Edward Kelly, *The Theatre of Terrestrial Astronomy.*
'Many books have been written on the art of Alchemy, which, by the multiplicity of their allegories, riddles, and parables, bewilder and confound all earnest students; and the cause of this confusion is the vast number and variety of names, which all signify and do set forth one and the same thing. For this reason I have resolved in my own mind to loosen and untie all the difficult knots of the ancient Sages. I will speak first of the inventors and restorers of the Art; secondly, of the mutual conversion of elements and how through the predominance of one element the substance of metals is generated; thirdly, I will shew the affinity and homogeneity of metals, procreated in the bowels of the earth, their sympathies and anti-pathies, according to the purity of their Sulphur and Mercury; and that as metals consist of Sulphur and Mercury, they can furnish us with the first matter of the Elixir'.

'Know that out of all metals a perfect Medicine can be made, which can transmute the remaining metals into gold and silver; for out of the perfect metals you get, by proper separation of elements, the Salt of Nature, otherwise Ore of the Philosophers, by some called Philosophical Lili, without which the work of the Sages cannot be accomplished. For Art presupposes a substance created by Nature alone, in which Art assists Nature and Nature assists art.'
— Text by John Dee, from *Cures and Curiosities. Inside the Welcome Library,* compiled and edited by Tony Gould, London 2005. R.Grossinger (ed) *Alchemy: pre-Egyptian Legecy, Millennial*

Promise. A Guide to the Alchemical writings of the Earth, Richmond ,California, 1979.

20. K. Thomas, *Religion and the Decline of Magic,* London, 1971. P. Lord, *Words with Pictures,* (ibid).

21. Tobyn, G, *Culpeper's Medicine. A Practice of Western Holistic Medicine,* London. 1997.

22. N. Cawthorne, *The Curious Cures of Old England,* London, 2005. G.C. Davies, *The Welsh Doctor as Poet,* in J.R Cule (ed) *Wales and Medicine* (ibid).

23. In 1683 a pamphlet by a William Cooper was published showing how to make *Aurum Potobile.* The process began with a block of tin heated in an iron pan until it was as ashes. Four ounces of this was mixed with three pints of strong wine and left to 'digest' for a few days. A distillation of the clear liquid was added to more red wine with the tin powder and left for ten days; the residule was to be filtered and distilled and mixed with a pint of vinegar; then heated and distilled again. This resulted in what he termed the *menstruum* which would take the infusion of pure refined gold and be heated for six days. An ounce of gold, costing nearly four pounds would be filed into dust and heated with equal parts of white salt. The distillation continued; the residule dried and powered and in a half pint of spirit of wine left for ten days and then poured off. This process was to be repeated three times and distilled to produce a kind of syrup. An ounce of this was to be put into a pint of red wine and the solution was then ready to be given to the patient.

24. Henry Vaughan, *The Complete Poems,* (ed) Alan Rudrum, London 1976.

25. H. Vaughan, *Hermetical Physic,* (translation of H. Nollius) 1654. F.E. Hutchinson, *Henry Vaughan; A Life and Interpretation,*

Oxford, 1947. S. Davies, *Henry Vaughan,* Bridgend. 1995. E. Holmes, *Thomas Vaughan and the Hermetic Philosophy,* Oxford, 1932.

26. E. Holmes, *Thomas Vaughan and the Hermetic Philosophy,* (ibid).

27. Thomas Vaughan, *Lumen de Lumine.* R. Grossinger (ed) *Alchemy,* (ibid)

> 'There is not an *Herb* here *below*,
> but he hath a *star* in *Heaven above*,
> and the *star* strikes him with her Beame,
> and sayes to him, *Grow*'.

'Eugenius' said she, 'I have many names, but my best and dearest is Thalia, for I am always green and shall never wither. Thou dost here behold the Mountains of the Moon, and I will shew thee the original of Nilus; for she springs from these invisible rocks. Look up and peruse the very tops of these pillars and cliffs of salt, for they are the true, philosophical, lunar mountains. Did'st thou ever see such a miraculous, incredible thing?'

28. G.P. Jones, *Folk Medicine in Eighteenth Century Wales,* Folkways Vol. 7. 1967.

29. Williams, E .R. *Welsh Physicians and the Renaissance,* Brit. Med. Jour. Dec. 1928.

30. Humphrey Lhwyd's translation into English of the *Chronicles of Wales,* attributed to Caradoc of Llancarvan under the title of *A Description of Cambria* was expanded in 1584 by David Powel into his *Historia of Cambria now called Wales.* Powel, a cleric and respected historian, used different fonts and other decorative devices to show his additions to Lhwyd's translation of a *Brut y Tywysogian*

manuscript that ended in the 13th century. A similar work written in Latin by Lhwyd and printed in Cologne in 1572, was done into English in the following year by the physician and astrologer Thomas Twyne entitled *The Breviary of Britayne.*

The treatise on Uroscopy by Humphrey Lhwyd was a translation of a much earlier work by John Vassey. It was written, he said, for those who wanted to know the state of their own bodies or were willing to help their friends. It indicated that as late as 1553 when the book was printed that diagnosis by examination of urine was still a prominent part of medical practice. The colour, smell and even the taste of a patient's urine was used diagnostically to assert the true condition of the inner body. It was commonly illustrated in medieval manuscripts by means of the figure of the physician holding his flask as if studying its contents.

31. William Salesbury of Llanrwst in the Vale of Conwy was a philologist and theologian that had studied medicine at Oxford where he became a Protestant and later probably attended the Inns of Court in London. Little is known of his life apart from his marriage to one sister of Dr. Elis Prys — known as *y Doctor Coch,* the Red Doctor — and his brother to another. After his brother died he was in dispute with Prys over their inheritance and in 1546 'put away' (divorced) his wife.

Salesbury Dictionary and the King's License, by J.H. Davies. Y Cymmrodor, Vol.XIV. London 1901. A copy of the Kynges Moste Gracious Priuiledge. Granted by Henry in the 37th year of his reign. Copied from the Shirburn Castle copy of the text. It was printed at the end of Epistles and Gospels published by William Salesbury in 1551.

32. Dr. Davies, *Dictionary Duplex, Dictionary in Welsh and English,* 1688; a facsimile by the Black Pig Press, Garreg Fawr, Porthyrhyd, Llanwrda, Dyfed, 1977. A. Breeze, *Dr. Sion Dafydd Rhys and Chinese Printing,* Trans. Hon. Soc. Cymmrodorion, 1999.

Sion Rhys deplored the reluctance of the poets to be open about their craft; a lack reflected in parts of his *Welsh Grammar*, written in Latin dealing with the arts of prosody. In his preface he refers to early Chinese printing, arguing that printing would save the early literature of Wales. He points out what others have done. 'They have gathered and brought together, and copied out, and printed, and put in order all the best books of historians and poets and rhetoricians and astronomers and astrologers and philosophers; and innumerable other illustrious men of learning that I might name'. And that the Chinese dwelling on the opposite side of the earth have put into print their splendid works, before any of the other nations in Europe; 'if what some historians say is true'.

33. A.V. Neale & H.R.E. Willis (eds) *Thomas Phaer, The Boke of Children*, London 1955. J. Cule, *Thomas Phaer M.D. of Cilgerran*, Trans. Hon. Soc. Cymmrodorion 1979.
The basic text of the *Regimen of Health* was considered a seminal work from the medical school of Salerno on the Bay of Naples in Southern Italy. It consisted of several hundred verses with advice on the maintenance of bodily health using herbal remedies, proper diet, sound sleep, regular exercise and moderation in all things. Salerno was the first teaching hospital in the modern sense with a course of medicine which lasted for five years and included anatomy — using pigs rather than human carcasses. Its students, including women, had to be over twenty-one to be accepted and to have studied logic. Trotula wrote a treatise on obstetrics in 1250; a teacher who may have been a man or perhaps as some assert was the prototype of the pantomime figure of Dame Trot.

34. J. Cule, John Jones Phistion, *on the Preservation of Bodie and Soule, 1578*, J. Cule, (ed) *Child Care Through the Centuries*, Swansea, 1996.

35. J. Phillips, *The Plague in Haverfordwest, 1651-52*. Arch. Camb. Series 5, Vol. X11.

Chapter 6. The Physic Garden

36. R. Brindley Jones, *W. Salesbury,* Cardiff,1994.

I. Edgar, *W. Salesbury's Plant Names, Plants & Medicine Forum.*
NLW 1993.
T. Lewis. *A Welsh Leech Book or Lllyfr a Feddyginiacht,* Liverpool.
1931. The original edition of 300 copies was published in 1914.

37. A. Pavord, *The Naming of Names. The search for order in the
world of plants.* London 2005.

Her fascinating and illustrated story is the business of naming
plants from Theophrastus in the 3rd century BC to the physic
gardens of the Italian Renaissance. The Geeek in his *Enquiry into
Plants* described what he could see with his own eyes, in terms of
similarities and dissimilarities. However it was the famous herbal
De Materia Medica of Dioscorides that engaged the plant lovers of
Islam, the mediaeval doctors of Salerno in Sicily and later the
European scholars; until Theophrastus was translated into Latin in
1483 by Theodoro de Gaza. This initiated the birth of modern
Botany. Anne Pavord ends her account with England in the 16th
century and the three-part *Herball* of Wiliam Turner, written in
English but published in Germany in 1551, 1562 and 1568.

38. S. Minton, *The Apothecaries Garden, A History of the Chelsea
Physic Garden,* London 2000.
M. Stuart (ed) *The Encyclopedia of Herbs and Herbalism,* London
1979.

It was the next generation of plantsmen after Turner that
exemplified the English love of gardens. From the formal creations
of the nobility to the physic town gardens and humble cottage-
garden of the peasant, all could share in making nature more
accountable to peoples' needs at a time when the Tudor ideas of

exploration, expansion, order and production had become popuar modes of expression.

A Niewe Herball (1578) by Henry Lyte; John Gerard's *Herbal* (1597) and its revised edition of 1631 by Thomas Johnson. He, in fact, was one of the early field explorers of plants in England and made a number of botanical visits to North Wales. The *Theatre of Plants* by John Parkinson (1640); Nicholas Culpepper's *The English Physician* (1652); and William Coles' *The Art of Simpling* (1656).

Alongside the herbals were many newly-published horticultural books that explained how to farm and cultivate the garden; the fruits to be preserved; and cooking the home-grown produce. Like the *briefe and plasaante treatyse* by Thomas Hyll, teaching readers how to dress, sow and set a garden (1563); the *five hundred points of good husbandry* by Thomas Tusser (1573); the *Countrie Housewifes Garden* (1617); and a *New Orchard and Garden*, particularly in the northern parts of England (1618); to the *Art of Cookery* (1654) and the *Queens Closet opened by her Cook* (1655).

These were but a few of the more popular publications available to an avid literate and interested readership. The high royal style had already been set at the earlier coronation banquets of the English monarchs such as Henry 1V in 1399 and again on his second marriage five years later. The manuscripts of two fifteenth century cookbooks with complete fish and fowl dishes were presented to Elizabeth I by Lord Stafford which she later gave to the Earl of Oxford. The dishes were strongly seasoned with pepper, ginger, cloves, garlic, cinnamon, galingale — an aromatic root of an East Indian plant also used as a medicine — vinegar, verjuice of green or unripe fruit, and wine.

Philip Ball, *The devil's Doctor, Paracelsus and the World of renaissance Magic and Science,* London 2007.

39. E. & R. Peplow, *In a Monastery Garden,* Newton Abbot, 1998.
K.V.Smith, *The Illustrated Earth Herbal,* (ibid).

Hortulus or the *Little Garden* by Walafrid Strabo (squint-eyed) was a Latin poem of 440 hexameters that was first printed in Venice in 1610. It had lain unnoticed in the monastery of St. Gall for 600 years. He had also written an account of the *Life of Gall* who had arrived on the continent as one of the chief disciples of St. Columbanus in 591. However he refused to accompany the saint when he made the journey with his group of Irish monks across the Alps to the south of Milan. The monastic settlement of Bobbio was to be the final resting place of perhaps the best known of the Irish peregrini who spent 25 years in the territory of the Franks. The Merovingian dynasty covered much of south-western France and large areas of Germany when the first Christian Emperor of the west sought to unify his kingdom and imposed the Rule of St. Benedict on monks within his empire. Benedict had believed that all monks, rich and poor alike, should work and that their communal activity was as important as private prayer. After a lifetime of living as a hermit he became the abbot of Monte Cassino where he wrote out his list of instructions of how monks should live, pray and behave, before he died in 544. When the monastery was sacked by the Lombards a century later the community dispersed with copies of the Rule.

40. John Gerarde in 1596 issued a list of plants he had created in his own garden. A work of twenty four pages; it seems to have been the first workable catalogue of any garden published — one copy of the first edition is in the British Library. *M Woodward, (ed) Gerard's Herbal.*

41. C. Davies, *Welsh Literature and the Classical Tradition,* Cardiff,

42. Local tradition asserts that some of the plants growing in Candy Lane, near Llanforda such as the Yellow Figwort, Blue Alkanet, Small Teazle and Golden Rod were introduced by Edward Lhuyd, who lived here until he was nine. In 1682, the twenty-two year old

Lhuyd made a list of 37 of the most interesting plants and where he found them:

Aran Branellyn: Starry and Cut-leaved Saxifrage, Cowberry, Fir Clubmoss. *Craig Verwin*: Alpine Clubmoss.

Cader Idris: Roseroot, Mountain Sorrel, Crowberry, Interrupted Clubmoss, Brittle Bladder-fern.

Breiddin Hill: Rock Cinquefoil, Red German Cathfly, Spiked Speedwell.

Snowdon: Alpine Mouse-ear Chickweed, Pondmoss, Dwarf Juniper, Prickly Shield-fern, Holly-fern, Green Spleenwort, Oblong Woodsia, Quilllwort, Moss Campion, Three-flowered rush, Few-flowered Scirpus, and Mountain Spiderword. The last example was named *Bulbosa alpine junncifolia uncio erecto in sumno cauliculo dodrantali.* It was shortened to *Bulbosa alpina* when the binomial system of naming plants with genus and species alone came in with Linnaeus. It was finally named *Lloydia serotina,* after the finder of this rare alpine plant that looks from a distance like a small Wood Anemone or Wood Sorrel; it is generally known as the Snowdon Lily. Due to global warming and the loss of its cold habitat on the north facing slopes of Snowdon, it may become an extinct species

43. D. Jones, *The Botanists and Guides of Snowdonia,* Llanrwst. 1996.

44. W. Linnard, & R. Gwyndaf, *William Morris of Anglesey: A Unique Gardening Book and a New Manuscript of Horticultural Interest,* Trans Cymmrodorion, 1979.

45. N. Culpeper's *The English Physician Enlarged,* published in 1653. The first English herbal to be made available in the native tongue, translated in 1816 by D.T. Jones and published soon afterwards by L.F. Jones of Carnarfon. Perhaps more popular and closer to Welsh needs was the translation of John Wesley's *Primitive Physic* by John Evans in 1759.

46.   G. Jenkins, *Dentristy & Teeth* (Unpublished Essay) Folk Archive No. 1894, St. Fagins, NMW.

47.   J. H. Wilks, *Trees of the British Isles in History and Legend* (ibid). Gilbert White in his *History of Selborne* remarks that a row of pollarded ash trees clearly showed that they had been cloven and had healed over. Wedges were used to keep young and flexible trees open at the splits; when the ailing children were stripped naked and pushed through the apertures. He added that the people were under the impression that such treatment would cure the young infants of rickets. Such ceremonies took place at 3 am in the morning, in other words in the middle of the night. The children were passed through the withen on three successive mornings. The split branches were then carefully closed and bound together. Later they were plastered with loam. The belief in the effective cures was based on (the notion) that if several parts of the tree healed and the tissue of the cambial area knitted, then the cure would be effective. If not, the whole operation would be a failure. Such trees were preserved with great care, for if during the life of the patients, the trees were felled or injured, the affliction would return or the person would die simultaneously with the tree itself. Gilbert thought that the practice was derived from the Saxons before their conversion to Christianity. However in Wales it was recorded as early as the 14th century and in relation to the Anglo-Saxons; such ceremonial use of nature medicine continued long after they became Christians.

48. W. Withering, *Arrangement of British Plants,* edited by his son (1776-1832).   Referring to the addition of Welsh names by the antiquarian or philologist, (rather than the botanist) it is presumed (that) the unusual appendage of our aboriginal names to each plant, so far as ascertainable, will be not an indescribable acquisition... even to the mysteries of the Meddygen (sic) (physicians) of Myddfai whose family, it is credibly asserted, practised the healing art at the same place in Caerarvonshire (sic) from the 12th to the 18th century. Whatever value may be contained in such obscure research, can

only be rendered available by the apprenhension of the proper (botanical) names. (Personal correspondence on William Withering, the Birmingham GP and the foxglove, from Gareth Evans).

49. A.E. Jones, *Folk Medicine in Living Memory in Wales,* Folklife No.18.
R. Price, *(Herbal) Llysieu-Lyfr Teuluaidd,* 1840.
J. Mooney, *the Medical Mythology of Ireland,* Proc. Amer. Philos. Soc. xxiv, 1887

50. D.E. Allen & G. Hatfield, *Ethnobotany, Medical Plants in Folk Tradition,* Cambridge, 2004.
D. Hoffmann, *Welsh Herbal Medicine,* Abercastle, 1978.

51. Jones, E, (ed) *The Welsh in London 1500-2000,* Cardiff, 2001.

Part Three. Rural Primitive Physic

Chapter 7. Herbs, Charms and Old Welsh Medicine

We go concerned
To Dr Harries
Because he is a cunning man
To ask about her fate;
He said she was lying
Near Maes yr On;
There is a tree full of poison
Growing by the place,
And a stream runs near
Where she was murdered by him'.

1. R.C. Allen, *Wizards or Charlatens — Doctors or Herbalists?: An Appraisal of the 'Cunning Men' of Cwrt y Cadno, Carmarthenshire.* N. American Journal of Welsh Studies, Vol 1, 2. 2001. The paper is available on http://spruce.flint.umich.edu/-ellisjs/Allen Pdf.

2. J, Rhys, *Celtic Folklore,* ibid.
O. Davies, *('Hedd Molwynog'), Dyn Hysbys Cwrt y Cadno* (Ph.D thesis). After the sudden death of John Harries from the fire when he slipped down the ladder in his cottage, even the spirits appeared to play a part in his funeral. As the body was being carried into the churchyard, the coffin became suddenly lighter. As this story was told, it widely explained the fact that those spirits that had once possessed his soul had now taken possession of his body. It was also alleged that a herd of cows in the nearby field took fright and were not rounded up until they reached a waterfall called *Hell's Pool* four miles away. Davies, commenting on these occurrences, noted that they buried the wizard in an isolated spot on the mountainside but left the headstone in the Caeo churchyard intact on his father's

grave. It is inscribed with Henry Jones who died in 1805 and his son John Harries, also of Pantcoy who died in 1839. R.C. Allen p. 83 (ibid).

3. Geraldus Cambrensis, *The Description of Wales,* London,1908.

Describing the country of Wales and its people; their manners, dress, habits; and love of ancient genealogy up to the 12th century, Gerald at the end of his preface says that he prefers praise to lucre, and reputation to riches. In Book I is a chapter 'concerning the Soothsayers of this nation, and Persons as it were possessed', known as *Awennddyon*. His term combines inspiration and the gift of poetry or rapture. It was also used as a designation of disciples and candidates for the giving of names in the Bardic Order. He describes these certain people who you will not find elsewhere; when consulted on any doubtful event they will roar out (so) violently (that) they are rendered beside themselves (to) become, as it were, possessed by a spirit. This is an apt description of what is now known as the shaman state. And when they do deliver answers amid their incoherent ramblings and ornamented speeches they do not recover till violently shaken by others and then do not remember any replies they had given. 'If consulted a second or third time upon the same point, they will make use of expressions totally different; perhaps they speak by means of fanatic and ignorant spirits'. Gerald quotes from Esdras. The Lord said unto me, open thy mouth, and I opened my mouth, and behold a cup full of water, whose colour was like fire; and when I had drunk it, my heart brought forth understanding, and wisdom entered into my breast.

4. G.P. Jones, *Folk Medicine in 18th century Wales,* (ibid) & E. Owen, *Welsh Folklore* (1857) record descriptions of the dyn hysbys with their extraordinary costumes and decorative head-dresses of animal furs and bird feathers. At St. Fagan's museum in the NMW, Cardiff, photographs of Dr. William Price show him dressed as a wizard at the burial of his children and also of his own grave with a fox fur head-dress hanging on his staff; (see notes 20-23 below).

291

5. E.A. Jones, *A Welsh Wizard,* The Carmarthen Antiquary, 1949.

The business prospectus that the Harries issued to prospective clients is no work of literature but it gives a flavour of the material aspirations of their astrological consultations.   Jones also mentions the locked magic tome and the supernatural occurances that were common in the earlier quasi-romantic and unrealistic accounts of the Harries.   The lives of the Harries, John (c1785-1839) father of Henry (1821-49) show that although recognised locally as 'doctors' without medical degrees, they gained notoriety as magicians, cunning men or conjurors. Such labels referring to the particular context of a white or black witchcraft were often indiscriminate but are generally inclusive in the common Welsh term *dyn hysbys.* Their lives, activities, and accounts of incidents in which they were involved, are reviewed with an extensive bibliography and reference to the Pantcoy papers in the N.L.W. Dr. Allen who is a Research Fellow in the University of Northumbria places it in the wider context of recent academic interest in witchcraft and magic, as in the works of Tim Harris (1995); Jim Sharpe (1979); Kathryn Smith (1999); Ronald Hutton (1999) and Owen Davies (1999) with seminal books on the Harries by earlier writers such as Arthur Mee, (1889 & 1912) and the brief biographical sketch by Mrs. Vaughan-Poppy in *The Harries Kingdom.* She described the favourite attire of John Harries as 'a full length heavy velvet cape which he had lined with red flannel...and fastened on the left shoulder with a three inch silver buckle'

From that earlier era the particular form of pre-modern medicine that healers like the Harries came to represent, was a special Welsh archetypical aspect of 19th century healing. It was much the same as with the so-called Physicians of Myddfai. Currently it is not only academic writers quoted by R.C. Allen who have become interested but also novelists like Brian John and Lloyd Jones whose Mr Cassini novel (published by Seren 2007) actually has some dialogues of a 'Harries' character quoting the same repetitive stories of the wizard's *mark* and the theft of a silver spoon. The woman told her servant she was going to contact John Harries in order to get it back. Scared of being so *marked*, the culprit returned the spoon.

B. John, *Martha Morgan's Little World,* Newport, 2006.

This is the essential companion to the Angel Mountain Saga, a series of five novels devoted to the central character of Martha Morgan. Her friend, Joseph Harries, is a healer or wizard and is one of the key people in the story. The saga is centred on Carningli the distinctive hill above Newport in North Pembrokeshire. The shape of the mountain itself was often regarded as that of a woman, an angel or goddess, and it is where the dramatic incidents of her life occurred as she aged, eventually becoming known as Mother Martha. According to the account in the first book, Harries lived in a small cottage on the north side of the mountain ridge at Werndew. He appeared to have been based on the more famous Dr. Harries of Cwrt y Cadno but according to the author his Joseph Harries was a local 18th century *knowing man.* Another character Shami Jenkins who is 'good with animals' is sent to be an apprentice in magic to Dr John Harries of Cwrt y Cadno. When he returns home, after the death of Harries of Werndew, he becomes the local conjurer or *dyn hysbys.* Other known wizards in Pembrokeshire were Abe Biddle of Millin Dingle, near Picton Castle; Will Tiriet of Caerfarchell by Middle Mill; John Jenkin a schoolmaster of Nevern; a cunning man of Pentregethin was most famous for his control of winds and he was able to sell fair or foul winds to sailers and sea captains. Old Levi Salmon of Cilgwyn above Newport was referred to as *Dr. Cwac* and lived in a house called Plas Y Ffynnon. Old Levi was one of the informants that W.Y. Evanz-Wentz talked with and mentions meeting him in *The Fairy Faith in Celtic Countries,* Oxford, 1902. Evans-Wentz conducted his research in Wales, Brittany, Ireland and Scotland.

6. G. Thomas, *The Visions of the Sleeping Bard, in B.Jarvis (ed) A Guide to Welsh Literature 1700-1800,* Cardiff, 2000.

Ellis Wynne is considered as one of the most famous Welsh prose writers of the 18th century. In 1692 he became an undergraduate at Jesus College Oxford and after graduation moved back to his home, Y Lasynys, a large farmhouse not far from Harlech. In between the marriage to his first wife, who died soon after in childbirth, and the second in 1702, he published his translation of a work by the English divine Jeremy Taylor. His next work *The Visions of the Sleeping Bard* was published in the following year and is the book on which his fame is based. It was also based on English translations from two versions of 17th century Spanish originals. It may appear to be an odd genesis of *y Bardd Cwsc* but according to Gwyn Thomas it was a genre of visionary literature on the Other World. Visions of Hell became a common satirical framework dealing with politics and religion of the period. Wynne's famous book was written around three dreams and three visions. The Angel's role in the first vision is to give the sleeping bard and the reader a close look at the world and its sinners. In the second, it is Master Sleep who guides him into the Kingdoms of Death, where many sinners go! After being given a sleeping potion he wakes on a barren plain full of 'medieval creepy crawlies' and a group of mythic figures such as Merlin and Taliesin; as well as his own namesake who had been left in peace here for nine hundred years. The third vision begins on the banks of the Severn with the bard reading a Welsh translation of a work that is similar to Wynne's own first publication. *The Practice of Piety* soon sends him to sleep. The Angel appears again and guides him through Hell which the *Bardd Cwsg* describes with familiar classical medieval details. He is especially fond of the tortures of the dammed. With its clear moral purpose the book is part of a long Christian tradition of moralizing, but enlivened with 'a verve and wit and a vivacity of language which sharpens the satire and enhances its comic aspects'. It even ends with a song on the tune called *Heavy Heart*!

7. A.O.H. Jarman & E. Jarman, *The Welsh Gypsies, Children of Abram Wood,* Cardiff, 1991.

This work is a revised and expanded translation of *Y Sipsiwn Cymreig* (1979) and it deals with the gypsy people of past days rather than travellers and tinkers, 'although there are no true Gypsies now travelling in Wales'. Eldra Jarman is a descendant of Abram Wood in the sixth generation. She is the grand daughter of John Roberts of Newtown and inherited the family gift for harp playing. The centre-piece of the work is the connection between the two families, *Teulu* Woods and *Teulu* Roberts who travelled around Wales from the beginning of the 19th century.

E. E. Roberts, *with Harp, Fiddle and Folktale,* Newtown, 1981.

The author of this work, a cousin to Eldra Jarman, died before the English version was published. A note by Selyf Roberts who had assisted with the original publication points out that it is a contribution of note to the memory of John Roberts, *Telynor Cymru* and at the same time a posthumous gift which enhances the romantic story of this talented Romany family. It includes John Robert's letters to Francis Hindes Croome edited by the late Dora E. Yates.

8. E. Owen, *Welsh Folk Tales, London 1857.* Reprinted by Llanerch, Felinfach, 1996.

9. T.G. Jones, *Welsh Folklore and Customs,* Aberystywth, 1930.

10. P.W. Nolan, *Folk Medicine in Rural Ireland,* Folk Ways vol. 27. Nolan, a lecturer in nursing studies in Birmingham, studied four healers or quacks in a small community he was familiar with in southern Ireland. He states that in common with folk-medicine in other countries, Irish folk-medicine does not locate illness within the biological or the pathological, but within the cultural. Their cures are based on suggestion techniques which harness the faith and beliefs of the culture that surrounds the sick person; adding that it is important not to confuse such present day healers with those of 18th century England, for the term 'quack' is not used in any derogatory

sense. In certain parts of Ireland their animal cures are so successful that the professional vets have requested the government to curb their activities. The vets claim that the quacks are not liable if anything goes wrong but the farmers point to their excessive high fees even if there is no improvement or if the animal dies. The particular focus of his study was in the west of Ireland, in an area of thirty square miles. The quacks he spoke with were 'ordinary'; elderly; lived like those around them; and preferred people to come to them. They have a special chair and spend as much time with the patient as is required. They never checked how effective their cures were and enjoyed the status and regard of their neighbours. There is often a performance of ritual such as the laying on of hands or breathing over a sick person; who may be asked to say special prayers or recite them later after the visit. Potions of plants and secret recipes from their gardens were also used. One quack explaining about the amount of time they spend with a person said, 'I know about the illness, but what I want to know is how the illness is affecting this particular person at this time'. Four individual treatments are described. For burns; for thrush, although he has no idea what it is or how people get it; for jaundice, shingles and eczema; and for slipped discs and other complaints. Maude, the only woman quack in her late forties, gets a pain on her left foot when depressed or more generally in the presence of suffering by others. Because of the numbers of people who were requesting help she confined her healing to two days a week. The author concludes from his studies that the quacks bring together religion, ethno-medicine and morality. Two were concerned with ridding the sick of their illness and two were more concerned to see their clients live more purposeful lives.

Chapter 8. Healers, Malpractice and the Law of the Land

11. R.C. Allen, *Wizards or Charlatan-Herbalists* (ibid).
   Many of the curious events involving them became part of Welsh folklore and one of the most known is the appearence in court of

John Harries after he discovered the body of a dead girl. Finding lost property, jewelry, stolen goods, and even wandering cattle were all recognised locally as part of the wizard's remit. At the same time the atmosphere generated by him was a part of his persona and it tended to produce slightly different versions of the same occurrence. So there was nothing usual when her family went to him after she was missing for some time. One account had it that he went into a kind of trance and without more ado led them to where she was, and taking a spade with him he dug where she had been buried. Richard Allen states that Harrries informed the police where they would find the corpse. Note however both the ease with which he found the body of the girl, whom he appeared to know quite well, and the fact that he claimed from carrying out an autopsy that she was pregnant. All of this led to her boyfriend being hanged for murder. The Welsh original of the popular verse is: Awn yn alarus /At Doctor Harries /Am ei fod yn hysbys, /I 'mofyn hanes bon; /Dywedai ei bod yn gorwedd /Gerllaw Maes yr On; /Mae ceu-bren mawr o wennyn /Yn tyfu buys y lle, /A nant yn rhedeg heibio /Lle'i lladdwyd ganddo fe. The last line of the poem on page 290 could have a dual meaning. The fact that he was charged as an accessory shows there was some doubt about the whole affair. Harries clearly did not wish to be questioned about it so he cleverly turned the issue around by asking the magistrates their hour of birth and he would tell them when they would depart from this life, and so he was discharged. His famous padlocked book of magic spells, that added a supernatural tinge to many accounts, could not be found among his effects stored in the National Library of Wales after his death. Some of his contemporaries were doubtful, even scathing, about the underhand methods used by Harries to gain information about people before they actually met him. He ran a small public house where gossip was frequently aired and even his wife's hospitality with oatcakes and ale made people that waited for him at ease and talkative, while the wizard could overhear everything in the next room. He could then magically inform them of their problems or illness and its causes, astrological or otherwise, before offering a cure and receiving a gift of money in return.

12. T.G. Davies, *Judging the Sanity of an Individual*, N.L.W. Journal Vol 19.No4. 1996.

In March 1856, Dr. William Price was called as a witness in a property case. He had drawn up the will of one of his patients shortly before he died. With a soliciter he took instructions concerning the man's new will, leaving the property to his wife for her life and afterwards to other relatives. The estate was valued at a hundred thousand pounds and Dr. Price was the only defence witness. The testator had hoped that the court would not allow the eccentricities of the doctor to prejudge the case, but in the event after two minutes the jury declared the earlier will was valid. As soon as he was called to the witness box, Price was asked to hand over the pistol he carried to the police. The opposing Councel began to tell of the doctor's own history, referring to the earlier post mortem on his father and the fact that he was known to the law on a number of occasions. Price ignored the barrister completely and when asked if he had been promised five hundred pounds for his testimony if they won the case, he replied: 'Oh that sum means nothing to me'. T. G Davies claimed that this behaviour showed Doctor Price's schizophrenia, but as in the court case of John Harries, it was probably that the doctor did not want to play along with what he probably thought was a charade and not worth his attention.

13. P.G. Jones, *Medicine in 18th Wales,* Folk Life (ibid) & G. Morgan, *History of Ceredigion* (ibid).

14. Daniel Defoe, *A Tour Through the Whole Island of Great Britain,* London, 1971

After travelling through the whole of Wales during the second decade of the 18th century, the stories of the well of saint Winifirid did not impress Defoe. In fact it all smelt too much of legend to take up his time. 'Romanists indeed believe it for it is obvious by their thronging here to receive the sanative virtue of the waters. A small town by the well may have risen from the confluence of the people hither for almost all the houses are either public ones or lodging houses. And the priests that attend the people are very numerous. They appear in disguise for sometimes they are physicians, sometimes surgeons sometimes gentlemen and sometimes as patients. No one takes any notice of them as to their profession although they know them well enough in private for they have their oratories in certain places. So good manners between the Roman Catholics and the Protestants have prevailed so far.'

15 F. Lynch, *The Holy Wells of Wales* (ibid) 1954.

16. T.I. Nicholas, *A Welsh Heretic,* London 1960.

17, J. Cule, *Dr.William Price (1800-1893) of Llantrisant: a study of an eccentric.* MD Thesis Univerity of Cambridge, 1960. Copy in the St. Fagan's Museum archive. Inoculation or 'variolation' was introduced into England by Lady Mary Wortley Montagu in 1717 after it had been performed on her own son in Turkey. She likened it to the engrafting of a bud in a garden. At the end of the century Edward Jenner a country doctor improved the procedure by using the related cowpox postule from the arm of a milkmaid and injecting it in a healthy boy.

18. Many prominent London physicians against inoculation in a campaign that claimed it had produced an 'ox-faced boy', whereas Dr. Price was against the wholesale scraping of pus on poor people by untrained doctors.

19. B.F. Roberts, *The Age of Resitution; Taliesan ab Iolo and the Reception of Iolo Morganwg,* in G.H. Jenkins (ed) *A Rattlesnake Genius, The Many faces of Iolo Morganwg.* (ibid).

20 T. Pennant, *A Tour of Wales Abridged by David Kirk,* Llanrwst, 1996.

T.G. Davies, *'Shrouded in Mystery', Events in the History of Psychiatry in Carmarthenshire,* The Carmarthenshire Antiquary Vol. xxxix, 2003.

In 1840, Dr. James Thomas, who worked as a general practitioner in Newcastle Emlyn for over forty years, wrote a long letter to *The Lancet* about a girl whose symptoms he had read of in the paper, *Seren Gomer.* He had not been asked to do so by her parents or anyone else but had decided to visit the girl. He left an account of his consultation that has similarities with the condition of the Fasting Girl of Pencader, who died in 1869. For over three years she was known to have had epilepsy and for most of the day lay in 'a state of perfect insensibility and unconscious' but woke up every evening around nine o clock. Thomas arrived earlier so he could watch the girl and note her every particular. She immediately flung herself into a sitting position and his impression was that she struggled for life and then lay back. Her mouth and eyes were wide open and her hands clenched and when raised into a sitting position she began to talk quite freely with her biscuits and tea. When a fit was about to return she described the pain as like a ball in her chest. He tested her eyes and even put a finger down her throat. As she took little by way of food and drink, he described her condition as from epilepsy or hysteria. Dr. Thomas intended to provide a further report if any change should occur, but appears not to have done so.

21. A few popular ballads on Sarah Jacob written in Welsh were published in Carmarthenshire during the late 1860's. In 1870 a number of case histories on the 'long-continued abstinence from food' that included Sarah and her father were published in London medical journals and in the following year Dr. R. Fowler's *A Complete History of the Case of the Welsh-fasting girl* appeared. Her story was subsequently turned into a play, *A Welsh Miracle* and published in 1928. S. Busby, *A Wonderful Little Girl, The True Story of Sarah Jacob, the Welsh fasting Girl,* London 2003. 'Sarah

Jacob may finally be credited with being the first recognised anorexic'

22 J. Cule, *The Wreath and the Crown, The Story of Sarah Jacob,* Llandyssul, 1967.

In his summing up of the case, Cule thought that when the final group of watchers that included some with medical experience was vigilant, she did not or could eat during the night as she had done during the previous two years. In his view 'She was a victim of her own personality (disorder) and that it was the child's 'duplicity' in convincing her parents that she had not been eating' which caused her death. This comment by a doctor who worked in St. David's mental hospital for many years as a psychiatrist is questionable given the circumstances of that time and place. In a small stone house where she would be in close proximity with them at all times, especially at night, it is a curious deduction to have made.

23 M.E. Owen & D. Jenkins, *Women in Welsh Law,* Cardiff, 1997.

24. M. Grufydd, *Witchcraft in Wales, Unpublished Essay 1973,* NMW – St. Fagan's Folk Archive index number 1997 - details of Dorthy Griffith 1656 and Anne Ellis 1657.
G. Morgan, *The History of Ceredigion* (ibid)
B. John, *Pembrokeshire Wizards and Witches,* Newport. 2001. (pp 23/24)

The reasons given by Brian John as to why the people of Wales did not become involved in the witch hunts were that they were generally accepted in society in the same way as labourers, coopers, millers, dairymaids and nurses were. In other words their skills were valued. Secondly they were acknowledged as successors of the priestesses and helpers who assisted in the rituals of pre-Christian religion. Linked with druids and bards, the people found it hard to accept (that) they were in league with the devil. Thirdly in the 16th & 17th centuries when the anti-witch hysteria was at its height the conflict between Catholics and Protestants in Wales was fairly low-keyed and, according to the author, only one woman was burned at the stake in 1558. Although individuals might have felt threatened, hexed or cursed by witches, the local communities as a whole did not react in a violent manner. People knew how to deal with bad or harmful magic – curses could be removed by negotiation as from the cursing wells of north Wales during the 19th century; or when necessary, use could be made of stronger magic, by a white witch or more generally the *dyn hysbys*.

25. M.E. Owen & D. Jenkins, *Women in Welsh Law* (ibid).

26. L.T. Davies & A. Edwards, *Welsh Life in 18th century Wales*, London , 1939.

27. *Dictionary of Welsh Biography down to 1950*, London 1959.
     Elizabeth Davis was born in Bala in 1782. She wrote and had published a two-volume autobiography about her eventful life that saw service as a nurse in the Crimea. Elizabeth Hoggan from Brecon was educated abroad and studied medicine in Zurich University. She moved back to Wales and was the first woman MD to be registered here in 1885. This was thirty-six years after Elizabeth Blackwell, who had moved with her family from England to America, had the 'honour' of breaking into the male medical lineage there. Dr. Hoggan was clearly concerned about the plight of Welsh women in terms of their health and physical education as the titles of some of her many publications indicate. Her last published works were still devoted to women's concerns and the internal complaints that affected them. The complete list of 29 medical works published by her and as joint author with her husband George Hoggan is in John Cule's Wales and Medicine, Aberystwyth, 1980. I am indebted to his bibliographical source list of published material relating to medicine in Welsh and English, throughout my research for the present book.
J. Williams, *The Autobiography of Elizabeth Davies,* London ,1857.

M. Jones, *Elizabeth Davies 1789-1860,* Cardiff,1960. A bilingual booklet based on the above.

F.E. Hoggan, *Women in Medicine, essays on the Woman Question in Europe,* 1884.

T. Onfel, *Biography of F.E. Hoggan,* Newport, 1970.

J. Boyd, *The excellent Doctor Blackwell,* Stroud, 2005

Growing interest in gender studies is evident in recently published research in Wales.

C. Lloyd-Morgan, *Welsh Women and the Written Word* in H. Price (ed) *Literacy in Medieval Celtic Societies,* Cambridge, 1998.

M. Roberts & S. Clare, *Women and Gender in Early Modern Wales,* Cardiff 2000, in which a total of fourteen cases of indictment for witchcraft during the period of 1550-1770 are recorded.

28. D. Davie, *Those were the days, Cardigan Cancer Healers,* Parts 1 & 2. Teifiside, 1984.

29. T.L. Jones & D.W. Jones, *Cancer Curers or Quacks? The story of a secret herbal remedy* Llandyssul, 1993.

30. H. Parri, *Meddygon y Ddafad Wyllt,* Caernarfon, 1984.

Owen Griffiths' instructions to one of his patients after the application of his magic salve: 'Keep the plaster on until the swellings begins to go down, and the matter to run out under the plaster (it will take as a rule two or thee days); do not take the small plaster off the wart (Epithelioma). Bathe around the wart with luke-warm water two or thee times a day, apply Olive Oil with a brush every time after bathing. Keep a plaster or anything to serve as a cover over it to prevent it being injured as some of the roots might be broken, and cause it to reappear and endanger your life. Let it come off itself, and when it will come, keep the sore place clean (by washing off the matter) and apply a little olive oil to the sore place till it heals up. Don't work and heal your blood.'

31. P. Logan, *Irish Country Cures*, Belfast, 1981.

A saying in Ireland: the doctor makes the diagnosis and the cancer curer treats the patient. The healer usually, with a severe complaint, will advise the person to see a doctor and then usually they come back to the healer. The essential ingredient in cancer plasters was arsenic which may be added to lard or butter and then applied as a plaster; even pitch or the juice of ivy leaves was used. This caused severe pain as the arsenic destroys all the tissues. The use of arsenic in the treatment of rodent ulcers was first described in a paper by Benjamin Rush, read to the American Philosophical Society in 1786. He learned of it from another doctor who had got the cure from some North American Indians. He examined the powder and found that the active ingredient was arsenic. Rush's method was to dissolve the powder in water and paint it on with a feather. This in fact was a method of application that the Evans brothers of Cardigan used, so perhaps they were aware of Rush's treatment. Later a small brush was used although there were some complaints that dipping the same brush into the bottle of 'magic oil' might contaminate other sufferers, so eventually they cleaned each brush after use. Patrick Logan adds that he had never heard of any folk treatment in Ireland for internal cancer. One of the points that David Rees Evans had put forward with his application to the Minister of Health, was that since his treatment for skin cancers was so effective some research might point to its possible internal use.

Chapter 9. The Secrets of Nature Revealed

32. J Cule, *Wales and Medicine*, Bibliographic Source-list, Aberystwyth, 1980.

33. A. Hayter, *Opium and the Romantic Imagination*, London, 1968.
G. Evans, *Poison Wine – John Keats and the Botanic Pharmacy*, The Keats-Shelley Review, 200?
J. Richards, *Opium and the British Indian Empire, the Royal Commission of 1895*, Cambridge. 2001; a lecture on the opium trade

with its politics, medical and social abuses to the final abolishment of the Indo-Chinese trade in the House of Commons in 1905.

In setting out the tradition of myths and poetic images that formed an important strand of the poetic imagination of Europe, Alethea Hayter begins in ancient Egypt where the poppy was advised for crying children in a medical treatise of the 16th century BC. For Dioscorides the drug would bring sleep and kill pain and the Roman physician Galen launched its compound of *mithridate* as an essential part of the European pharmacopoeia. For the poet Virgil it was a sophorific and the Arab doctor Avicenna is said to have been an opium addict. The use of it was brought back to Europe by the Crusaders who learned of it from the Arabs. The writings of Marco Polo, Mandeville and the travellers' tales gave form to the mythology of opium so that by the time *Purchas his Pilgrimage* was published in 1613 it had become a normal medical remedy. As a narcotic it was mentioned by Chaucer, Shakespeare, and Dryden; but it was the Welsh doctor, John Jones, Chancellor of Llandaf cathedral, who has the honour of first describing both its *Joy and happy Refreshment of the spirit* as well as its physical and mental symptoms from excessive use. Between 1700 when his book *The Mysteries of Opium Reveal'd* was published and 1822 with the publication of *The Confessions of an English Opium Eater* by Thomas De Quincey, Hayter examines its effects on the dreams and contemporary images in the consciousness of poets and writers. She explores the case histories of writers such as Poe, Baudelaire; De Quincey, George Crabbe, Samuel Taylor Coleridge, Wilkie Collins, Francis Thompson; and poets like Keats and Shelley who took opium occasionally but whose absorption in dreams and sleep and poetry is full of its evocative references.

John Keats was a doctor and as a member of the Society of Apothecaries he made the traditional herbal excursions to the Chelsea garden. Gareth Evans shows how the apothecary profession supplied a rich source for the often splintered imagery of his poetry. The opening lines of the 1819 *Ode on Melancholy* have often been referenced to his reading of Burton's *The Anatomy of Melancholy,* but the wealth of poisons and medical associations of plants like henbane, hemlock and the woody nightshade his *bittersweet fruit* are often bypassed. ...'and aching Pleasure nigh / Turning to Poison while the bee-mouth sips; / Ay, in the very temple of Delight / Veil'd Melancholy has her Sovran shrine.'

34. C.H. Jenkins, *Facts, Fantasy and Fiction,* (ibid*).*

35. M. Fitzpatrick, *The Cultivated Understanding and Chaotic Genius of David Samwell,* in G.H. Jenkins, (ed) *A Rattleskull Genius,* (ibid).

36. Very little is known about Richard Hakluyt the cosmographer other than his tireless gathering, editing and publication of accounts of other mens' voyages to the New World. Whether he himself explored the Americas is not known but he certainly encouraged the Elizabethian adventurers, as well the dreams of Iolo Moganwg, to find the Welsh descendants of Prince Madoc.

37. H. Walters, *Myfyrv Morganwg and the Rocking-Stone Gorsedd,* in G.H. Jenkins (ed) *A Rattleskull Genius,* (ibid).
Brutal Truth of Cook's final Minutes. The Guardian, 13.07.2004.
   He died on a beach in Hawaii on February 14, 1779. The official painting of the death of Captain Cook by John Clevely shows him as a heroic figure with his hand up as if signalling his ships to hold their fire on a large crowd of unruly natives. More recently a different version was auctioned at Christie's London. It is a work by the same painter that was based on sketches of the incident by his brother, a ship's carpenter, and shows Cook fighting for his life with a few companions and using his useless rifle as a club while the natives close in on him at the water's edge. The painting, and three other watercolours on display, was made about 1784 and may have been owned by Cook's widow. After the death of the artist the engraving was published but then altered to match the official account of the story.

38. C.W. Lewis, *Iolo Morganwg,* in B. Jarvis (ed) *A guide to Welsh Literature c.700-1800,* Cardiff, 2000.
M.A. Constantine, *In a Very Deranged State,* Planet 171, 2005; & *Seeing Daylight All the Way,* Planet 172, 2005.

Both articles are based on the life and work of Iolo Morganwg as revealed in the massive archive of his papers at the NLW. She is the leader of a research project at the Centre for Advanced Welsh and Celtic Studies which is currently mining the archive to bring it to the attention of of an English academic audience worldwide. The most recent book is a collection of essays edited by Professor G.H. Jenkins, titled *A Rattlesnake Genius.* As well as his own introduction, there are 21 contributions divided into 'Contexts'; 'The Bard'; 'Iolo's Preoccupations'; and 'Iolo's Friends and Enemies'. All the references used throughout this extraordinary critique including every individual paper or scrap of paper as used by Iolo, are itimised with a NLW number so university departments elsewhere can create their own mini archive by purchasing copies from the National Library of Wales in Aberystwyth.

39. J. Pollack, *John Wesley,* London 1989 & B. Griggs, *Green Pharmacy,* London 1981.

40. A. Hall, *John Wesley among the Physicians,* Studies in 18th Century London, London 1958;
J. Cule, *The Rev. John Wesley, The Naked Empiricist in Orthodox medicine,* Jour.Hist.Med. Vol.5, 1990.

41. F. Lynch, *Holy Wells of Wales, Cardiff,* (ibid)

42. James Graham studied medicine at Edinburgh and went to America as an eye surgeon in Philadelphia. It was when he saw the electrical demonstrations of Benjamin Franklin that he realised its potential in healing people. In 1775 he came to London and provided electricity or what he grandly terms *aetherial balsam* to ladies in high society such as Georgina, Duchess of Devonshire that

made his name. Towards the end of that decade he opened his Temple of Health with Graham himself acting as a guide to explain the magnetic and electric effects that his grandiose carnival-like attractions would induce in the human body. Further stimulation was provided by the scantily dressed young ladies trying out his machines as examples of perfect health available to the rich visitors with its combination of an electrified spa and gift shop. However his financial investment failed to draw the crowds so he returned to his hometown of Ediburgh a few years later. He continued to lecture on the good life through healthy eating and frequent bathing in mud, before dying suddenly at the age of forty nine.

43. G.P. Jones , *Folk Medicine in 18th Century Wales,* (ibid).

44. David Jenkins, *A Refuge in Peace and War,* National Library of Wales, 1952.

45. R. Porter, *The Greatest Benefit to Mankind,* (ibid).

46. T. Herbert & G.E. Jones (ed*) People and Protest:* Wales 1815-1880.

47. L.T. Davies & A. Edwards, *Welsh Life in the 18th Century,* London, 1939.

48. H.O. Thomas, *Dictionary of Welsh Biography up to 1940,* (ibid).

49. K.P. Thomas, *Some early Welsh contributions to American medicine,* in J. Cule (ed) *Wales and Medicine* (ibid).

50. Guton Owain who lived from 1460 to the end of the century was a bardic disciple of Dafydd ab Edmwnd, and he became a skillful poet. He was a scholar, a noted genealogist and copier of manuscripts that included the Mostyn 88 MS now in the collection

of the National Library of Wales. It contains the Life of St. Martin of Tours written by his uncle who was abbot of Valle Crucis, and a medical manuscript which begins with some unusual illustrations in a Welsh context, although common elsewhere at this period. They include a chart with the names in Welsh of a number of recognized Points on the body for bloodletting; a uroscopy diagram in circular form relating to the examination of urine, and a finely drawn Zodiac Man. It illustrates those areas of the body connected with the signs of the Zodiac showing a Christ-like figure covered in astrological signs where they were thought to govern the body or influence the human spirit. At the top Aries the Ram is sitting on his head. Taurus the Bull is wrapped around the neck. A pair of Gemini Twins cling to the outstretched arms. Cancer the Crab is on the breast. Leo the Lion guards the heart. Virgo the Virgin is at the stomach with the Scales of Libra hanging below and Scorpio the Scorpion between them and the genetalia. Sagittarius the Archer is across the thighs and Capricorn the Goat over the knees. Aquarius the young water-carrier is between the legs. The feet with marks of the Nails stand on a crossed pair of Pisces, the Fish. The library also has the earlier Peniarth 28 manuscript with illustrations from a Welsh lawbook. In common with medieval art it relied on imitating earlier models to illustrate the laws of Hywel Dda. The king is shown sitting on a throne, in a late 12th century style, although he had died two centuries earlier. The remainder of the twenty-two colorful pen and ink drawings are of officials of the court such as the chief of the household, groom, steward, doorkeeper and huntsman each shown holding the symbols of their functions. There are pictures of animals, bees, trees and birds. A woman with a dish begins a section on the laws of women; one man is shown pulling another's hair whilst fighting; and there is a decorated letter C on the law of land.

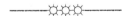

APPENDIX

Here is a list of plants and fruits, useful herbs and others that every doctor should know and use to treat wounds in the human body. Original list reproduced from the 1861 edition of Meddygon Myddfai.

Llyma bellach ddangos enwau y llysiau, a'r ffrwythau, a'r defnyddiau Llyseugael ag eraill a ddylai pob meddyg eu gwybod ag ymarfer a nhwy er iachau doluriau, a chlefydau ynghorph dyn.

A.

Agnus castus, y bendigaid, dail y twrch, dail fendigaid.

Asarabacca, llysiau'r cyfog, y fflamgoed.

Anigrifoliwm, y pump dalen.

Athemesia, y mâs.

Agrimonia, y tryw.

Anibrotana, llysiau'r corph.

Absinthiwn, chwerwyn, chwerwyn y twyn.

Abrosianwm, chwerwlys yr eithin, llysiau'r bystwn.

Apiwm, yr halogan, y perllys y môr.

Aliwn, garlleg, craf y gerddi, craf ffrengig.

Arnoglosa, llydan y ffordd,

Agrigida, rhuddos, gold, rhuddaur, sensegl.

Aleluia, surion y coed.

Arnogloswm, y llwynhidydd.

Agrioselinwm, dulys, alisantr, march berllys, perllys y berllan.

Agriophylwm, ysgall y moch.

Anetiwm, anis, gwewyrllys.

Asiantws, y rhydd redyn.

Acanthws, troed yr arth.

Artiplex, y llygwyn.

Arunda, corsen.

Aurantiwm, auronwydd, auronen, afal euron,

Anuncia, y fabcoll.

Amarista, amranwen, y tormwyth.

Amarica, yr eliniawg.

Aliscandriwm, marchberllys y gerddi, alisantr.

Acrifoliwm, y clwt, yr egrai.

Asblebion, tafod yr hydd.

Andram, y dorllwyd.

Amatoria, ffrwt i wared.

Artemisia, y ganwraidd lwyd.

Agrium, y torwynt, llysiau Cadwgan, y falerian.

Alum, y gieulys, llysiau'r giau, y glydlys.

Agripalma, babanllys, dynhaden ddall, torloes.

Auricula, clustiau'r arth, y ffrydd, blodau'r fann.

Alaria, adain y llew.

Anemonia, blodau'r gwynt, y ffrithogen.

Auripimentwm, aurbib, yr aurbibau.

Agria molosia, malw'r perthi, malwen y meusydd.

Agrostis, dant y ci.

Agrocinaria, ysgall Mair, ysgallen fraith.

Agrifoliwm, celyn.

Apiastrwm, llysiau'r gwenyn, gwenynddail, melorllys.

Acedula, penlon.

Archangelica, dalfedel.

Assa nigrwm, y bengaled.

2 o

Attramendwm, yspargam yr
  hesg, y gellesc.
Aspargws, y merllys, magwr-
  llys, gwiflan.
Aristologia, yr henllydan.
Assafetida, baw diawl, y drewgi.
Argilla, dail y clas.
Avalana, cnau'r gerddi.
Amaranthws, ammorlys, blodau
  ammor.
Aletorolofws, arianllys.
Acopus, drewgoed.
Abiga, y dorllwyd.
Acorwm, gellesk, elestr.
Argentaria, y dinwen, y din-
  llwyd.
Apios, clor, clorlys
Alicubi, ffiol y ffrith.
Acetabwlwm, crynddail.
Acipitrina, gwlaeth y waun,
  llaethygen y waun.
Aconitwm, llysiau'r blaidd,
  bleiddan, bleiddlys.
Anaglis, llysiau'r cryman.
Aptiaca, gwŷg, pys gwyllton.
Apolinaris, y belai, llewyg y iar.
Aristologia, llysiau'r galon, ys-
  garllys.
Angelica, llysiau'r angel, y
  wreiddber.
Alsinc, gwlydd y perthi, llau'r
  perthi.
Asphodelwm, y gilgain.
Anethwm, gwewyrllys.
Athanasia, tanclys, llysiau'r tanc,
  tanced, tancedlys.
Antylys, palf y gath.
Asplenwm, rhedyn y graig,
  rhedyn y gwelydd.
Alliarwm, troed yr assen.
Andrachne, troed y cyw.
Anti rhinwm, trwyn y llo, safn
  y llo, llwnc y trothwy.
Arwm, pidyn y gweew.
Alcea, malwen Alis.
Alicampania, marchalan.
Aquileia, troed y ceiliog.
Acetaria, melynsur.
Amera, had y rhos, grawn y
  rhos, gwyfon rhonwydd.
Anatolia, llorwydden.
Ardaliwm, corsen, cyrs.

Alga, gwimon, gwigmor.
Alwmen, elyf.
Andonica, gwrlys.
Argimonia, y dinllwyd.
Argentina, arianwen, y dinllwyd.
Alcea, malwen Alis.
Arbutus, mefynwydd, mewydd,
  mewydden.
Aquilegia, madwysc.

B.

Bacca, gwyfon, gwyfonen, mac-
  cwn, maccynen, grawn coed,
  greol, egroes, manaeron coed.
Baccalina, bae, baewydd.
Balania, greol gwin, grabon,
  ffrwyth gwinwydd.
Balsamwm, balmwydden.
Balsaminwm, balm.
Bambata, morwynwyn.
Betonica, cribau sanffred, y bit-
  tain, y bitton, y feddyges
  lwyd, dannogen.
Betonica aquatica, dannogen y
  dwr, y feddyges ddu.
Barba aeron, pys y ceirw, pwys
  y ceirw.
Barba sacti, y ganwraidd lwyd.
Buglosswm, tafod yr ych.
Bursa pastoris, pwrs y bugail,
  llysiau'r tryfal.
Batinwm, mwyar y perthi.
Buboniwm, y serlys, serenllys,
  dail y tenewyn, blodau
  gwydion.
Botrus, gwinwyfon.
Byglosa, glesyn y coed.
Beneria, grug, grel.
Bibilis, brwynen.
Burneta, y rhwyddlwyn.
Borago, tafod yr ych, tafod y
  fuwch.
Barba Jovis, llysiau pen tai, y
  ferllys, berllys.
Bellis, llygaid y dydd.
Bipnelia, gwyddlwyn.
Biciona, pys y llygod, gwŷg.
Barba capri, barf y bwch, er-
  waint, barfogan.
Batis, corn y carw mor, eliglys.
Bardana, cyngaw, caresgar.

Botris, derwen Gaersalem.
Bransi, crynllys, crynddail, y gron doddaid.
Brassicca, breswg, bresych.
Brionia, coedrwym, greol y cŵn, eirin gwion, gwion y perthi.
Belliwm, priellau Mair, deigren Mair, sammwl.
Beata, } melged, sewlys,
Beta, } y chwecclys.
Bardana, cyngaw, baw mwcci.
Barba senis, barf yr hen wr.
Branca, trigon, tygron.
Bonia, hiawl.
Boletus, grion, grionen.
Bacca palustris, llus, llusi.
Bacchar, menig Mair, meddyg y bugail.
Bacciferia, gruglys.
Barbarcea, berwr Ffrainc.
Batws, mwyarwydd, mwyar.
Benedicta, y fabcoll.
Berberis, y pren melyn, drain ysbin, greol ysbin.
Bifoliwm, gefellys.
Bipennula, gwlydd Mair.
Bismalva, malw yr hêl.
Blephara, alaw, llynnon.
Blitum, blithan.

C.

Caro, garddwy.
Chamaerops, dail yr ysgyr.
Chelidonia, melynllys, llysiau'r wenol, y ddilwydd felen.
Centauria, bustl y ddaiar.
Calamentha, mynt y mynydd.
Cariophiliwm major, benigan, clawen ffrengig.
Cariophiliwm minor, pinc, ceian, ceilys.
Cumminwn, llysiau'r hedydd.
Cochlearia, chwerfwr, y chwerfell, golofau.
Cyperus, ysnoden Fair, gelinllys.
Consolida regia, yspardunllys, yspardun y marchog.
Ceraswin, ceiros.
Capina, corwynwyn, ceninog.
Cœpa, gwynwyn, egryn, egran.
Chamaedaphne, perfagl.

Clematitis, ysgarllysc bychan.
Cardus niger, ysgall duon.
Cardus maculatus, ysgallen fraith.
Crassula minor, y ffaflys, yr orpin.
Cardamonia, grawn Paris.
Capillis Veneris, gwallt y Forwyn.
Caprifoliwm, gwyddfid, gwyddfel.
Cynanthemis, llygad yr ych.
Capnonia, mwg y ddaiar.
Carex, hesg, gellesg, gelesg.
Cassythia, llysiau'r llindag.
Cardus Veneris, cribau'r pannwr.
Calendula, sensegl, rhuddos.
Chinilla, y feidiog las.
Coronopus, dant y llew.
Consolida major, cyfardwf.
Crithmwm, ysgyrydlys y mor.
Cardus benedictus, ysgall bendigaid.
Chamepitys, palf y gath.
Cornus silvestris, pisgwydden.
Camilon, ysgall y blaidd.
Cineria, llysiau'r llydw.
Capsella, mwstarth.
Consolida minor, llygaid y dydd.
Coronopus, erilyriad y mor,
Cyclamenis, didol, didenol.
Carota, moron, dawean goch, ciwig yr ardd.
Calaminthus, mynt y gath, mynt bendigaid.
Cynosrhodes, rhos y cwn, breilwy y perthi.
Convolvulus, y taglys.
Cicerbita, ysgall y moch.
Canopican, cyfoglys.
Cimbaria, llysiau'r geinog.
Consolida media, glesyn y coed.
Crispinus, yspinwydd, y pren melyn.
Cucumerasinus, dynaid gwynnon.
Crithamon, eliglys, githrell.
Cannabis, cywarch.
Cawlis, cawl, callorlys.
Castania, cestin, cnau cestin, cestinen, cestinwydd.
Chameleucis, troed yr ebol.
Cinamoniwm, canel.
Crocus, saffar, y feddyges felen.

Consolia, mader, llysiau Mair.
Chamaemiliwm, milwydd.
Cedrus, cedryswydd, llibanwydd.
Clobina, dulys, alisantr,
Clutumws, yr engraff.
Cladiolws, yr hylythr, y gloria.
Cariophilis, claw, clawen, y clawan, y clewyn.
Centoria, ystol Crist.
Concloida minor, yswinfri.
Cetra, redyn y gogau.
Cisampelis, berthlys.
Cristagalli, arian gwion.
Comeria, barf y bwch.
Cicuta, cegyr, cegyr ocr, cegyr Bened.
Cnita mattifera, y bumystl, pymystl.
Catabrica, blodau'r gog.
Cynoocrambia, yr yscedd, yscedd y cwn.
Crambe sativa, yscedd y gerddi, yscedd lledfegin.
Ciglesia, pigle, woodstarre.
Coliandria, coliawndwr, coliandrwn, coliandr, brwysgedlys.
Cyanws, y clafrlys.
Crenaria, bwlwg yr ŷd.
Calendula, swyn-ystres.
Craspula, y ganhewin.
Cardamwm, berw'r lledfegin.
Culaniwm, llysiau'r dom, y dinllys, dail y dindost.
Confeiria, gludoglys y cwmffri, llysiau'r cwlan.
Cadania maria, berwr.
Casofoliwm, craf y geifr.
Canfeged, cyflaith.
Colocasia, mynt y meirch.
Castania, castain, cneuwydden, gestin, cestinen.
Convolvulws major, cloffrwym y cythraul, cloffrwym y mwcci.
Codyla, yr amranwen.
Cam, claer, orchwyrydd.
Calemintwm, mynt y feisdon.
Cifrwm, erwaint.
Carifoliwm, y fabcoll.
Cessesta, banadl, banal.
Cucnander, us maeldaf, zena.
Crimillimwm, y gromil.

Canufenta, corfanadl.

D.

Dans leonis, dant y llew.
Dastys, nele, y gandoll.
Dragontia, neitrlys.
Diapensia, clust yr arth, yr olchyddes.
Digitalis, ffiol y ffrith, byssedd y cwn.
Dancus, nyth yr aderyn, panygan, panwg, ciwig.
Daphnoides, clust yr ewig, glas y gaiaf, nidwydden las.
Dictamen, y ddittain.
Dactytia, gofyslys.
Dardana, cyngaw.
Deliteria, clych Enid.
Damasconia, llydan y ffordd.

E.

Enulacampana, marchalan y llwyglas.
Ebulwm, ysgaw bendigaid, gwaed y gwyr, corysgaw.
Endiva, yr ysgellog.
Elleborwm, pelydr ysbain, y torrgos, y torrlaeth.
Enfragon, y waedlys fawr.
Erythrodanwm, y wreiddrudd, y gochwraidd, madr.
Erygiwm, ysgall boglynog.
Erywm, pys yr aran.
Ebulusia, y greulys fawr.
Erigerwm, y benfelen.
Enfatorwm, y feon chwerw.
Efatica, cynglennydd.
Erratica, treigledlys, elinog goch, y benrudd.
Eleboniwm nigrwm, y gloerllys fawr.
Eruca, y pybyr gwynn.
Erisimwm, berw'r gauaf.
Ebuntia, ysgaw bendigaid, gwaed y gwyr.
Elebiarni, cyflaith.
Equisetwm, rhawn y march.
Elatine, llysiau'r gerwyn.
Eleborws, troed yr arth, llewyg y llynger, llyngerllys.

Eupatoriwm, y drydon, troed y dryw, drywlys.

Euphrasia, golwg Crist.

Eringo, morgelyn, y cwsglys.

Erica, grug, y grelys.

Eleniwm, marchalan.

Ervilia. gwyg, pys yr adar.

Filicula virginea, gwallt y For-wyn.

Fragania, corwynwyn, cibellau, cibellys, y cebyddlys.

Filitis, tafod yr hydd,

Funda sexsanet, ysgall.

Filape, dywlath, dywla.

F.

Fabaria. berwr Taliesin, yr orpin, ffatlys, y fywydog.

Febrifuga, tormwyth, chwerwyn gwynn, yr amranwen.

Fungus, grion, madarch, ffwngc y ddaiar, mwg y ddaiar.

Farfara, troed yr ebol, pesychlys.

Farfaria, y bittain, dannogen, cribau sanffred.

Filex, rhedyn, ffil-lys.

Fragaria, gwlydd syfi.

Fraga, syfi.

Fistularia, bolog y waun, llys-iau'r cwn.

Flos Veneris, boled Olwen, y taglys mawr, y tagwydd.

Felterre, y ganrhi goch.

Ffurfur, y greifion.

Fumws terræ, mwg y ddaiar.

Ffenicula, ffunel, ffenigl.

Ffascoli, ffa ffreinig.

Filix boretica, llawredyn.

Ficaria, gwenith y gog.

Flos Adonis, pabi lledfegin, bwlwg lledfegin.

Filix aquatica. rhedyn y gors, rhedyn Crist, rhedyn cyfr-dwy.

Ffebilion, y tresgl.

Fflamula, y fflamboeth, blaen y gwayw, y fflammog.

Filix aquatica, rhedyn y gors, rhedyn Crist, rhedyn bendig-aid.

Faba, ffa, panar.

Ffemolin, ffunel, ffenigl.

Filipendula, y grogedyf.

Fontinalia, llyriad y llynn.

Farinaria, cannllys, y paill, rhe-dyn y mynydd.

Fascula aurea, ysgubaur, llwyn euron, yr eurwaith.

G.

Gicumala, y ddalen ddu, y goed-wyrdd, glas y gauaf.

Grosula, gwyfon barfog, gwyfon-en farfog, grwys eirin, grwys eirin Mair.

Grossularia, grwyswydd.

Galingal, ysnoden Fair, ysnoden llys.

Gingibera, sini, sinsyr, ginber, y torwynt.

Gallicristi, y geiniogwellt.

Gramen, glaswellt, porwellt, ton-wellt, maeswellt, ffwynwellt, gweirwellt, gwyran.

Grifoliwm, emeillion.

Grifoliwm minus, meillion.

Grifoliwm albwm, meillion Olwen.

Grifoliwm rubrwm, marchfeill-ion, meillion cochion, rhudd-feillion.

Glastwm, gweddlys, llasarlys, y glaslys, glaston.

Granwm gnidwm, pybyr y myn-ydd.

Graphaliwm, llwydym y ffordd, y llwydlys,

Gith, llysiau'r bara, gith, y gith-lys.

Geminalis, y ganhewin, y clym-lys, clymmogan.

Gabsus, y flewog, blewlys, blew-ynog.

Grinaletwm, yr iororth, llysiau iororth.

Gruina, y droedrudd.

Galiwm, melynllys, llysiau'r cower, melyn y twyn.

Glycyrrhiza, melottai, glyr, glyf, melanllys.

Gladiolus, gelesc, yr hylythr.

Geraniwm, robinllys, y droed-rudd.

Gyrytelaeth }
barbatus }

Grana Parisi, grawn Paris.

Gesticlws, salmaiog, craf y nadredd.

Garaseca, tanclys, tanced, tancedlys, tansi, tansli.

Generum, hefyd yw.

Glaucis, marchfeillion, meillion cochon.

Geribiwm ola, perwaint.

Geum, y fabcoll.

Gromentwm, magmodor, ystraf llob.

Gratia Dei } gras Duw,
Gratiola } yr yrddon, yr orddon.

Gnadwm, y glaslys, y glaiarllys, y lasog.

Geribiwm ola, perwaint.

Granum, grawn, had, ceri, ascer, cnewyll.

Glans, més, mesen, castinen, cneuen, cestin.

Gith, grawn Rhufain, hefyd ŷd.

H.

Herba regia, yr odrwyth.

Herba perforata, eiriullys, erinllys, godwallon, y gandoll.

Herba Roberti, y droedrudd.

Herba sardonia, troed yr erydd.

Herba pulicaris, y chweinllys, llysiau'r chwain, llewyg y chwain.

Herba prati, chwys Arthur, erwaint, melys y waun.

Herba paralysis, priellau, samwl, samylau, llysiau'r parlys, y dewbannog, clych Euron.

Herba Joauis, llysiau Ieuan, y gandoll.

Herba Jovis, llysiau'r gwayw, y fywlys fawr, bywlys mawr.

Herba pedicularis, y llaullys, llewyg y llau.

Herba crucis, llysiau'r grog.

Herba Walteri, llysiau Gwallter.

Herba stipiti, wodsawr.

Hedera, ciddew, iddieu, iorwg, eiddionwg, eiddan, eidwydd.

Hedera terrestris, y feidiog las, llysiau'r gerwyn, eiddiau'r ddaear, y cyrflys, y gerwynllys.

Hedopnis, dant y llew lleiaf.

Heliochrysos, blodau'r haul, euros, eurbenn.

Helnus, hesg, gelesg.

Heptapleurws, llwynhidydd.

Heptapleuron, llydan y ffordd.

Heleniwm, marchalan, llysiau'r eli.

Helionwm, tafod yr hydd.

Heptaphylwm, tresgl melyn, melyn yr eithin.

Hepatica, yscenllys, llysiau'r afu, goferllys, clust yr assen, cynglennydd y dwr.

Helleborus niger, troed yr arth.

Helxine, y berthlys, y cynghafog, cwlm y gwydd, cwlm y coed, y gylmog.

Hirudinaria, melynllys, llygadlys, llygadlym, llysiau'r wenol.

Hieraciwm, y felenydd.

Hipposelinon, dulys, alisantr, marchberllys, perllys y berllan.

Horminiwm, clais, had llygaid, y werddonell.

Hyacinthus, sanau'r gog, groeso'r haf, glas y llwyni, clych yr cos.

Hyperia, llysiau Ieuan, y gandoll fechan.

Hpericwm, llysiau Ieuan, y gandoll fawr, y godwallon fawr.

Hipoglosswm, tafod y march.

Hypogesia major, llysiau'r gwayw, y fyddarllys, bywlys mawr.

Hypogesia minor, bywlys bach, llysiau'r to, briweg y cerrig, cynffonllys.

Hypomarathrwm, ffunel y cwn, iororth.

Hyoscyamos, llewyg y iàr.

Hydrolapathwm, suran, hirion, tafol y dwr.

I.

Jacca alba, y benlas, y gaswenwyn.

Juncus, brwynen, pabwyren.

Jacea nigra, y bengaled.
Janis barba, llysiau pen tai, llys-
iau tai, tolys, y toflwyn.
Janipiwm, egroes.
Jayrys, y fyddarllys.
Introlewm, y ieuawd, yr wr-
nerth.
Jarucia, iarwg, madar.
Jassa nigra, mad felen, llysiau'r
hadfelen.
Ibiscus, malw y morfa, malw
yr hel, meddalai.
Jecoraria, cynglennydd, y llefan-
og, llinwysg yr afon.
Inguinalis, dail tenewyn, tene-
wynllys.
Juniperus, beryw, berywydd,
eithinen bêr, eithin y cwrw,
berweddlys.
Ischas, huddygl y march.
Iris, elestr, elestron, y gelesg, y
gleiflys.
Inguinaria, y dinllwyd.
Ipericon, eurinllys, y gandoll,
godwallon.
Ipia minor, y wenolydd.
Junonis, alaw'r dwr, y gannaid,
gwili.
Isopus, isob, ysgyllys.

L.

Labwrnwm, pyswydd.
Laurus, llorwydd, dail y cwrw,
diodwydd, y bae, y bae-
wydd.
Lactuca, gwylaeth, llaethoglys,
llaethlys, llaethogan.
Lactuca saliva, llaethlys, gwy-
laeth, lledfegin.
Lactuca sylvatica, llaethlys y
maesydd, gwalchlys.
Laver, perllys y nant, dyfrllys.
Lactucella, ysgall y moch.
Lavendula, llafant, llafanllys,
llysiau'r dillad, llogellys.
Lanceolata, llwynhidydd.
Lappago, cribau'r pannwyr.
Lattyris, llysiau'r cyfog.
Lagopus, meillion cedenog.
Lappa, y cyngaw.
Laureola, clust yr ewig.

Laurentiana, glesyn y coed, glas
y coed, y goedwyrdd.
Labeo, dynhaden ful.
Lapathwm, suran y maes.
Lanandula
Lestagiwm omnigawne, tafod
yr hydd.
Lapa, tafol, "parel dock."
Laparwm,) athulm, trwython,
Lapaewm, (trwythlys.
Lactuca agrestis, y gwla.
Latacea ortril diwrpletus.
Lapaciwm rocudiwm, cyngaw.
Lemoniwm, lemwn, euronen sur.
Lentistws, yr yswydd.
Ledea, y benlas, y glafrllys.
Leucacantha, ysgallen wenn,
gwynysgall, ysgallen fraith.
Levisticwm, perllys y meirch.
Leucophyllwm, y dewbannog
fawr, gwynllys.
Lencacanthamis, amranwen.
Lepidwm, berwr gwyllt.
Lens palustris, bwyd hwyaid,
llinhad y llynn.
Libadiwm, y ganrhi goch, yr
heinllys.
Liliwm, alaw, lili, blodau Essyllt,
elestron.
Liliwm convaliwm, clych Enid,
gwenonwy, alaw crewyll.
Liliastrwm, y taglys, llindag y
perthi, y llinclwm, cyfnydd.
Libanotis, pyglys, ffenigl y moch.
Limonia, ffrithlys, y ffrithogan,
y goedwyrdd.
Ligwstrwm, gwyros, gwewydd.
Lichen, yscenllys, y llefanog, y
lleglyn, cynglynydd.
Linagina, llindag, llindro.
Lithospemwm, tormaen.
Lingua canis, tafod y ci.
Lingua cervina, tafod yr hydd.
Lingua leonis, tafod y llew.
Lingua hircina, tafod y bwch.
Lingua bovis, tafod yr ych,
bromwerth yw.
Ligustrwm, priellyn, priallen.
Lingen avituli, glesyn y coed.
Lingua avis, tafod yr edn.
Lintistws, yr yswydd.
Litoria, yr un yw.

Lodwin, pys y ceirw.
* * pabi yw.
Loliwm, gwyg, bwlwg yr yd.
Lotus urbanus, pys y ceirw.
Lolia, craf y nadredd.
Ligna omnia, tafod yr hydd.
Lobgyry, y tewlaeth.
Lucoion, melyn y gauaf, melyn y gwelydd, murwyll.
Lupinus, llewyg y blaidd
Lycopus, llysiau'r fam.
Lychnis, rhoscampau, yr elfannog, bannogan.
Lysimachiwm, helyglys, gwaedlys.
Lichen marina, llaswyr.
Libanws, llibanwydd, y tuswydden.
Lycopsis, tafod yr ych mawr.
Lycopodiwm, crafanc y blaidd, gwinedd y blaidd, mwswn y mynydd.
Lychnitis, cas gan y cythraul.
Luteola, aurfanal, y corrfanal, melynog y waun.
Lunaria, gwlanllys, y wlanog, cadenllys, y lloerlys, canwyll adar.
Luciola, tafod y neidr.

M.

Malva, malw, malwedlys, malwottan, malwedlys, malwedog, malwydd, y feddalac, melfedlys, hoccys.
Malva sacra, malw bendigaid, yr holihocc yw, hoccys Mair.
Malvaviscus, malw y morfa, malw yr hel.
Mastic, gwm, llysnof. llysnofedd y gwydd, llysnodd.
Macia, y mas.
Matrisilva, gwyddfid, y melwydd, melwydd y perthi.
Mamoria, crafanc yr arth.
Maturalis, craf y geifr.
Marmorilla, y drydon, llysiau cychwlyn, cychwlyn.
Majorana, eidran.
Magistrantia, pelydr ysbain.

Marubiwm rubens, morddynaid cochon, morddynaid duon.
Marabiwm albwm, morddynaid gwynnon, morddynaid llwydon, llwyd y cwn, llwydyn chwerw, perwherwyn.
Mala, afalau, pwmmod.
Malwm aurantiwm, afal euron, euronen, eurbwmp.
Malwm terræ, bara'r moch, y mochwraidd, egel.
Melampyrwm albwm, biwlith, buelith.
Melilotus, meillion y ceirw.
Melisa, gwenynllys, gwenynddail, llysiau'r gwenyn, llysiau'r mêl, gwenynog, llysiau'r mel, mellys.
Melaniwm, ysgidiau'r gog.
Melanthiwm, bwlwg Rhufain, bwlwg lledfegin.
Mentha, mynt, fflorlys.
Mespilws, ceri, cerien sarphwydden, sarphwydd.
Meticulwm, dail meiwon.
Mercurialis, sawdl y crydd, llysiau'r gwr da.
Melitotwm, y wydroeth, y wewyrllys.
Mercuralia, craf y geifr.
Mercuriwm, argyry, arian byw.
Mentastiwm, mynt y meirch.
Mentha aquatica, mynt y dwr.
Merica, banal, banadl.
Minera, glist, mynor.
Mezerion, llosglys, llysiau'r llosg, y bliwyn, bliw, bliwlys, godrwyth.
Mezerion albwm, yr odrwyth weun, canys blodau gwynnon a fydd arno, nidwydden weun.
Mezerion rubwm, yr odrwyth rudd, blodau rhuddgochion a fydd arno, nidwydden goch.
Mirica, dynhaden, epome.
Millifoliwm, y filwydd, llysiau'r gwaedlin, milddail.
Morwm, mwyaren.
Morus, mwyarwydd, mieri, drysi.
Morus arbaria, mwyarbren, mwyarwydden, morwydd.

Morella major, mochlys.
Morella minor, y droedrudd.
Morsus caline, y glwydd.
Morsus galina, gwlydd, brech-
lys, y llymorlys.
Morsus diaboli, y gaswenwyn,
bara'r cythraul, tamaid y
cythraul.
Milesolis, y gromil, y gromel.
Miety atoreu, yr yswydd, ys-
wydden.
Morsella major, llysiau'r môr, y
morllys.
Morsella minor, llysiau Bened,
benediglys.
Myrta, llysiau'r giau, gieulys,
gewynllys.
Myrtus, myrtwydd, mordywydd.
Myrtus silvestris, gwyrlin, gwir-
linwydd, gwyrlinen, helygen
bêr, helyg y waun, helyg y
chwain, mordywydd y gors,
helyg y gors, corrhelyg y gors.
Myrtus hortensis, gwyrlin y
y gerddi, gwirlin lledfegin,
myrtwydd, mordywydd.
Muraliwm, y muriwyn, pelydr
y gwelydd, llysiau'r murddin.
Muscus, mwswrn, mwswgl.
Mysotis, clust y lygoden.
Myacanthon, celyn y mor, morgelyn, y cysglys.
Myriophyllwm, milddail iororth, milwydd.
Myrra, myrr, gwm.
Myrtoselinon, clust y lygoden.

N.

Napus, erfinen, erfin.
Nappiwm, yr erfinog, erfinllys.
Nasturtiwm, berwr, mwstarth.
Nastwrtiwm hortensis, berwr
gerddi.
Nastwrtiwm aqaticwm, berwr
dwr, berwr ffynonau.
Nastwrtiwm gallicwm, berwr
ffrengig, berwr gerddi.
Nastwrtiwm porciawm, berwr
moch.
Nastwrtiwm pratensis, berwr
meusydd.

Nastwrtiwm agrestis, berwr
gwyllt.
Nastwrtiwm lapidwm, berwr
cerrig.
Nastwrtiwm sylvestris, garlleg
y ferwr.
Nardus, nardd, yr eliog, gwrthlys
yr ardd.
Nectaria, marchalan.
Neurospaston, mieri Mair, rhos
y cwn, breilenllwyn bêr.
Navce, ysgyllys.
Nepta, mynt y gath.
Nepte, erfin.
Nicea, y bengaled.
Nice alba, y beulas.
Nigea nigra, y bengaled.
Nigella, ysgithlys, githlys, llys-
iau'r gith, hefyd dynaid.
Nigella Romana, bwlwg Rhufain.
Nomma, y llwyn gyfagwy, y
facewyog, hacewyog.
Numularia, y canclwyf, yr holl-
gur, ariaullys.
Nux juglans, cnau ffreinig.
Nux avelana, cnau cestin.
Nymphea, alaw, rhos y dwr,
breilen y dwr.
Nucus, collen, cneuwydden, coll-
wydden.
Nucus sylvestris, collen wyllt.
Nucus barbaratus, collen led-
fegin.

O.

Odorata, rhocelys, fflorlys, ys-
pigan, yspiglys, bleision,
sychlysiau.
Occularia, llysiau'r olwg, y
wyrddonell.
Occulis Dei, ut spensolis, llysiau
Crist, golwg Crist.
Occulis Christi, y wyrddonell,
gwerddonllys, golwg Crist,
llygad Crist, goleudrem.
Occulis bovis, llygad yr ych.
Olusatrwm, march berllys y
gerddi, perllys y cestyll.
Olus, cawl, march ferwr, berwr
teulu.
Olibanwm, ystor, tus gwyllt.

2 D

Occulus caninus, llygad y ci.

Oleoselinon, march berllys yr hel, march berllys y môr, yr helogan.

Occulus leporis, llygad yr ysgyfarnod.

Oenanthe, y tormaen, yr eglyn, y gromil.

Os mundi, pŷs y llygod, gwyg.

Osimwm, brenhinllys.

Organ, mesuriaid, meswraidd, y mysyriad.

Oreoselinon, perllys y mynydd, gwidigdda.

Origanwm sativwm, corfynt y gerddi.

Origanwm sylvestris, corfynt y crieigiau, mynt y creigiau.

Oriewm, blorlys, bloran.

Orchis, yr erith, ceilliau'r ci, y galdrist, tegeiriau ystongroes.

Orpina, y fywydog, yr orpin, briweg.

Orobanche, tagwyg.

Ostris, y gingroen.

Osiliwm, tringol, suran.

Organwm, myntmaenau,maenaullys, maenllys, mynt y graig.

Olewm, eliw, gliw, olew.

Olea, gliwydden, eliwydden, olewydden.

Ophioscorodon, garlleg gwyllt, craf y meusydd.

Oxys, suran y coed.

Oxalis corvi, suran y frân.

Oxalys, suran yr yd.

Oxylapathwm, tafol Mair, tafol surion.

Oxytriphyllwm, meillon cochon, rhuddfeillion, hefyd suran, tringol.

Ophioglosswm, tafod y neidr.

P.

Pacitaria, coantafawl

Patoria, bibasinpen, gyta y ffer rhag pob gweli.

Peretus, pelydr.

Panis oncli, surion y coed.

Petilion, peuros, breilan segli.

Paralys, samwl, samylen, deigreu Mair,llygad Ebrill, corfannog y waun, y dewbannog fechan, priellau penclwm.

Polianthys, corfannog yr ardd, sammwl y gerddi, priellau'r ardd, priellau corbi, corbien, corbiod.

Panis euculi, suran y gog, suran y coed, surfeillion.

Phalaris, yr eigryn, gwenith yr ysgyfarnog, crydwelit.

Paniewm, y gibog, ciboglys.

Panis porcinws, clor, cnau'r moch, bara'r hwch.

Parietaria, llysiau'r pared, paredlys.

Partheniwm, tormwyth gwynn, amranwen.

Palmus, y llymddreiniog, y llewydd, y palflys.

Papaver, bwlwg, pabi y cysglys, drewlys.

Papaver erratiewm, bwlwg yr yd, cysglys yr yd.

Papaver sativwm, bwlwg yr ardd, bwiwg lledfegin.

Palma Christi, llun llaw Crist, llysiau'r fam.

Pastinacia hortense, pannas.

Pastinacia agrestis, pannas y moch, efyrllys.

Peplws, llaeth y cythraul.

Petalitis, corn y carw, corn yr hydd.

Pedram, y bybyrllys.

Pespalle, hefyd ∤ gwrthlys, yr
l'escaballe,   ∫ alan hen.

Pesroliwm, bing, y droedrydd.

Pelitaiewm, llawredyn y ddaear.

Porrwm, cenin.

Pes leonis, troed y llew, y feidiog lwyd, (gwel ymlaen I.G.)

Peristerios, y dderwen fendigaid, cas gan gythraul, gwylldarf, tarfellyll.

Persicaria, dail y dindost, cliniog goch, y bengoch.

Perforata, y gandoll, gowallon, godwallon.

Pes leporina, troed yr ysgyfarnog.

Pes milvi, troed y barcud.

Pes corvi, troed y frân.
Pes anserina, troed yr wydd.
Pes puli, troed y eyw.
Portulaca, troed y cyw.
Potamogitwm, llynnwellt, dyrwellt, gwellt y dwr.
Perpacantha, troed yr arth.
Pes alauda, troed yr hedydd, blodau'r hedydd.
Pesvituti, y fabcoll.
Pentafoliwm, pump dalen.
Pervincia, perfagl.
Periphoron, pluf y waun, pluf y gors, pluf y brwyn.
Pes muli, y fabcoll.
Pesiliwm, llysiau sllin.
Pes leonis, troed y llew, y feidiog las, llysiau'r gerwyn, y gerwynllys, llysiau'r cwrw, cyrflys.
Perpensa, bolgarn yr ardd, y gwrthlys.
Pencedauwm, ffenigl y moch, piglys, pyglys.
Pedicularia, y lleulys, llysiau'r llau, llewyg y llau.
Pentaffilwm, dail y pumpys.
Philistis, tafod yr hydd, y tanllys, dail y tanllosg.
Philochares, chwerwyn llwyd, llwyd y cwn, llwyd y galchen.
Phaseolus, ffa ffreinig, ffa marchell.
*Petrosiliwm perllys, mynachlys, sewlys.
†Petrosiliwm olioselinwm, yr halogan, yr helogan, marchberllys yr hêl.
Piganiwm, hefyd } blodau'r
Pipnia } brenin, rhos y brenin, rhos y mynydd, pioni.
Pisosella, clustiau'r llygoden.
Pilocella, y dorllwyd.
Pimpinela stepmodo, llysiau llysyrawt, llysyrlys.
Plantago major, llydan y ffordd, yr egorllys.
Plantago minor, y llwynhidydd, ystelynês, ystelynllys.

Pix, pyg.
Picea, pygwydden, ffyrwydden, terrwydden.
Pigula minor, tafod yr edn, tafod y deryn.
Polygonwm, y ganhewin.
Polyanthemwm, blodau'r menyn, y beneurad, troed y frân.
Pœonica casta, * * * blodau'r brenin.
Pœonoia, blodau'r brenin, coronllys.
Polypodiwm, rhedyn y deri, rhedyn y canddo, llawredyn y derw.
Polipopiwm, llawredyn y llwyf, llwyfredyn.
Pinus, pinwydden, ffinydwydd.
*Polipopiwm lilinwm, llawredyn y llwyf.
Pneunomanthe, blodau Mihangel.
Portulaca, porpin.
Polygalwm, llysiau Crist.
Potamogeton, llyriad y llynn, llyriad y dwr.
Potentilla, y dinllwyd, y dorrllwyd.
Pulegiwm, pigle y brymlys, breflys, coluddlys.
Pulmonaria, llysiau'r ysgyfaint, callodr y derw.
Prosepis, cyngaw, y gyccwallog, cyccwallys.
Prunioli, bwyd llyffaint, ellyllys, yr ellyllog.
Pursa pastoris, pwrs y bugail, llysiau'r tryfal.
Prunella, y feddyges ddu.
Pulagiwm, berge.
Puenica, puinge.
Pseudo narcissus, yr ylfinog, croeso gwanwyn.
Psillion, llysiau'r chwain, y chweinllys.
Psychotrophon, bittain, dannogen, y ddeiniog.
Pulicaria, llysiau'r chwain.
Pternica, ystrawlys, trewlys, dail y trew.

---

* Petroselinon. I. M.
† Petrosilion Oleoselinon. I. M.

* Polypodium, yn ddiamau. I. M.

Pungentia, sinsir y gors, yr ithrog, githran y gors, y boethwraidd.

Primilavois, priellan, priellen, samwl.

Pympyrnel, llysiau'r cryman, brathlys.

Pyretrwm sylvestris, pelydr gwyllt.

Pyrola, y goedwyrdd. gwyrdd y gauaf, gwyrdd y coed.

Pyrus, geligwydd, peranwydd,

Pyrwin, peranen, geligen, grwnen, grwnigen, rhwnigen.

Pyren, cerien; ceri, had neu gnewyll, ffrwythau a llysiau.

Pyrethrwm, pelydr, y pelydre.

Q.

Quercus, derwen, darwydden, deri, derwydd, derw.

Querculus, derwen Gaersalem.

Quercula benedicta, y dderwen fendigaid, cas gan gythraul.

Quinquefoliwm, y pumpys, dail y pumpys.

Quinquenervia, ystylynes, y llwyn hidydd.

R.

Rapum, erfinen, erfin.

Ranunculus, troed y frân, chwys Mair, blodau'r menyn, egyllt.

Raspis, afan, mafon, meiwon, meiwydd, mefynwydd, mefynen.

Rhaphanus hortensis, rhuddugl lledfegin.

Rhaphanus agrestis, rhuddugl y meirch, rhuddugl gwyllt.

Rhamnus, rhafn, pren rhafn, rhafnen, rhafnwydden, mwyar ffrengig.

Rhabarbarwm, y suranog fawr, march dafol y gerddi.

Rhesta bovis, cas gan arddwr, hwp yr ychen, drain y gafaelon, tegwch meinwen.

Ronilla, eunof, ewnof gwyllt.

Rosa, rhos, brail, breilwy, egroeswydd.

Rosa canina, rhos gwylltion, breilwy gwyllt, rhos crewyll, ciros, rhos y cwn, rhos y perthi.

Rosa solis, y dawddrudd, toddedigrudd, y dawddlys, *arianllys, gwlithlys.

Rosmaris, rhosmari.

Rhibes, rhyf, rhyfwydden, rhyfon, rhyfonwydd.

Rhibes aquatica, rhyf y nentydd, rhyfon y nentydd, rhyfon duon.

Rhibes hortensis, rhyfon lledfegin, rhyfon y gerddi, rhyfon cochon.

Rubia silvestris, y fandon, llysiau'r erydd.

Rubia minor, friwydd wenn, briwydd, briwlys.

Rubia, y wreiddrydd, cochwraidd, cochlys.

Rubus, mwyarwydd, mwyaren.

Rumex, tafol, suranog.

Rumex medicinalis, marchdafol y meddig, tafol briwddail.

Ruscus, celyn Mair, celyn Ffrainc, celyn Gwent, corgelyn, celyn y wrach.

Ruta, rhud, rhuw, torrwenwyn, gwenwynllys, llysiau'r echrysaint.

S.

Sata, yd, ceri, cnewyll, had, gwyfon, grawn.

Satoria, yr heonllys, yr uchelfar, gwysglys, gwysgonllys.

Satella, ydig, efr, gwenith y cythraul, had y drwg.

Satyriwm, tegeiriau.

Satureia, sewyrllys, y selsiglys, llysiau'r selsig, y sorelys.

Salix, helig, gwielwydd.

Salix equina, rhawn y march, cedor y wrach.

---

* Arienllys, undoubtedly. 1. M., i. e. the same as gwlithlys.

Salvia, y geidwad.
Salvia agrestis, y geidwad wyllt.
Sambucus, yscaw, yr yscewydd.
Sauguinaria, y canclwm, y gan-
hewin, y waedlys.
Sanicula, clust yr arth, yr olch-
wraidd.
Sanamwndi, y bendigeidlys, y
fabcoll.
Sardonia, troed yr erydd.
Saxifragiwm, tormaen, llysiau'r
tostedd.
Saponaria, yr olchyddes, y sebon-
llys.
Savina, y gyrllys, gwaredlys.
Saurion, mwstwrdi, y llymmin-
og, llymminllys.
Seda Maria, ystol Fair.
Sedwm major, llysiau'r gwayw.
Sedwm minor, briweg y cerrig,
maenllys, cynffon y lygoden,
y friweg.
Sempervivwm, y fyw fyth, byw-
lys.
Senecio, y benfelan, y greulys
fawr, y greulys fenyw, llych-
lyn y dwr.
Septinea, yr henllydan.
Sesarwm, grug, grelys.
Securiadaca, llewyg y iâr.
Seriphiwm, chwerwyn y mor.
Serpentaria, llysiau'r neidr.
Serica pratense, sidan y waun,
serig y waun, seriglys, sidan-
llys, serigwellt, sidanwellt, y
sidanog, serigog.
Scabiosa, y bengaled, y glafrllys.
Scandwlaciwm, mwstarth.
Scandix, nodwydd y bugail.
Scelerata, troed yr erydd.
Scirpws, brwynen y môr.
Scopa regia, y milddail, llysiau'r
gwaedling.
Scolopendria, rhedyn y gwelydd,
tafod yr hydd.
Scrofularia major, danogen y
y dwr, y feddyges ddu.
Scrofularia minor, dynhaden
fenw, dynhaden ful.
Scolopendriwm, rhedyn y fam.
Scorodwm, garlleg, craf.
Scorodina, y geidwad wyllt.

Sinapi silvestre, berwr yr yd,
bresych yr yd, y carl, y cer-
lyn.
Sinilax, coedgwlm, cwlm y coed,
cynghafog.
Sinyrnion, dulys, perllys y berllan, marchberllys y gerddi.
Solanwm somnifera, y gedow-
rach.
Solanwm lignoswm, y manyg-
log.
Solidago, glesyn y coed, y goedwyrdd, gwyrdd y gauaf.
Souilana, gwynwyn y moch,
gwynwyn gwylltion, gwyn-
wyn y mensydd.
Sorbus, cerwydden, cerwigen,
cerdinwydd, sarphwydd.
Spinus albus, draenen wenn, yspyddaden, draen yspyddaid,
egfaenwydd.
Spinus, duddraenen, draenen
ddu, eirinwydd.
Spineolus, coreirin, cirin y
perthi.
Spina, draen, draenen.
Spinacia, yspinllys.
Spicus, tywysen, hefyd llysiau
sychon, yspiglys, yspiccedlys.
Sparganiwm, yspargan, y gledd-
yflys, y gleiflys, gellesg, yr
inclys.
Staphys agria, llewyg y llau,
llysiau'r llau, y lleulys.
Staphylinws, pannas y moch.
Stachys, y fedwen chwerw,
chwerwlys yr eithin, dail y
bystwn, y geidwad wyllt.
Strobilwm, llydylys.
Struthiwm, cribau'r pannwr.
Succus, sudd, sugn, sug, nof,
llynnor, irder, gweisgion,
gwysgon.
Secisa, bara'r cythraul.
Sulphur, ufelfaen, llosglist.
Syringa, pibellwydd, pibwydd,
chwibellwydd.
Syriac * * * *
*dd*sn * * *

T.

Tanaecetwm, tancedlys, tanclys,
dail y tanced, tansli.

Thalictrwm, arianllys.
Thlaspi. mwstarth.
Thryalis, rhoscampau, bannogan yr ardd.
Thymus, gryw, grywlys, teim.
Thymus agrestis, grywlys, y twynau.
Thymus hortensis, grywlys, lledfegin.
Tipha, calaf felfed, cynffon y gath.
Telephiwm, orpin, llysiau Taliesin, y ffaflys.
Tithymal, llysiau'r cyfog.
Tormentilla, tresgl y moch.
Tremularia, yr eigryn crydlys, crydwellt, gwenith yr ysgyfarnog, crydwellt.
Triorchis, teircaill.
Trifoliwm, meillion.
Trifoliwm rubwm, meillion cochon, marchfeillon.
Trifoliwm albwm, meillon gwynnon, meillon Olwen, corfeillon.
Trifoliwm aurewm, meillion aur, pig y deryn.
Trifoliwm silvestre, meillon edring.
Tubera, bwyd y llyffaint.

V.

Vaccinia, llus duon, llus y mynydd, llusi.
Vacciniwm, llygeiriau, ceiroes y waun.
Valeriana, llysiau Cadwgan, cynffon y cabwllt, gysynorllys.
Verbena, y dderwen fendigaid.
Vernilagiwm, yr ysgallen ddu.
Veronica, yr ornerth.
Verbwrnwm, cwyrwiail, ffyllwydd.

Verbasewm, y dewbannog, yscedlys, panllys.
Vetonica, cribau St. Ffred.
Viola, mill, gwiolydd, y fioled.
Viscus, gwysglys, gwysgonllys, uchelfar, yr heonllys.
Ulmus, elmwydd, llwyf, y claswydd, elmeunwydd.
Ulmus Romanus, llwyfen Rhufeinig, llwyf Rhufain, y claswydd.
Umbilicus Veneris. bogail y forwyn, bottynog.
Voluerwm major, taglys, tagwydd.
Voluerwm minor, yr yttag, taglys yr yd, taglys bychan, taglys y gerddi.
Volubilis, ewlm y coed.
Urtica, dynaid.
Uvæ, gwyfon, greol, bacewyon, gwyfon, gwin, gwinwyfon.
Uvæ passac, rhesinod, rhesinau, rhesinwyf, gwynwyfon sychon.
Uvæ ursina, gwyfon yr yspinwydd, greol y pren melyn, ffrwyth yr arthwydden.
Uvularia, tafod y march.

Z.

Zura, hegfaen, gwyfon, yr yspyddaden, yr yspyddwy.

A'r gwydd a'r llysiau hynn, sef y nifer a aller o honynt, a ddylai bob Meddyg eu cadw mewn gardd yn lledfegin, ag mewn perllanau, a hynny mewn parel o dir a fo da'r ddaear, ag yn wasgodig, a cherwyneb haul, fal au caffer wrth raid ag achos.

****

323

Also published by Llanerch:

The Physicians of Myddfai
a facsimile of the edition
edited by John Pugh,
published at Llandovery
in 1861.
ISBN 1897853157

For a complete list of Llanerch Press Ltd

publications, please visit our website:

www.llanerchpress.com

or all telephone orders to 01278 781278

INDEX

This index contains the names of most of the persons mentioned in the text and those of authors mentioned in the notes; it also includes names of books mentioned in the text only. The Appendix includes a list of herbs from the original book of the Physicians of Myddfai.

Edwards, A 246, 302, 308
Edwards, Evan 192
Edwards, John 190
Edwards, N. 267
Ellis, Anne 202, 301
Elyot, Thomas 122, 131
Etheldrida 36
Evan, Richard ap 236
Evans, Arise 118-9
Evans brothers 304
Evans, Daniel 206,207
Evans, Daniel Rees 206, 208
Evans, Dr. John 109, 110
Evans, Gareth 242, 288-289,
                    305-6
Evans, John 149, 190, 206, 207,
                    288
Evans, John of Bala 223
Evans, John of Waunfawr 217
Evans, Mary 204
Evans, Mrs. 204
Evans Rhys 118
Evans, David Rees 206, 304
Evans, Richard 236
Evans, Theophilus 226, 230,
                    275
Evans-Wentz, W.Y. 293
Fardd, Myrddin 176, 213
Fenton, R. 78, 245, 267
Ffynnon Elian 188
Ffynon Elian, Jac 190
Fisher, J. 264
Fisher, John 245
Fitzpatrick, M. 306
Flavius Justinius 30
Fleetwood, J. 243, 270
Fleming, Alexander 208
Freeman, Dr. 113
French, P. J. 279
Friar Glyn of Kilkenny 51

Fuchs, Leonhard 138
Friar Forest 104, 278
Gaddesden, John of, 184
Galen 22-3, 42, 111, 121, 123,
                    153, 249, 305
Garyn, Gwilym 189
Gerald of Wales, *(Geraldius
Cambrensis)* 29, 47, 65-66, 70-
72, 127, 169-170, 261, 264,
                    277, 291
Gerard's Herbal 21, 138, 145,
                    165, 285, 286
Gerard, John 145, 223, 285-
                    286
Gethin, Iuann 53
Gethin, John 168-169
Gibson, J. 262
Gildas 27-28, 33, 36-37, 47, 66,
                    68-69, 251, 255-257
Globe-flower 144
Glyn, Guto'r 201, 204
Glynne, Thomas 145
Goat's Hole Cave 8-9, 244
Goch, Gwen 201
Goodyer, John 25, 145, 250
Gozbert, Abbot 140
Graham, James 171, 229, 307-
                    308
Great Plague of London 133
Gregory, Pope 35
Grieve, M. 138
Griffith, David ap 150
Griffith, Dorothy 202, 301
Grifith family 170, 210
Griffith, G. 242, 262
Griffith, Griffiths 208-211
Griffiths, Owen 303
Griffiths, R.A. 91, 260, 272
Gruffydd, Elis, 73, 122, 127,
Griggs, Barbara 97, 243, 247,

John, Augustus 175
John, Brian 292, 301
John of Arderne 90, 203
John of Gaunt 90
Johns, T. 264
Johnson, H. 253
Johnson, Thomas 145, 285
Jones, A. 150, 161, 275, 289
Jones, D. 287
Jones, Daniel 188
Jones, David 213
Jones, D. W. 243, 303
Jones, Dewi 146, 243
Jones, D. T., Dr. 149, 287
Jones, Edward, Dr. 239
Jones, E. 289
Jones, E. A. 292
Jones, Francis 34, 63, 64, 76
Jones, G. E 277
Jones, Harry 171
Jones, Henry 290
Jones, John: see pages 213-221;
       also131, 132, 188,240, 283,
                                    305
Jones, G. E. 278, 308
Jones, G. P., Dr. 171, 185, 260,
                     281, 291, 308
Jones, Griffith 226
Jones, L. E. 147
Jones, L. F. 287
Jones, Lloyd 292
Jones, M. 303
Jones, Owen 221
Jones, P. G. 298
Jones, Robert 236-237
Jones, Samson, Dr. 148
Jones, T. G. 179, 295
Jones, T. L. 243, 303
Jones, William 188
Julius Caesar 25, 83

Julius Martinus 33
Justinus Consul 30
Justinian plague 30, 45, 252
Juvenis, Julius 33
Keats, John 215, 304-305
Kelley (Kelly), Edward 108-
                   109, 242, 279
Kelly, J. 260
Kew 136
Keys, D. 252
Knight, J. 251-252
Kokard, Iannik 58-59, 242, 262
Kymer, Gilbert 91
Lacnunga 40, 41, 256
Lady Wells 64
Laws, Edward 77
Laws of Compensation 93
Laws of Howell (Hywel) Dda
                          62, 92
Lay of the Nine Herbs 40, 257
Leland, John 124
Leprosy 29, 54-58, 62, 66, 68,
                   230, 260-262
Lewis, C. W. 307
Lewis, Daniel, Dr. 149
Lewis of Caerleon 101
Lewis, T. 274, 284
Lhuyd, Edward 64, 77, 144-
146, 190, 227, 262, 264, 275,
                               286
Lhuyd or Lhwyd, Humphrey
          121-124, 218, 281-282
Liber landavensis 47
Lillly, William 108-110
Lindner, Dr. Dietric Wessel
                               230
Linnaeus, Carl 142, 287
Linnard, W. 244, 287
Livre de Seyntes Medicines 89
Lloyd, Edward 144